General Biology Laboratory Manual for Science Majors

BIOL 1407 LAB

Custom Edition for North Lake College

James W. Perry | David Morton | Joy B. Perry

Edited by: Mark Manteuffel

Contributions to Animal Diversity: Ronald E. Barry, Jr.

And Evolutionary Agents: James H. Howard

CENGAGE Learning·

Australia · Brazil · Japan · Korea · Mexico · Singapore · Spain · United Kingdom · United States

**General Biology Laboratory Manual
for Science Majors: BIOL 1407 LAB, Custom
Edition for North Lake College**

Lab Manual for Majors General Biology, 1st Edition
James W. Perry | David Morton | Joy B. Perry

© 2009 Brooks/Cole, Cengage Learning. All rights reserved.
Library of Congress Control Number: 2008927240

Senior Project Development Manager:
 Linda deStefano

Market Development Manager:
 Heather Kramer

Senior Production/Manufacturing Manager:
 Donna M. Brown

Production Editorial Manager:
 Kim Fry

Sr. Rights Acquisition Account Manager:
 Todd Osborne

For product information and technology assistance, contact us at
Cengage Learning Customer & Sales Support, 1-800-354-9706
For permission to use material from this text or product,
submit all requests online at **cengage.com/permissions**
Further permissions questions can be emailed to
permissionrequest@cengage.com

This book contains select works from existing Cengage Learning resources and
was produced by Cengage Learning Custom Solutions for collegiate use. As such,
those adopting and/or contributing to this work are responsible for editorial
content accuracy, continuity and completeness.

Compilation © 2012 Cengage Learning
ISBN-13: 978-1-285-55800-4

ISBN-10: 1-285-55800-6

Cengage Learning
5191 Natorp Boulevard
Mason, Ohio 45040
USA
Cengage Learning is a leading provider of customized learning solutions with
office locations around the globe, including Singapore, the United Kingdom,
Australia, Mexico, Brazil, and Japan. Locate your local office at:
international.cengage.com/region.

Cengage Learning products are represented in Canada by Nelson Education, Ltd.
For your lifelong learning solutions, visit **www.cengage.com/custom.**
Visit our corporate website at **www.cengage.com.**

Printed in Mexico

Brief Contents

Preface

Greetings from the authors! We're happy that you are examining the results of our efforts to assist you and your students. We believe you'll find the information below a valuable introduction to this laboratory manual.

Audience

This manual is designed for students at the college majors level. You'll find that the exercises support any biology text used in a majors course.

Features of This Edition

Inquiry Experiments and the Methods of Science

We realize that the best way to learn science is by doing science. Thus, in this edition, you will find numerous **inquiry-based experiments.** Some are extensions of a preceding activity, while others stand alone. Each follows the cognitive techniques whose foundations are laid in the first exercise, "Scientific Method."

Throughout the manual, we place more emphasis on testing predictions generated from hypotheses. We strongly believe that all biology students—benefit by repeating the logical thought processes of science.

New and Updated Exercises

As always, we strive to provide students with exciting, relevant activities and experiments that allow them to explore some of the rapidly developing areas of biological knowledge. We have added an additional animal diversity exercise and re-ordered and re-grouped some of the microbe, plant and invertebrate phyla.

Updated Taxonomy

An attempt to provide accurate systematic information is like trying to hit a moving target. As new information floods in, our best understanding of taxonomy and systematic relationships sometimes seems to change daily. The taxonomy in our exercises is completely updated and reflects the most widely accepted information at the time of publication.

What's Important to Us

In preparing this lab manual, we paid particular attention to pedagogy, clarity of procedures and terminology, illustrations, and practicality of materials used.

Pedagogy

The exercises are written so the conscientious student can accomplish the objectives of each exercise with minimal input from an instructor. As suggested by the publisher, the procedure sections of the exercises are more detailed and step-by-step than in other manuals. Instructions follow a natural progression of thought so the instructor need not conduct every movement.

We attempted to make each portion of the exercise part of a continuous flow of thought. Thus, we do not wait until the post-lab questions to ask students to record conclusions when it is more appropriate to do so within the body of the procedure. Answers to in-lab questions are to be found in the *Instructor's Manual* as well as online.

Terms required to accomplish objectives are **boldface.** Scientific names and precautionary statements, or those needing emphasis, are *italic.*

The use of scientific names is deemphasized when it is not relevant to understanding the subject. However, these names generally do appear in parentheses because the labels on many prepared microscope slides bear only the scientific name.

Format

Each exercise includes:

1. Objectives: a list of desired outcomes.
2. Introduction: to stimulate student interest, indicate relevance, and provide background.
3. Materials: a list for each portion of the exercise so a student can quickly gather the necessary supplies. Materials are listed "Per student," "Per pair," "Per group," and "Per lab room."
4. Procedures: including safety notes, illustrations of apparatus, figures to be labeled, drawings to be made, tables to record data, graphs to draw, and questions that lead to conclusions. The procedures are listed in easy-to-follow numbered steps.
5. Pre-lab Questions: ten multiple-choice questions that the student should be able to answer after reading the exercise, but prior to entering the laboratory.
6. Post-lab Questions: questions that draw on knowledge gained from doing the exercise and that the student should be able to answer after finishing the exercise. These post-lab questions assess **recall** (preparing students for lab practical assessments), **understanding,** and **application.**

Practical Post-lab Questions

Virtually all courses use laboratory practical examinations. We explain to our students the difference between lecture-type questions, which they need to read and provide an answer based on the written word, and practical-type questions, for which a response depends on observation.

We believe the post-lab questions should draw on the knowledge gained by observation. Consequently, we've incorporated as many illustrations as possible into the post-lab questions. These illustrations typically are similar, but not identical, to those in the procedures. Thus, they assess the student's ability to use knowledge gained during the exercise in a new situation.

Post-lab questions are identified by exercise section. This allows the instructor to easily assign or use only those questions relevant to portions of exercises performed by students. The questions also have been revised and are directly tied to the learning outcomes expected from each exercise.

Flexible Quiz Options

Each exercise has a set of pre-lab questions. We have found through nearly 80 combined years of experience that students left to their own initiative typically come to laboratory unprepared to do the exercise. Few read the exercise beforehand. One solution to this problem is to incorporate some sort of graded pre-exercise activity. At the same time, we recognize that grading a large number of lab papers each week can put an unreasonable burden on instructors. Consequently, we decided on a multiple-choice format, which is easy to grade but still accomplishes the pedagogical goal.

In our own courses, we have students take a pre-lab quiz consisting of the questions in their lab manual in scrambled order to discourage memorization. These scrambled quizzes are reproduced in our *Instructor's Manual.* Our quiz takes about five minutes of lab time and counts as a portion of the lab grade, thus rewarding students for preparation.

Other instructors have told us they use the pre-lab questions to assess learning after the exercise has been completed. We encourage you to be creative with the manual; do what you like best.

Lab Length and Exercise Options

We realize there is wide variation in the amount of time each instructor devotes to laboratory activities. To provide maximum flexibility for the instructor, the procedure portions of the exercises are divided by major headings, and the approximate time it takes to perform each portion indicated. Once the introduction has been studied, portions of the procedures can be deleted or conducted as demonstrations without sacrificing the pedagogy of the exercise as a whole.

It's our experience that if the lecture section covers the topic prior to the lab, students find the exercise much more relevant and understandable. We strive to create this situation in our courses, and thus no time is spent on a lecture-style introduction in the lab itself before the exercise begins. Therefore, we have two to three full hours for real scientific investigation and need to delete very little material to complete most exercises in the time allotted.

Illustrations

Perhaps our illustrations are more noticeable than anything else as you thumb through the manual. We continued our incorporation of a generous number of high-quality color illustrations, including everything a student needs visually to accomplish the objectives of each exercise. While there is no need for students to purchase supplemental publications, students may find the *Photoatlas for Biology*, ISBN 0-534-23556-5, to be a useful reference for this course and other biology courses.

Most illustrations of microscopic specimens are labeled to provide orientation and clarity. A few are unlabeled but are provided with leaders for students to attach labels. In other cases, more can be gained by requiring the student to do simple drawings. Space is included in the manual for these, with boxes for drawings of macroscopic specimens and circles for microscopic specimens.

Materials

Most of the equipment and supplies used in the exercises are readily available from biological and laboratory supply houses. Many others can be collected from nature or purchased in local supermarket, discount or office supply stores. (Our department budgets are not large!) We've attempted to keep instrumentation as simple and inexpensive as possible.

Anyone who lives in a temperate climate knows it may be necessary to adjust the sequence of the laboratory exercises to accommodate seasonal availability of certain materials. However, we provided alternatives, including the use of preserved specimens wherever possible, to avoid this problem.

Instructor's Manual

There is no need to worry, "Where can I get that?" or "How do I prepare this?" Our *Instructor's Manual* includes:

- Material and equipment lists for each exercise
- Procedures to prepare reagents, materials, and equipment
- Scheduling information for materials needing advance preparation
- Approximate quantities of materials needed
- Answers to in-text questions
- Answers for pre-lab questions
- Answers for post-lab questions
- Tear-out sheets of pre-lab questions, in scrambled order from those in the lab manual, for those who wish to duplicate them for quizzes
- Vendors and ordering information for supplies

And in the End . . .

There are very few things in life that are perfect. We don't suppose that this lab manual is one of them. We hope your students will enjoy the exercises. We **know** they will learn from them. Perhaps you and they will find places where rephrasing will make the activity better. Please contact us with your opinions and any ideas you wish to share; encourage your students to do likewise.

James W. Perry
Department of Biological
Sciences
University of Wisconsin
Fox Valley
1478 Midway Road
Menasha, WI 54952-1297
(920) 832-2610
james.perry@uwc.edu

David Morton
Department of Biology
Frostburg State University
Frostburg, MD 21532-1099
(301) 689-4355
dmorton@frostburg.edu

Joy B. Perry
Department of Biological
Sciences
University of Wisconsin
Fox Valley
1478 Midway Road
Menasha, WI 54952-1297
(920) 832-2653
joy.perry@uwc.edu

About the Editor

Mark Manteuffel holds a doctorate in ecology and evolutionary biology from the University of Miami. He is currently a faculty member at Washington University and St. Louis Community College, where he involves students in research learning experiences and teaches courses in biology, ecology, and environmental science. He teaches field courses around the world that focus on the conservation of biodiversity, sustainable development, and ecosystem function and health.

Professor Manteuffel also develops innovative interdisciplinary undergraduate and graduate science programs that cover global education and environmental sustainability. This focus led him to work with colleagues from the University of Missouri, Columbia, converting laboratory investigations into more inquiry-based and student-directed biological investigations. This work is currently ongoing, funded by National Science Foundation grant DEB-0618817, *Connecting Undergraduates to the Enterprise of Science* (CUES).

The inquiry-based lab modules in this edition of the laboratory manual are an extension of Professor Manteuffel's work on the CUES grant. These modules are designed to introduce students to the process and content of science. Students read and critique the lab modules' scientific reports and extend the research reported. The goal of these modules is for students to learn not only content matter, but also the process of science through their own direct experience. They design their own research that will extend the research reported in the modules. The intent is that students will benefit from learning science by doing science, thereby increasing their ability to read and interpret scientific literature.

To the Student

Welcome! You are about to embark on a journey through the cosmos of life. You will learn things about yourself and your surroundings that will broaden and enrich your life. You will have the opportunity to marvel at the microscopic world, to be fascinated by the cellular events occurring in your body at this very moment, and to gain an appreciation for the environment, including the marvelous diversity of the plant and animal world.

We offer a number of suggestions to make your college experience in biology a pleasant one. We have taken the first step toward that goal; we have written a laboratory guide that is user friendly. You will be able to hear the authors speaking as though we were there to share your experience. The authors share a personal belief that the more comfortable we make you feel, the more likely you will share our enthusiasm for biology. One thing we all must realize is that we are citizens of "spaceship Earth." The fate of our spaceship is largely in your hands because you are the decision makers of the future. As has been so aptly stated, "We inherited the earth from our parents and grandparents, but we are only the caretakers for our children and grandchildren."

As caretakers, we need to be informed about the world around us. That's why we enroll in colleges and universities with the hope of gaining a liberal education. In doing so, we establish a basis on which to make educated decisions about the future of the planet. Each exercise in this manual contains a lesson in life that is of a more global nature than the surroundings of your biology laboratory.

To enhance your biology education, take the initiative to give yourself the best possible advantage. Don't miss class. Read your text assignment routinely. And, read the laboratory exercise before you come to the lab.

Each exercise in the manual is organized in the same way:

1. Objectives tell exactly what you should learn from the exercise. If you wish to know what will be on the exam, consult the objectives for each exercise.

2. The Introduction provides background information for the exercise and is intended to stimulate your interest.

3. The Materials list for each portion of the exercise allows you to determine at a glance whether you have all the necessary supplies needed to do the activity.

4. The Procedure for each section, in easy-to-follow step-by-step fashion, describes the activity. Within the procedure, spaces are provided to make required drawings. Questions are posed with space for answers, asking you to draw conclusions about an activity you are engaged in. You'll find a lot of illustrations, most of which are labeled and others which are not but have leaders for you to attach labels. The terms to be used as labels are found in the procedure and in a list accompanying the illustration. We believe it best for you to sometimes make a simple drawing, and have inserted boxes or circles for your sketches. Where appropriate, tables and graphs are present to record your data.

5. Pre-lab questions can be answered easily by simply reading the exercise. They're meant to "set the stage" for the lab period by emphasizing some of the more salient points.

6. Post-lab questions are intended to be answered after the laboratory is completed. Some are straightforward interpretations of what you have done, while others require additional thought and perhaps some research in your textbook. In fact, some have no "right" or "wrong" answer at all!

It is our experience that students are much too reluctant to ask questions for fear of appearing stupid. Remember, there is no such thing as a stupid question. Speak up! Think of yourselves as "basic learners" and your instructors as "advanced learners." Interact and ask questions so that you and your instructors can further your/their respective educations.

Laboratory Supplies and Procedures

Materials and Supplies Kept in the Lab at All Times

The following materials will always be available in the lab room. Familiarize yourself with their location prior to beginning the exercises.

- Compound light microscopes
- Dissection microscopes
- Glass microscope slides
- Coverslips

- Lens paper
- Tissue wipes
- Plastic 15-cm rulers
- Dissecting needles
- Razor blades
- Assorted glassware-cleaning brushes

- Detergent for washing glassware
- Distilled water
- Hand soap
- Paper towels
- Safety equipment (see separate list)

Laboratory Safety

None of the exercises in this manual are inherently dangerous. Some of the chemicals are corrosive (causing burns to the skin) and others are poisonous if ingested or inhaled in large amounts. Contact with your eyes by otherwise innocuous substances may result in permanent eye injury. **Remember, once your sight is lost, it's probably lost forever.** Locate the following safety items and then study the list of basic safety rules.

1. Eyewash bottle or eye bath

   Should any substance be splashed in your eyes, wash them thoroughly.

2. Fire extinguisher

   Read the directions for use of the fire extinguisher.

3. Fire blanket

   Should someone's clothing catch fire, wrap the blanket around the individual and roll the person on the floor to smother the flames.

4. First-aid kit

   Minor injuries such as small cuts can be treated effectively in the lab. Open the first-aid kit to determine its contents.

5. Safety goggles

   Eye protection should be worn during the more experimental exercises.

Safety Rules

1. Do not eat, drink, or smoke in the laboratory.
2. Wash your hands with soap and warm water before leaving the laboratory.
3. When heating a test tube, point the mouth of the tube away from yourself and other people.
4. Always wear shoes in the laboratory.
5. Keep extra books and clothing in designated places so your work area is as uncluttered as possible.

6. If you have long hair, tie it back when in the laboratory.
7. Read labels carefully before removing substances from a container. Never return a substance to a container.
8. Discard used chemicals and materials into appropriately labeled containers. Certain chemicals should not be washed down the sink; these will be indicated by your instructor.

Caution: Report all accidents and spills to your instructor immediately!

Instructions for Washing Laboratory Glassware

1. Place contents to be discarded in proper waste container as described in exercise.
2. Rinse glassware with tap water.
3. Add a small amount of glassware cleaning detergent.
4. Scrub using an appropriately sized brush.

5. Rinse with tap water until detergent disappears.
6. Rinse three times with distilled water (dH_2O).
7. Allow to dry in inverted position on drying rack (if available).

When glassware is clean, dH_2O sheets off rather than remaining on the surface in droplets.

Evolutionary Agents

OBJECTIVES

After completing this exercise, you will be able to

1. define *evolutionary agent, natural selection, fitness, directional selection, stabilizing selection, disruptive selection, gene flow, divergence, speciation, mutation, genetic drift, bottleneck effect, founder effect;*
2. determine the allele frequencies for a gene in a model population;
3. calculate expected ratios of phenotypes based on Hardy–Weinberg proportions;
4. describe the effects of nonrandom mating, natural selection, migration, genetic drift, and mutation on a model population;
5. describe the effects of different selection pressures on identical model populations;
6. identify the level at which selection operates in a population;
7. describe the impact of the founder effect on the genetic structure of populations.

INTRODUCTION

Heredity itself cannot cause changes in the frequencies of alternate forms of the same gene (alleles). If certain conditions are met, then the proportions of genotypes that make up a population of organisms should remain constant generation after generation according to the equation that describes the Hardy–Weinberg equilibrium:

$$p^2 + 2pq + q^2 = 1.0 \text{ (for two alleles)}$$

If p is the frequency of one allele, and q is the frequency of the other allele, then

$$p + q = 1.0$$

For example, if two alleles for coat color exist in a population of mice and the allele for white coats is present 70% of the time, then the alternate allele (black) must be present 30% of the time.

The Hardy–Weinberg equation describes the proportions of phenotypes present in succeeding generations, as long as conditions don't change. In our example, since $p = .7$, we would expect 49% (p^2) of the mice in our population to be homozygous for white coats. Thus, 42% ($2pq$) would have one of each allele and would appear gray if neither allele is dominant (that is, both alleles would have equal expression in the phenotype). What percentage of our population is homozygous for black coats? _____ %

In nature, however, the frequencies of genes in populations change over time. Natural populations never meet all of the conditions assumed for Hardy–Weinberg equilibrium. *Evolution is a process resulting in changes in the genetic makeup of populations through time;* therefore, factors that disrupt Hardy–Weinberg equilibrium are referred to as **evolutionary agents.** This exercise demonstrates the effect of these agents on the genetic structure of a simplified model population.

10.1   Natural Selection (75 min.)

The populations you will work with are composed of colored beads. White beads in our model represent individuals that are homozygous for the white allele ($C^W C^W$). Red beads are individuals homozygous for the red allele ($C^R C^R$), and pink beads are heterozygotes ($C^W C^R$). These beads exist in "ponds"—plastic dishpans filled with smaller beads. Counts of white, pink, and red individuals in the pond are made after straining the beads through a sieve. The smaller beads pass through the mesh, which retains the larger beads. Figure 10-1 shows the initial experimental setup.

When the individuals are recovered, the frequencies of the color alleles are determined using the Hardy–Weinberg equation. The alleles in our population are codominant. Thus, each white bead contains two white alleles; each pink bead, one white and one red allele; and each red bead, two red alleles. The total number of color alleles in a population of 40 individuals is 80. If such a population contains 10 white beads, 20 pink beads, and 10 red beads the frequency of the white allele is

$$p = \frac{(2 \times 10) + 20}{80} = .5$$

Because $p + q = 1.0$, the frequency of the red allele (q) must also be .5 if there are only two color alleles in this population.

different sized and colored beads

sieve

long forceps

(Photo by D. Morton.)

Figure 10-1 Experimental setup used to demonstrate natural selection.

MATERIALS

Per student group (4):

- plastic dishpan (12″ × 7″ × 2″)
- 50 large (10-mm-diameter) white beads
- 50 large red beads
- 50 large pink beads
- 4000 small (8-mm diameter) white beads
- 4000 small red beads (optional)

- ruler with a cm scale
- pair of long forceps
- coarse sieve (9.5 mm)
- scientific calculator

Per lab room:

- clock with a second hand

PROCEDURE

A. Experiment: Natural Selection Acting Alone

Natural selection disturbs the Hardy–Weinberg equilibrium by discriminating between individuals with respect to their ability to produce young. Those individuals that survive to reproduce perpetuate more of their genes in the population. These individuals exhibit greater **fitness** than do those who leave no offspring or fewer offspring.

This experiment addresses the hypothesis that *individuals are more likely to survive and reproduce when their coloration makes it easier to hide from predators in the environment.*

1. Work in groups of four with each group member assuming one of the following roles: Predator, Data Recorder/Timer, Calculator, or Caretaker. Predators search for prey. Data Recorders/Timers record numerical results and time events. Calculators use a scientific calculator to crunch numbers as needed. Caretakers look after and manipulate the experimental setup.
2. Create a white pond by filling a dishpan with small white beads to a depth of about 5 cm and establish an initial population by mixing into the pond 10 large white beads, 10 large red beads, and 20 large pink beads. The Predator will prey on the large beads, removing as many as possible in a limited amount of time. The survivors will then reproduce the next generation and predation will begin again. This cycle will be repeated several times. Make a prediction as to the changing frequency in the population of the red allele over time and write it in the Prediction (Selection Alone) row of Table 10-3.
3. Search the pond for prey (large beads) and, using a pair of long forceps, remove as many of them as possible in 30 seconds.
4. Strain the pond with the sieve, and count the number of large white, pink, and red beads. Record the totals in the After row under Initial in Table 10-1.
5. Calculate the frequencies of the white (p) and red (q) alleles remaining in the population after selection and record them in First Generation after selection of Table 10-2. For example, if 6 white, 8 pink, and 8 red beads remain, the frequency of the white allele is

$$p = \frac{(2 \times 6) + 8}{44} = .45$$

TABLE 10-1 Large-Bead Counts Before and After Four Rounds of Simulated Predation

Population	White Beads	Pink Beads	Red Beads	Total Beads
Initial				
Before	10	20	10	40
After	_____	_____	_____	_____
Second Generation				
Before	_____	_____	_____	50
After	_____	_____	_____	_____
Third Generation				
Before	_____	_____	_____	50
After	_____	_____	_____	_____
Fourth Generation				
Before	_____	_____	_____	50
After	_____	_____	_____	_____

TABLE 10-2 Allele and Genotype Frequencies Due to Selection by Simulated Predation

Population	p	q	p^2	$2pq$	q^2
Initial	.5	.5	.25	.5	.25
First generation after selection					
Second generation after selection					
Third generation after selection					
Fourth generation after selection					

6. Using the new values for allele frequencies, calculate genotype frequencies for homozygous white (p^2), heterozygous pink ($2pq$), and homozygous red (q^2) individuals, and record them in Table 10-2. For example, if p now equals .45, the frequency of homozygous white individuals is

$$p^2 = (.45)^2 = .20$$

Assuming that 50 individuals comprise the next and succeeding generations (maximum number of individuals the pond can sustain), calculate the number of white, pink, and red individuals needed to create the population of a new pond and record these numbers in the Before row under Second Generation in Table 10-1. Here and in future calculations to generate new numbers of individuals, round up or down to the nearest whole number. For example, if $p^2 = .20$, the number of white beads needed is

$$p^2 \times 50 = .20 \times 50 = 10 \text{ white beads}$$

Using these numbers, construct a new pond.

7. Repeat steps 2–6 for three more rounds, filling in the remaining rows in Tables 10-1 and 10-2. When you are finished, copy the frequency of the red allele from Table 10-1 to Table 10-3 (Selection Alone column) and plot this data in Figure 10-2.

TABLE 10-3 Frequency of Red Allele (q) Due to Selection and Migration

Prediction (Selection Alone):

Prediction (Selection and Migration):

Generation	Selection Alone	Selection and Migration
1		
2		
3		
4		

Conclusion (Selection Alone):

Conclusion (Selection and Migration):

8. Write your conclusion as to your prediction in the Conclusion (Selection Alone) row of Table 10-3.
9. If you had started with a pond filled with small red beads as a background, how would the frequency of the red allele change?

_____

_____

_____

Figure 10-2 Effects of predation on allele frequencies.

10. Selection that favors one extreme phenotype over the other and causes allele frequencies to change in a predictable direction is known as **directional selection.** When selection favors an intermediate phenotype rather than one at the extremes, it's known as **stabilizing selection.** Selection that operates against the intermediate phenotype and favors the extreme ones is called **disruptive selection.** Which kind of selection is illustrated by simulated predation of white, pink, and red beads in a white pond? Explain why you made this choice.

_____

_____

_____

It is important to realize that selection operates on the entire phenotype so that the overall fitness of an organism is based on the result of interactions of thousands of genes.

11. If two identical populations (such as the mix of beads described in step 2) inhabited different environments (such as red and white ponds), how would the frequency of the color genes in each pond compare after a large number of generations?

_____

_____

_____

As two populations become genetically different through time (**divergence**), individuals from these populations can lose the ability to interbreed. If this happens, two species form from one ancestral species. This process is called **speciation.**

B. Experiment: Effect of Gene Flow on Natural Selection

The frequencies of alleles in a population also change if new organisms immigrate and interbreed, or when old breeding members emigrate. **Gene flow** due to *migration* may be a powerful force in evolution. This activity demonstrates its effect.

1. Establish an initial population as in the previous section, step 2.
2. Begin selection as before, *except* add five new red beads to each generation before the new allele frequencies are determined. These beads represent migrants from a population where the red allele confers greater fitness. This experiment addresses the hypothesis that *gene flow resulting from the migration of a significant number of individuals into a population undergoing predation affects the change in allele frequencies expected from selection alone.* Write your prediction as to how the change in frequency of the red allele will be affected in the Conclusion (Selection and Migration) row of Table 10-3.
3. For each generation, record the frequencies of the red allele obtained with both selection and migration in Table 10-3.
4. How does migration influence the effectiveness of selection in this example?

_____

_____

_____

5. Write your conclusion as to your prediction in the Conclusion (Selection and Migration) row of Table 10-3.
6. How would migration have influenced the change in gene frequencies if white instead of red individuals had entered the population?

_____

_____

_____

Gene flow keeps local populations of the same species from becoming more and more different from each other. Things that serve as barriers to gene flow can accelerate the production of new species. Migration can also introduce new genes into a population and produce new genetic combinations. Imagine the result of a black allele being introduced into our model population and the new heterozygotes (perhaps gray and dark red) it would produce.

Note: If time is short, any or all of the remaining sections may be done as thought experiments, i.e., doing it in your head rather than actually setting it up.

10.2   Mutation *(About 15 min.)*

Another way new genetic information enters a population is through **mutation.** This usually represents an actual change in the information encoded by the DNA of an organism. As such, most mutations are harmful and will be eliminated by natural selection. Nevertheless, mutations do provide the raw material for evolution.

MATERIALS

Per student group (4):

- small bowl
- 10 large white beads
- 10 large red beads

- 20 large pink beads
- 1 large gray bead
- scientific calculator

PROCEDURE

1. Establish an initial population by placing 10 large white beads, 10 large red beads, and 20 large pink beads in a small bowl (without the small beads).
2. For the sake of expediency, establish a new generation by one group member picking, without looking, 20 large beads from the bowl. Replace one white bead with a gray bead. This represents a mutation in a gamete that one parent contributed to this generation.
3. Calculate the allele frequencies of the new generation, including the frequency of the new color allele (r). Record them in Table 10-4.

TABLE 10-4 Change in Allele Frequencies Due to Mutation

Population	p	q	r
Initial	.5	.5	
New generation with mutation			

4. Three alleles are present ($p + q + r = 1.0$), so the Hardy–Weinberg equation is expanded to $p^2 + 2pq + q^2 + 2pr + 2qr + r^2 = 1.0$, and in addition to white, pink, and red phenotypes, we now have gray, dark red, and potentially, in subsequent generations, black. If the next generation contains 50 individuals, how many offspring of each phenotype would you expect? Use Table 10-5 to calculate these numbers.

TABLE 10-5 Numbers of Each Phenotype Two Generations After a Single Mutation

Color	Genotype	Frequency	× 50	Number of Individuals
White	p^2			
Pink	$2pq$			
Red	q^2			
Gray	$2pr$			
Dark red	$2qr$			
Black	r^2			

Imagine a population made up of individuals in these proportions. What effect will natural selection have on these phenotypes in a white pond?

_____

_____

_____

How could conditions change to favor the selection of the rare black allele?

_____

_____

10.3   **Genetic Drift** *(About 30 min.)*

Chance is also a factor that results in shifts in gene frequencies over several generations (**genetic drift**). This is primarily due to the random aspects of reproduction and fertilization. Genetic drift is often a problem for small populations in that they can lose much of their genetic variability. In very small populations, chance can eliminate an allele from a population, such that p becomes 0 and the other allele becomes fixed ($q = 1.0$). This loss of genetic variation due to a small population size is known as the **bottleneck effect.**

MATERIALS

Per student group (4):

- small bowl
- 10 large white beads
- 10 large red beads

- 20 large pink beads
- scientific calculator

PROCEDURE

1. As in the previous section, place 10 large white beads, 10 large red beads, and 20 large pink beads in a small bowl. Listed in Table 10-6 are the expected allele frequencies for color in this population given all individuals participate in reproduction.

TABLE 10-6 Allele Frequencies Produced by Genetic Drift

| | Expected Frequency | Actual Frequency in | |
		Small Cluster	Large Cluster
n			
p	.5		
q	.5		

2. Establish a cluster of reproductively lucky individuals by a group member choosing, without looking, 10 beads from the bowl.
3. In the second column of Table 10-6, record the allele frequencies present in this cluster.
4. Now replace the 10 beads you removed in step 2. Select beads at random again, but this time select 30 beads representing a larger cluster of reproductively lucky individuals.
5. Calculate the allele frequencies for this larger cluster and record them in the third column of Table 10-6.
6. Compare the allele frequencies in the three columns of Table 10-6. Sometimes chance determines whose gametes contribute to the next generation. What effect does the size of the number of individuals participating in reproduction have on gene flow to the next generation?

_____

_____

_____

7. Another way in which chance affects allele frequencies in a population is when migrants from old populations establish new populations. To model this effect, choose at random six individuals from an initial population to represent the migrants.
8. Move these individuals to a new unoccupied pond. (It is not necessary to actually set up a new pond for this demonstration. Use your imagination.)
9. Now calculate the allele frequencies in the new pond and record them in Table 10-7. How do they compare with the frequencies that characterized the pond from which these migrants came?

_____

_____

_____

The genetic makeup in future generations in the new population will more closely resemble the six migrants than the population from which the migrants came. This effect is known as the **founder effect.** The founder effect may not be an entirely random process because organisms that migrate from a population may be genetically different from the rest of the population to begin with. For example, if wing length in a population of insects is variable, we might expect insects with longer wings to be better at founding new populations because they can be carried farther by winds.

TABLE 10-7 Allele Frequencies in a Founder Population

	p	q
Initial Population	.5	.5
Founder Population		

Hardy–Weinberg equilibrium is also disturbed if individuals in a population don't choose mates randomly. Some members of a population may show a strong preference for mates with similar genetic makeups. This activity models this effect.

MATERIALS

Per student group (4):

- small bowl
- 10 large white beads
- 10 large red beads

- 20 large pink beads
- scientific calculator

PROCEDURE

1. Establish an initial population as in Section 10.3.
2. Assume that individuals will mate only with individuals of the same color. Arbitrarily assign sex to every bead so there are equal numbers of males and females in each color group.
3. If each pair of beads produces four offspring, record the number individuals with the same phenotype present in the next generation in Table 10-8. Remember that the pink pairs will produce one red, one white, and two pink individuals on average.

TABLE 10-8   Phenotype Changes Due to Nonrandom Mating Color

| | Number in | |
Color	Initial Generation	Next Generation
White	10	
Pink	20	
Red	10	

4. Calculate the genotype frequencies in this generation, record them in Table 10-9, and compare these with the frequencies in the initial generation.

TABLE 10-9   Genotype Frequency Changes Due to Nonrandom Mating

Genotype Frequency	Initial Generation	Next Generation
p^2		
$2pq$		
q^2		

5. What happens to the frequency of the heterozygote genotype in subsequent generations?

_____

_____

_____

_____ 1. If all conditions of Hardy–Weinberg equilibrium are met,
  (a) allele frequencies move closer to .5 each generation
  (b) allele frequencies change in the direction predicted by natural selection
  (c) allele frequencies stay the same
  (d) all allele frequencies increase

_____ 2. If a population is in Hardy–Weinberg equilibrium and $p = .6$,
  (a) $q = .5$
  (b) $q = .4$
  (c) $q = .3$
  (d) $q = .16$

_____ 3. Natural selection operates directly on
  (a) the genotype
  (b) individual alleles
  (c) the phenotype
  (d) color only

_____ 4. The process that discriminates between phenotypes with respect to their ability to produce offspring is known as
  (a) natural selection
  (b) gene flow
  (c) genetic drift
  (d) migration

_____ 5. Two populations that have no gene flow between them are likely to
  (a) become more different with time
  (b) become more alike with time
  (c) become more alike if the directional selection pressures are different
  (d) stay the same unless mutations occur

_____ 6. A process that results in individuals of two populations losing the ability to interbreed is referred to as
  (a) stabilizing selection
  (b) fusion
  (c) speciation
  (d) differential migration

_____ 7. Two ways in which new alleles can become incorporated in a population are
  (a) mutation and genetic drift
  (b) selection and genetic drift
  (c) selection and mutation
  (d) mutation and gene flow

_____ 8. If a new allele appears in a population, the Hardy–Weinberg formula
  (a) cannot be used because no equilibrium exists
  (b) can be used but only for two alleles at a time
  (c) can be used by lumping all but two phenotypes in one class
  (d) can be expanded by adding more terms

_____ 9. A shift from expected allele frequencies, resulting from chance, is known as
  (a) natural selection
  (b) genetic drift
  (c) mutation
  (d) gene flow

_____ 10. Genetic drift is a process that has a greater effect on populations that
  (a) are large
  (b) are small
  (c) are not affected by mutation
  (d) do not go through bottlenecks

EXERCISE 10

Evolutionary Agents

POST-LAB QUESTIONS

10.1 Natural Selection

1. What effect does increasing gene flow between two populations have on their genetic makeup?

2. How can selection cause two populations to become different with time?

3. Describe how the effects of directional selection can be offset by gene flow.

10.2 Mutation

4. In addition to mutation, what other mechanism allows for new genetic information to be introduced into a population? Explain your answer.

5. What is the fate of most new mutations?

6. If a population has three codominant color alleles, how many phenotypes are possible?

10.4 Nonrandom Mating

7. What effects can nonrandom mating exert on a population?

Food for Thought

8. What two evolutionary agents are most responsible for decreases in genetic variation in a population?

9. If a population has three color alleles and one is dominant over the other two, how many phenotypes are possible?

10. In humans, birth weight is an example of a characteristic affected by stabilizing selection. What does this mean to the long-term average birth weight of human babies? How might the increasing number of Caesarean sections be affecting this characteristic?

Evidences of Evolution

OBJECTIVES

After completing this exercise, you will be able to

1. define *evolution, fossil, natural selection, population, species, fitness, mass extinction, adaptive radiation, anthropologist, hominid;*

2. explain how natural selection operates to alter the genetic makeup of a population;

3. describe the general sequence of evolution of life forms over geologic time;

4. recognize primitive and advanced characteristics of skull structure of human ancestors and relatives;

5. describe the evolutionary relationships among *Dryopithecus, Australopithecus afarensis,* and other australopith species, and the various *Homo* species.

INTRODUCTION

Have you ever marveled over the diversity of animals in a zoo? Lions, antelopes, zebras, giraffes, elephants, and chimpanzees are all mammals, as are we humans. All mammals living today, and many forms that are extinct, descended from a mammalian ancestor who lived more than 200 million years ago. The process by which this incredible diversity of mammals (and all the other living and extinct species) came to exist is called **evolution,** the focus of this exercise.

Evolution, the process that results in changes in the genetic makeup of populations of organisms through time, is the unifying framework for the whole of biology. Less than 200 years ago, it seemed obvious to most people that living organisms had not changed over time—that dandelions looked like dandelions and humans looked like humans, year after year, generation after generation, without change. As scientists studied the natural world more closely, however, evidence of change and the relatedness of all living organisms emerged from geology and the fossil record, as well as from comparative morphology, developmental patterns, and biochemistry.

Charles Darwin (and, independently, Alfred Russel Wallace) postulated the major mechanism of evolution to be **natural selection**—the difference in survival and reproduction that occurs among individuals of a population that differ in one or more alleles. (See Exercise 8 for the definition of *allele.*) A **population** is a group of individuals of the same species occupying a given area. A **species** is one or more populations that closely resemble each other, interbreed under natural conditions, and produce fertile offspring.

Individuals in a population that have particular combinations of alleles better adapted to their environment survive and produce more offspring than individuals with different genetic makeups. The offspring have received alleles that also make their chances for survival and reproduction greater, and so it goes, generation after generation. The population evolves as some traits become more common and others decrease or disappear over time.

Many people think of evolution in historic terms—as something that produced the dinosaurs or the Galapagos finches Darwin studied but that no longer operates in today's world. Remember, though, that *the process of genetic change over time continues today* and is a dominant force shaping the living organisms of our planet.

The scientific evidence for evolution is overwhelming, although scientists continue to debate the exact mechanisms by which natural selection and other evolutionary agents change allelic frequencies. In this exercise, you will observe the effects of natural selection in a living plant population; consider the time over which evolution has occurred; and examine the fossil record for evidence of large-scale trends and change among our human ancestors and relatives.

Natural selection discriminates among individuals with respect to their ability to produce offspring. Those individuals that survive and reproduce will perpetuate more of their alleles in the population. These individuals are said to exhibit greater **fitness** than those who leave no or fewer offspring.

You will examine individuals of two different populations of dandelions. Dandelions are interesting because, despite their showy yellow flowers, they reproduce primarily asexually. Instead of the sexual reproduction that typically occurs in flowers, dandelions form seeds without fertilization. Thus, each dandelion is essentially genetically (and physically) identical to its parent plant.

One set of dandelion seedlings in your laboratory was grown from seeds collected from an area that has endured frequent, close mowing for many years. The second group of seedlings was grown from seeds collected from plants mowed infrequently, if at all. Your instructor will describe in more detail the conditions under which the parent plants of your seedlings have grown.

This experiment tests the hypothesis that *dandelion populations grown for generations under different mowing regimes will have different growth forms.* Write a prediction regarding this experiment in Table 11-2. What would you predict the dandelion plants grown from seeds produced in mowed and unmowed areas to look like?

MATERIALS

Per student group (4):

- flat of dandelion seedlings, labeled Mowed or Unmowed
- trowel or large spoon
- metric ruler
- knife or single-edged razor blade
- calculator

Per lab room:

- several dishpans half-filled with water
- paper towels

PROCEDURE

1. Observe the flats of young dandelion plants. Note and describe any general differences in appearance between those grown from seeds of unmowed plants versus those grown from seeds of mowed plants.

   _____

   _____

   _____

2. Take one flat of plants to your lab bench. Remove the plants carefully from the flat with a trowel or spoon. Be careful to remove all the root system but do not damage or lose root material. Wash each plant gently in the dishpan provided, *not in the sink,* to remove the residual soil. Blot the plants dry with the paper towels.

3. Cut each plant at the region separating the root from the leafy shoot, keeping each root portion with its corresponding shoot. See Figure 11-1.

4. Measure shoot length to the nearest millimeter as the length between the cut surface and the tip of the longest leaf. Record this measurement in Table 11-1.

5. Measure root length to the nearest millimeter as the length between the cut surface and the tip of the longest tap root. Sometimes it's hard to tell where the tap root ends, but try to avoid measuring branch roots. See Figure 11-1. Record this data in Table 11-1.

6. For each plant, divide the shoot length by the root length to calculate the shoot-to-root ratio. Record the ratio in Table 11-1.

Figure 11-1 Dandelion plant.

_____

*Adapted from an exercise by Thomas Hilbish and Minnie Goodwin, University of South Carolina.

TABLE 11-1	Measurements of Dandelions (Mowed or Unmowed?		
Plant	Shoot Length (mm)	Root Length (mm)	Shoot-to-Root Ratio
1			
2			
3			
4			
5			
Total number of plants =			Average =

7. Graph the distribution of the shoot-to-root ratio of each plant in your flat in Figure 11-2.

Figure 11-2 Distribution of shoot-to-root ratios of length measurements of dandelions.

8. Calculate the average shoot-to-root ratio of your plants by adding the shoot-to-root ratios of all the individual plants and dividing that number by the total number of plants.

9. Your instructor has drawn two graphs like that in Figure 11-2, one for mowed plants and one for unmowed plants. Pool your data with those of your classmates who have measured plants of the same type and enter that pooled data in Table 11-2 and on the corresponding graph. Calculate the average shoot-to-root ratio of the pooled data for each set of plants.

Are there noticeable differences in the distribution of shoot-to-root ratios between descendants of dandelions from intensely mowed versus unmowed areas? _____

If so, what are those differences?

_____

_____

_____

Do the results support your hypothesis? Write a conclusion accepting or rejecting the hypothesis in Table 11-2.

TABLE 11-2 Class Shoot-to-Root Ratios for Mowed and Unmowed Plants		
Prediction:		
Group	Mowed	Unmowed
1		
2		
3		
4		
5		
6		
7		
8		
Average		
Conclusion:		

If you failed to detect a difference between seeds grown from plants of mowed versus unmowed populations, speculate on the reason(s) for this failure. Does this failure necessarily mean that natural selection is not occurring?

_____

_____

Explain the results of this demonstration in terms of the effects of natural selection on the genetic makeup of the two dandelion populations.

_____

_____

11.2   Geologic Time *(About 30 min.)*

Our earth is an ancient planet that formed from a cloud of dust and gas approximately 4.6 billion years ago.

Life formed relatively quickly on the young planet, and the first cells emerged in the seas by 3.8 billion years ago. For more than a billion years, the only living organisms on earth were prokaryotic bacteria and bacterialike cells. Eventually, though, more complex, eukaryotic organisms evolved. The seas were colonized by single-celled organisms first, followed by multicelled and colonial plants and animals (Figure 11-3). Only much later did life move onto the land.

Throughout the history of life on earth, there have been many episodes of **mass extinctions** (catastrophic global events in which major groups of species are wiped out) followed by **adaptive radiation** (in which a lineage fills a wide range of habitats in a burst of evolutionary activity). For example, scientists postulate that a huge asteroid impacted the earth about 65 million years ago. The resulting environmental destruction caused a mass extinction in which nearly all the dinosaurs and marine organisms became extinct. After this extinction, the early mammals underwent an adaptive radiation and filled the habitats that had previously been occupied by dinosaurs.

Geologic time, "deep time," is difficult for humans, with our recent evolution and 75-year life spans to grasp. In this section, you will construct a geologic time line to help you gain perspective on the almost incomprehensible sweep of time over which evolution has operated.

MATERIALS

Per student pair:

- one 4.6-m rope or string
- meter stick and/or metric ruler

- masking tape
- calculator

PROCEDURE

1. Obtain a 4.6-m length of rope or string. The string represents the entire length of time (4.6 billion years) since the earth was formed. On this time line, you will attach masking-tape labels to mark the points when the events below occurred. Measure from the starting point with the meter stick or metric ruler.
2. Locate and mark with tape on the time line the following events (bya = billion years ago, mya = million years ago, ya = years ago):

4.6 bya	Formation of earth
3.8 bya	First living prokaryotic cells
2.5 bya	Oxygen-releasing photosynthetic pathway
1.2 bya	Origin of eukaryotic cells
580 mya	Origin of multicellular marine plants and animals
500 mya	First vertebrate animals (marine fishes)
435 mya	First vascular land plants and land animals
345 mya	Great coal forests; amphibians and insects undergo great adaptive radiation
240 mya	Mass extinction of nearly all living organisms
225 mya	Origin of mammals, dinosaurs; seed plants dominate
135 mya	Dinosaurs reach peak; flowering plants arise
65 mya	Mass extinction of dinosaurs and most marine organisms
63 mya	Flowering plants, mammals, birds, insects dominate
6 mya	First hominid (upright walking) human ancestors
2.5 mya	Human ancestors (*Homo*) using stone tools, forming social life
200,000 ya	Evolution of *Homo sapiens*
6400 ya	Egyptian pyramids constructed
2000 ya	Peak of Roman Empire
225 ya	Signing of the Declaration of Independence
In A.D. 1969	Humans step on earth's moon

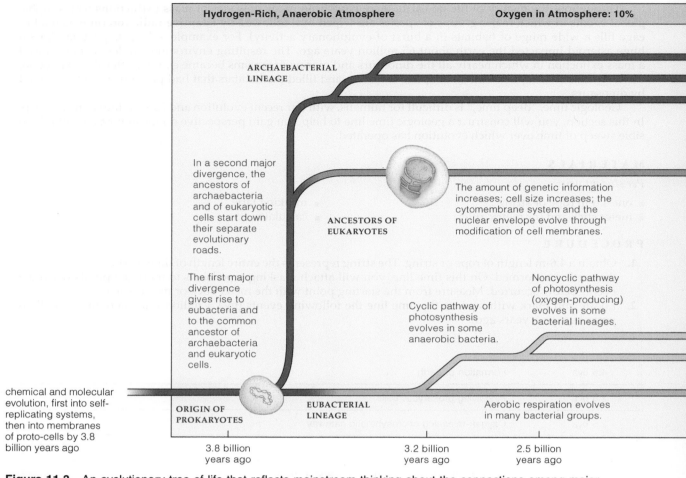

Figure 11-3 An evolutionary tree of life that reflects mainstream thinking about the connections among major lineages and origins of some eukaryotic organelles. (After Starr, 2000.)

Over what proportion of the earth's history were there only single-celled living organisms? _____

Over what proportion of the earth's history have multicelled organisms existed? _____

Over what proportion of the earth's history have mammals been a dominant part of the fauna? _____

Over what proportion of the earth's history have modern humans existed? _____

11.3 The Fossil Record and Human Evolution *(About 30 min.)*

The fossil record provides us with compelling evidence of evolution. Most fossils are parts of organisms, such as shells, teeth, and bones of animals, or stems and seeds of plants. These parts are replaced by minerals to form stone or are surrounded by hardened material that preserves the external form of the organism.

Anthropologists, scientists who study human origin and cultures, are piecing together the story of human evolution through the study of fossils, as well as through comparative biochemistry and anatomy. The fossil record of our human lineage is fragmentary at times and generates much discussion and differing interpretations. However, scientists agree that **hominids,** all species on the evolutionary branch leading to modern humans, arose in Africa between 10 and 5 million years ago from the same genetic line that also produced gorillas and chimpanzees.

Many anatomical changes occurred in the course of evolution from hominid ancestor to modern humans. Arms became shorter, feet flattened and then developed arches, and the big toe moved in line with the other toes. The legs moved more directly under the pelvis. These features allowed upright posture and bipedalism (walking on two legs), and they also allowed the use of hands for tasks other than locomotion.

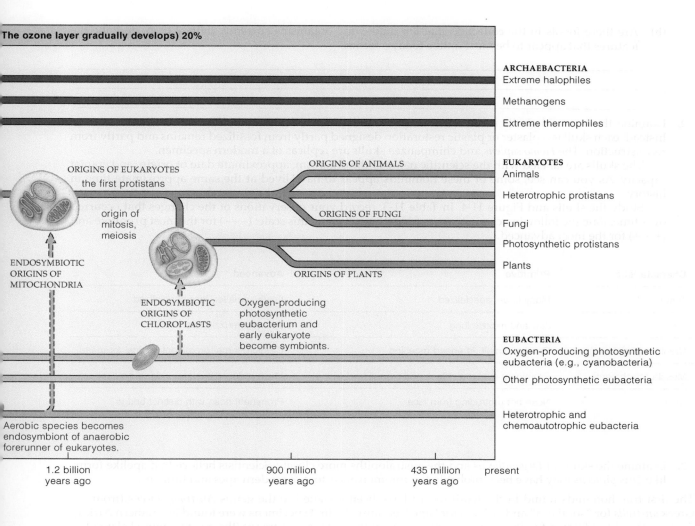

The ozone layer gradually develops) 20%

ARCHAEBACTERIA
Extreme halophiles

Methanogens

Extreme thermophiles

EUKARYOTES
Animals

Heterotrophic protistans

Fungi

Photosynthetic protistans

Plants

ORIGINS OF EUKARYOTES
the first protistans

ORIGINS OF ANIMALS

origin of
mitosis,
meiosis

ORIGINS OF FUNGI

ENDOSYMBIOTIC
ORIGINS OF
MITOCHONDRIA

ENDOSYMBIOTIC
ORIGINS OF
CHLOROPLASTS

ORIGINS OF PLANTS

Oxygen-producing
photosynthetic
eubacterium and
early eukaryote
become symbionts.

EUBACTERIA
Oxygen-producing photosynthetic
eubacteria (e.g., cyanobacteria)

Other photosynthetic eubacteria

Aerobic species becomes
endosymbiont of anaerobic
forerunner of eukaryotes.

Heterotrophic and
chemoautotrophic eubacteria

1.2 billion
years ago

900 million
years ago

435 million
years ago

present

Still other anatomical changes were associated with the head. In this section, you will observe some of the evolutionary trends associated with skull structure by studying reproductions of the skulls of several ancestors and relatives of modern humans.

MATERIALS

Per laboratory room:

- 1 set of skull reproductions and replicas, including *Dryopithecus africanus, Australopithecus afarensis, Australopithecus africanus, Paranthropus robustus, Homo habilis, Homo erectus, Homo neandertalensis, Homo sapiens,* and chimpanzee (*Pan troglodytes*)

- collection of fossil plants and animals (optional)
- guide to fossils (optional)
- wall chart of human evolution (optional)

PROCEDURE

1. If they are available, examine the fossil collection and field guide to fossils. Note which fossils are forms that lived in the seas and which lived on land.

    (a) Do any of the fossils resemble organisms now living? If so, describe the similarities between fossil and current forms.

    _____

    _____

    _____

(b) Are there fossils in the collection that are unlike any organisms currently living? If so, describe the features that appear to be most unlike today's forms.

_____

_____

_____

2. Examine the hominid skulls in the laboratory. Note that these skulls are not actual fossils themselves. Instead, each skull is a plaster or plastic restoration designed partly from fossilized remains and partly from reconstruction. The *Homo sapiens* and chimpanzee skulls are replicas of a modern specimen.

The skulls are labeled with the scientific name of the organism, approximate date of origin, and cranial capacity. As you can see, some of these hominids appear to have lived at the same approximate time in history.

Study the skulls and Figure 11-4. In Table 11-3, record your observations of the changes that occurred over time. Rate the following characteristics for each skull using this scale: (− − −) for the most primitive and (+ + +) for the most advanced.

Characteristic	Primitive	Advanced
Teeth	Many large, specialized	Fewer, smaller, less specialized
Jaw	Jaw and muzzle long	Jaw and muzzle short
Cranium (braincase)	Cranium small, forehead receding	Cranium large, prominent vertical forehead
Muscle attachments	Prominent eyebrow ridges and cranial keel (ridge)	Much reduced eyebrow ridges, no keel
Nose	Nose not protruding from face	Prominent nose with distinct bridge

3. Examine the skulls of *Dryopithecus* and the australopiths more closely. Scientists believe that apelike forms like *Dryopithecus* may have been probably the common ancestors of modern apes and humans.

The first true hominids found in the fossil record have been assigned to the genus *Australopithecus* (from the Greek *australis* for "southern" and *pithecus* for "ape," because the first specimens were found in southern Africa). Some of the oldest known fossils of *Australopithecus* are of the species *A. afarensis* (the most famous skeleton has been named Lucy). Lucy and her conspecifics (members of the same species) lived approximately 3.5 million years ago and may have been the ancestors to the later forms of *Australopithecus*. (See Figure 11-5.)

(a) Study the skull of *Dryopithecus* and the skull of *A. afarensis*. What resemblances do you see between the two specimens?

_____

_____

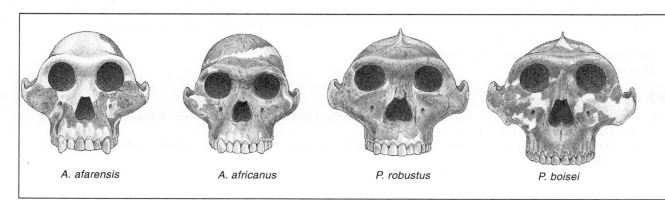

| A. afarensis | A. africanus | P. robustus | P. boisei |

Figure 11-4 Comparison of skull shapes of human ancestors and relatives. (After Starr and Taggart, 1992.)

TABLE 11-3 Skull Characteristics of Human Ancestors and Relatives, from (− − −) = Most Primitive to (+ + +) = Most Advanced

Genus and Species	Teeth	Jaw	Structure	Cranium	Muscle	Attachments	Nose
Dryopithecus							
Australopithecus afarensis							
Australopithecus africanus							
Paranthropus robustus							
Homo habilis							
Homo erectus							
Homo neandertalensis							
Homo sapiens							
Pan troglodytes							

(b) What structural differences do you see between the two skull specimens?

_____

_____

(c) What advances do you see in skull characteristics between *Dryopithecus* and *Australopithecus africanus*?

_____

_____

(d) Between *Dryopithecus* and *Paranthropus robustus*?

_____

_____

The genetic line(s) of *Australopithecus africanus* and *P. robustus* became extinct approximately 2–1.5 million years ago. There is clear evidence, though, that these hominids were fully bipedal, though not as upright in stance as modern humans. These australopiths also probably used unworked stones and pieces of wood as tools.

4. Now turn your attention to the skulls of the *Homo* lineage. There is debate also about the lineage of our own genus, *Homo* ("Man"). *Homo habilis,* often dubbed simply "early *Homo,*" lived in eastern and southern Africa from about 2.5–1.6 million years ago. *Homo erectus* ("upright man") also arose in Africa. However, it was *Homo erectus* whose populations left Africa in waves between 2 million and 500,000 years ago. Our own species, *Homo sapiens* ("wise man"), arose from other *Homo* ancestors.

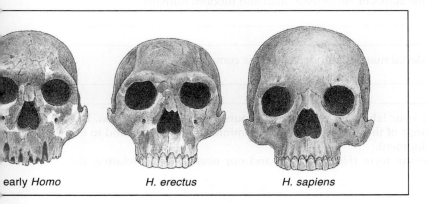

early *Homo*   *H. erectus*   *H. sapiens*

Figure 11-5 Timeline for appearance and extinction of major hominid species.

(a) What changes from primitive to advanced characteristics do you see in the evolutionary line from *A. afarensis* to *Homo sapiens*?

_____

_____

_____

(b) What is the trend in cranial capacity between the ancestral *A. afarensis* and *Homo erectus*?

_____

_____

(c) Between *Homo erectus* and *Homo sapiens*?

_____

_____

Fossils of the Neandertals (*Homo neandertalensis*) are known from Europe, the Near East, and China. These humans hunted and gathered food, made many kinds of tools, and buried their dead, which has been interpreted as showing their capability for abstract and religious thought. The Neandertals disappeared mysteriously 40,000–35,000 years ago, soon after the modern form of *Homo sapiens* arrived from Africa in their range.

(d) What differences do you see between the skulls of Neandertal man and modern humans?

_____

_____

(e) How do the cranial capacities of Neandertal man and modern humans compare?

_____

_____

5. If one is available, study the wall chart in your lab room showing the course of human evolution. Pay particular attention to the conceptual drawings of the appearance of the hominids and humans, and to the evolution of tool making and cultural development.

6. Finally, study the skulls of the modern human form (*Homo sapiens*) and our nearest living relative, the chimpanzee (*Pan troglodytes*).

Fossil evidence, biochemistry, and genetic analyses indicate that chimpanzees and humans are the most closely related of all living primates. In fact, comparisons of amino acid sequences of proteins and DNA sequences show that chimpanzees and humans share about 99% of their genes! Other evidence shows that the separation from the hominid line of the lineage that led to chimpanzees occurred no more than 4–6 million years ago.

(a) How does the chimpanzee skull compare to the human skull with respect to primitive and advanced anatomical features?

_____

_____

(b) How does the chimpanzee skull compare to the skull of *Dryopithecus*, the apelike hominid ancestor?

_____

_____

_____ 1. Evolution is
  (a) the difference in survival and reproduction of a population
  (b) the process that results in changes in the genetic makeup of a population over time
  (c) a group of individuals of the same species occupying a given area
  (d) change in an individual's genetic makeup over its lifetime

_____ 2. The major mechanism of evolution is
  (a) adaptive radiation
  (b) drift
  (c) fitness
  (d) natural selection

_____ 3. An organism whose genetic makeup allows it to produce more offspring than another of its species is said to have greater
  (a) fitness
  (b) evolution
  (c) adaptive radiation
  (d) selection

_____ 4. The earth was formed approximately
  (a) 4600 years ago
  (b) 1 million years ago
  (c) 1 billion years ago
  (d) 4.6 billion years ago

_____ 5. The first living organisms appeared on the earth approximately
  (a) 4.6 billion years ago
  (b) 3.8 billion years ago
  (c) 1 billion years ago
  (d) 6400 years ago

_____ 6. A catastrophic global event in which major groups of species disappear is called
  (a) adaptive radiation
  (b) natural selection
  (c) mass extinction
  (d) evolution

_____ 7. Fossils
  (a) are remains of organisms
  (b) are formed when organic materials are replaced with minerals
  (c) provide evidence of evolution
  (d) are all of the above

_____ 8. The organism believed to be the common ancestor of modern apes and humans is
  (a) _Australopithecus africanus_
  (b) _Homo habilis_
  (c) the chimpanzee
  (d) _Dryopithecus_

_____ 9. Hominids with evolutionarily advanced skull characteristics would have
  (a) many large, specialized teeth
  (b) a large cranium with prominent vertical forehead
  (c) prominent eyebrow ridges
  (d) a long jaw and muzzle

_____ 10. The human ancestor whose populations dispersed from Africa to other parts of the world was
  (a) _Homo sapiens_
  (b) _Australopithecus afarensis_
  (c) _Dryopithecus_
  (d) _Homo erectus_

EXERCISE 11

Evidences of Evolution

POST-LAB QUESTIONS

Introduction

1. Define the following terms.
   a. evolution

   b. natural selection

11.1 Experiment: Natural Selection

2. Describe how natural selection would operate to change the genetic makeup of a dandelion population that had been growing in an unmowed area if that area became subject to frequent low mowing.

11.2 Geologic Time

3. Which event occurred first in the earth's history?
   a. Photosynthesis or eukaryotic cells? _____
   b. Vertebrate animals or flowering plants? _____
   c. Extinction of dinosaurs or origin of hominids? _____

11.3 The Fossil Record and Human Evolution

4. What primitive characteristics are visible in the skull pictured here?

(Photo by J. W. Perry.)

5. Describe anatomical changes in the skull that occurred in human evolution between a *Dryopithecus*-like ancestor and *Homo sapiens*.

6. Compare the slope of the forehead of chimpanzees with that of modern humans.

7. Compare the teeth of *Australopithecus afarensis* and *Homo sapiens*.
   a. Describe similarities and differences between the two species.

   b. Write a hypothesis about dietary differences between the two species based on their teeth.

Food for Thought

8. Why was the development of bipedalism a major advancement in human evolution?

9. Do you believe humans are still evolving? If not, why not? If yes, explain in what ways humans may be evolving.

10. Humans have selectively bred many radically different domestic animals (for example, St. Bernard and chihuahua dog breeds). Does this activity result in evolution? Why or why not?

Taxonomy: Classifying and Naming Organisms

OBJECTIVES

After completing this exercise, you will be able to

1. define *common name, scientific name, binomial, genus, specific epithet, species, taxonomy, phylogenetic system, dichotomous key, herbarium;*

2. distinguish common names from scientific names;

3. explain why scientific names are preferred over common names in biology;

4. identify the genus and specific epithet in a scientific binomial;

5. write out scientific binomials in the form appropriate to the Linnean system;

6. construct a dichotomous key;

7. explain the usefulness of an herbarium;

8. use a dichotomous key to identify plants, animals, or other organisms as provided by your instructor.

INTRODUCTION

We are all great classifiers. Every day, we consciously or unconsciously classify and categorize the objects around us. We recognize an organism as a cat or a dog, a pine tree or an oak tree. But there are numerous kinds of oaks, so we refine our classification, giving the trees distinguishing names such as "red oak," "white oak," or "bur oak." These are examples of **common names,** names with which you are probably most familiar.

Scientists are continually exchanging information about living organisms. But not all scientists speak the same language. The common name "white oak," familiar to an American, is probably not familiar to a Spanish biologist, even though the tree we know as white oak may exist in Spain as well as in our own backyard. Moreover, even within our own language, the same organism can have several common names. For example, within North America a gopher is also called a ground squirrel, a pocket mole, and a groundhog. On the other hand, the same common name may describe many different organisms; there are more than 300 different trees called "mahogany"! To circumvent the problems associated with common names, biologists use **scientific names** that are unique to each kind of organism and that are used throughout the world.

A scientific name is two-parted, a binomial. The first word of the binomial designates the group to which the organism belongs; this is the **genus** name (the plural of genus is *genera*). All oak trees belong to the genus *Quercus*, a word derived from Latin. Each kind of organism within a genus is given a **specific epithet.** Thus, the scientific name for white oak is *Quercus alba* (specific epithet is *alba*), while that of bur oak is *Quercus macrocarpa* (specific epithet is *macrocarpa*).

Notice that the genus name is always capitalized; the specific epithet usually is not capitalized (although it can be if it is the proper name of a person or place). The binomial is written in *italics* (since these are Latin names); if italics are not available, the genus name and specific epithet are underlined.

You will hear discussion of "species" of organisms. For example, on a field trip, you may be asked "What species is this tree?" Assuming you are looking at a white oak, your reply would be *"Quercus alba."* The scientific name of the **species** includes *both* the genus name and specific epithet.

If a species is named more than once within textual material, it is accepted convention to write out the full genus name and specific epithet the first time and to abbreviate the genus name every time thereafter. For example, if white oak is being described, the first use is written *Quercus alba,* and each subsequent naming appears as *Q. alba.*

Similarly, when a number of species, all of the same genus, are being listed, the accepted convention is to write both the genus name and specific epithet for the first species and to abbreviate the genus name for each species listed thereafter. Thus, it is acceptable to list the scientific names for white oak and bur oak as *Quercus alba* and *Q. macrocarpa,* respectively.

Taxonomy is the science of classification (categorizing) and nomenclature (naming). Biologists prefer a system that indicates the evolutionary relationships among organisms. To this end, classification became a **phylogenetic system;** that is, one indicating the presumed evolutionary ancestry among organisms.

Current taxonomic thought separates all living organisms into six kingdoms:

- Kingdom Bacteria (prokaryotic cells that include pathogens)
- Kingdom Archaea (prokaryotic organisms that are evolutionarily closer to eukaryotes than bacteria)
- Kingdom Protista (euglenids, chrysophytes, diatoms, dinoflagellates, slime molds, and protozoans)
- Kingdom Fungi (fungi)
- Kingdom Plantae (plants)
- Kingdom Animalia (animals)

Let's consider the scientific system of classification, using ourselves as examples. All members of our species belong to

- Kingdom Animalia (animals)
- Phylum Chordata (animals with a notochord)
- Class Mammalia (animals with mammary glands)
- Order Primates (mammals that walk upright on two legs)
- Family Hominidae (human forms)
- Genus *Homo* (mankind)
- Specific epithet *sapiens* (wise)
- Species: *Homo sapiens*

The more closely related evolutionarily two organisms are, the more categories they share. You and I are different individuals of the same species. We share the same genus and specific epithet, *Homo* and *sapiens*. A creature believed to be our closest extinct ancestor walked the earth 1.5 million years ago. That creature shared our genus name but had a different specific epithet, *erectus*. Thus, *Homo sapiens* and *H. erectus* are *different* species.

Like all science, taxonomy is subject to change as new information becomes available. Modifications are made to reflect revised interpretations.

12.1   Constructing a Dichotomous Key *(About 45 min.)*

To classify organisms, you must first identify them. A *taxonomic key* is a device for identifying an object unknown to you but that someone else has described. The user chooses between alternative characteristics of the unknown object and, by making the correct choices, arrives at the name of the object.

Keys that are based on successive choices between two alternatives are known as **dichotomous keys** (*dichotomous* means "to fork into two equal parts"). When using a key, always read both choices, even though the first appears to describe the subject. Don't guess at measurements; use a ruler. Since living organisms vary in their characteristics, don't base your conclusion on a single specimen if more are available.

MATERIALS

Per lab room:

- several meter sticks or metric height charts taped to a wall

PROCEDURE

1. Suppose the geometric shapes below have unfamiliar names. Look at the dichotomous key following the figures. Notice there is a 1a and a 1b. Start with 1a. If the description in 1a fits the figure you are observing better than description 1b, then proceed to the choices listed under 2, as shown at the end of line 1a. If 1a does *not* describe the figure in question, 1b does. Looking at the end of line 1b, you see that the figure would be called an Elcric.
2. Using the key provided, determine the hypothetical name for each object. Write the name beneath the object and then check with your instructor to see if you have made the correct choices.

——————   ——————   ——————   ——————   ——————

Key		
1a.	Figure with distinct corners	2
1b.	Figure without distinct corners	Elcric
2a.	Figure with 3 sides	3
2b.	Figure with 4 or more sides	4
3a.	All sides of equal length	Legnairt
3b.	Only 2 sides equal	Legnairtosi
4a.	Figure with only right angles	Eraqus
4b.	Figure with other than right angles	Nogatco

3. Now you will construct a dichotomous key, using your classmates as subjects. The class should divide up into groups of eight (or as evenly as the class size will allow). Working with the individuals in your group, fill in Table 12-1, measuring height with a metric ruler or the scale attached to the wall.

4. To see how you might plan a dichotomous key, examine the following branch diagram. If there are both men and women in a group, the most obvious first split is male/female (although other possibilities for the split could be chosen as well). Follow the course of splits for two of the men in the group.

Note that each choice has *only* two alternatives. Thus, we split into "under 1.75 m" and "1.75 m or taller." Likewise, our next split is into "blue eyes" and "nonblue eyes" rather than all the possibilities.

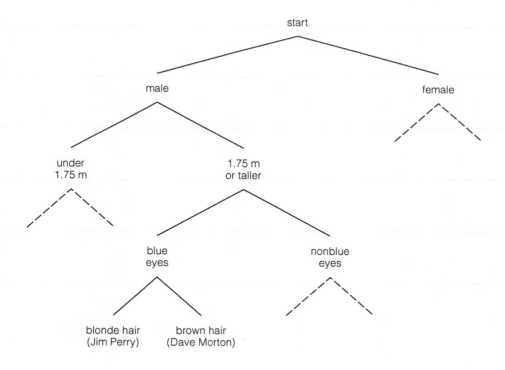

5. On a separate sheet of paper, construct a branch diagram for your group using the characteristics in Table 12-1 and then condense it into the dichotomous key that follows. When you have finished, exchange your key with that of an individual in another group. Key out the individuals in the other group without speaking until you believe you know the name of the individual you are examining. Ask that individual if you are correct. If not, go back to find out where you made a mistake, or possibly where the key was misleading. (Depending on how you construct your key, you may need more or fewer lines than have been provided.)

TABLE 12-1	Characteristics of Students					
Student (name)	Sex (m/f)	Height (m)	Eye Color	Hair Color	Shoe Size
1.					
2.					
3.					
4.					
5.					
6.					
7.					
8.					

Key to Students in Group _____

1a.
1b.
2a.
2b.
3a.
3b.
4a.
4b.
5a.
5b.
6a.
6b.
7a.
7b.
8a.
8b.

12.2   Using a Taxonomic Key

A. *Some Microscopic Members of the Freshwater Environment* (About 30 min.)

Suppose you want to identify the specimens in some pond water. The easiest way is to key them out with a dichotomous key, now that you know how to use one. In this section, you will do just that.

MATERIALS

Per student:

- compound microscope
- microscope slide
- coverslip
- dissecting needle

Per student group (table):

- cultures of freshwater organisms
- 1 disposable plastic pipet per culture
- methylcellulose in dropping bottle

PROCEDURE

1. Obtain a clean glass microscope slide and clean coverslip.
2. Using a disposable plastic pipet or dissecting needle, withdraw a small amount of the culture provided.
3. Place *one* drop of the culture on the center of the slide.
4. Gently lower the coverslip onto the liquid.
5. Using your compound light microscope, observe your wet mount. Focus first with the low-power objective and then with the medium or high-dry objective, depending on the size of the organism in the field of view.
6. Concentrate your observation on a single specimen, keying out the specimen using the Key to Selected Freshwater Inhabitants that follows.
7. In the space provided, write the scientific name of each organism you identify. After each identification, have your instructor verify your conclusion.
8. Clean and reuse your slide and coverslip after each identification.

Key to Selected Freshwater Inhabitants

1a.	Filamentous organism consisting of green, chloroplast-bearing threads	2
1b.	Organism consisting of a single cell or nonfilamentous colony	4
2a.	Filament branched, each cell mostly filled with green chloroplast	*Cladophora*
2b.	Filament unbranched	3
3a.	Each cell of filament containing 1 or 2 spiral-shaped green chloroplasts	*Spirogyra*
3b.	Each cell of filament containing 2 star-shaped green chloroplasts	*Zygnema*
4a.	Organism consisting of a single cell	5
4b.	Organism composed of many cells aggregated into a colony	6
5a.	Motile, teardrop-shaped or spherical organism	*Chlamydomonas*
5b.	Nonmotile, elongate cell on either end; clear, granule-containing regions at ends	*Closterium*
6a.	Colony a hollow round ball of more than 500 cells; new colonies may be present inside larger colony	*Volvox*
6b.	Colony consisting of less than 50 cells	7
7a.	Organism composed of a number of tooth-shaped cells	*Pediastrum*
7b.	Colony a loose square or rectangle of 4–32 spherical cells	*Gonium*

Organism 1 is _____

Organism 2 is _____

Organism 3 is _____

Organism 4 is _____

Organism 5 is _____

Organism 6 is _____

Organism 7 is _____

Organism 8 is _____

Suppose you want to identify the trees growing on your campus or in your yard at home. Without having an expert present, you can now do that, because you know how to use a taxonomic key. But how can you be certain that you have keyed your specimen correctly?

Typically, scientists compare their tentative identifications against *reference specimens*—that is, preserved organisms that have been identified by an expert *taxonomist* (a person who names and classifies organisms).

If you are identifying fishes or birds, the reference specimen might be a bottled or mounted specimen with the name on it. In the case of plants, reference specimens most frequently take the form of *herbarium mounts* (Figure 12-1) of the plants. An **herbarium** (plural, *herbaria*) is a repository, a museum of sorts, of preserved plants. The taxonomist flattens freshly collected specimens in a plant press. They are then dried and mounted on sheets of paper. Herbarium labels are affixed to the sheets, indicating the scientific name of the plant, the person who collected it, the location and date of collection, and often pertinent information about the habitat in which the plant was found.

It is likely that your school has an herbarium. If so, your instructor may show you the collection. To some, this endeavor may seem boring, but herbaria serve a critical function. The appearance or disappearance of plants from the landscape often gives a very good indication of environmental change. An herbarium records the diversity of plants in the area, at any point in history since the start of the collection.

Label indicates name of specimen, site and date of collection, associated species at same site, name(s) of collector(s)

(Photo by J. W. Perry)

Figure 12-1 A typical herbarium mount.

MATERIALS

Per student group (table):

- set of 8 tree twigs with leaves (fresh or herbarium specimens) *or*
- trees and shrubs in leafy condition (for an outdoor lab)

PROCEDURE

Use the appropriate following key to identify the tree and shrub specimens that have been provided in the lab or that you find on your campus. Refer to the *Glossary to Tree Key* and Figures 12-2 through 12-9 when you encounter an unfamiliar term. When you have finished keying a specimen, confirm your identification by checking the herbarium mounts or asking your instructor.

Note: **Some descriptions within the key have more characteristics than your specimen will exhibit. For example, the key may describe a fruit type when the specimen doesn't have a fruit on it. However, other specimen characteristics are described, and these should allow you to identify the specimen.**

Note: **The keys provided are for *selected* trees of your area. In nature, you will find many more genera than can be identified by these keys.**

Common names within parentheses follow the scientific name. A metric ruler is provided on page 204 for use where measurements are required.

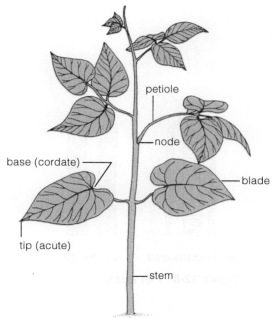

Figure 12-2 Structure of a typical plant (bean).

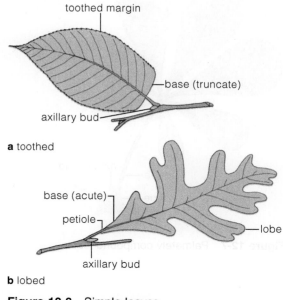

a toothed

b lobed

Figure 12-3 Simple leaves.

Figure 12-4 Pinnately compound leaf.

Figure 12-5 Simple leaves—alternating.

Figure 12-6 Simple leaves—opposite.

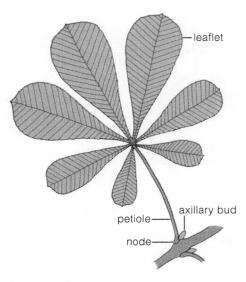

leaflet

petiole

axillary bud

node

Figure 12-7   Palmately compound leaf.

a pith chambered   **b** pith solid

Figure 12-8   Pith types.

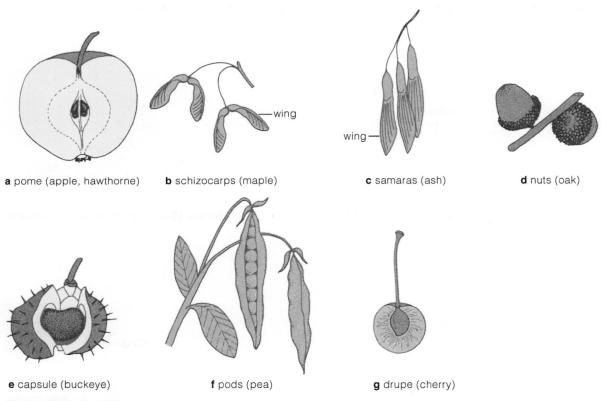

wing

wing

a pome (apple, hawthorne)   **b** schizocarps (maple)   **c** samaras (ash)   **d** nuts (oak)

e capsule (buckeye)   **f** pods (pea)   **g** drupe (cherry)

Figure 12-9   Fruit types.

0   1   2   3   4   5   6   7   8   9   10   11   12   13   14   15

centimeters

Key to Some Common Genera of Trees of the Midwestern and Eastern United States and Canada

1a.	Leaves broad and flat; plants producing flowers and fruits (angiosperms)	2
1b.	Leaves needlelike or scalelike; plants producing cones, but no flowers or fruits (gymnosperms)	22
2a.	Leaves compound	3
2b.	Leaves simple	9
3a.	Leaves alternate	4
3b.	Leaves opposite	7
4a.	Leaflets short and stubby, less than twice as long as broad; branches armed with spines or thorns; fruit a beanlike pod	5
4b.	Leaflets long and narrow, more than twice as long as broad; trunk and branches unarmed; fruit a nut	6
5a.	Leaflet margin without teeth; terminal leaflet present; small deciduous spines at leaf base	*Robinia* (black locust)
5b.	Leaflet margin with fine teeth; terminal leaflet absent; large permanent thorns on trunk and branches	*Gleditsia* (honey locust)
6a.	Leaflets usually numbering less than 11; pith of twigs solid	*Carya* (hickory)
6b.	Leaflets numbering 1 or more, pith of twigs divided into chambers	*Juglans* (walnut, butternut)
7a.	Leaflets pinnately arranged; fruit a light-winged samara	8
7b.	Leaflets palmately arranged; fruit a heavy leathery spherical capsule	*Aesculus* (buckeye)
8a.	Leaflets numbering mostly 3–5; fruit a schizocarp with curved wings	*Acer* (box elder)
8b.	Leaflets numbering mostly more than 5; samaras borne singly, with straight wings	*Fraxinus* (ash)
9a.	Leaves alternate	10
9b.	Leaves opposite	21
10a.	Leaves very narrow, at least 3 times as long as broad; axillary buds flattened against stem	*Salix* (willow)
10b.	Leaves broader, less than 3 times as long as broad	11
11a.	Leaf margin without small, regular teeth	12
11b.	Leaf margin with small, regular teeth	13
12a.	Fruit a pod with downy seeds; leaf blade obtuse at base; petioles flattened, or if rounded, bark smooth	*Populus* (poplar, popple, aspen)
12b.	Fruit an acorn; leaf blade acute at the base; petioles rounded; bark rough	*Quercus* (oaks)
13a.	Leaves (at least some of them) with lobes or other indentations in addition to small, regular teeth	14
13b.	Leaves without lobes or other indentations except for small, regular teeth	16
14a.	Lobes asymmetrical, leaves often mitten-shaped	*Morus* (mulberry)
14b.	Lobes or other indentations fairly symmetrical	15

15a.	Branches thorny (armed); fruit a small applelike pome	*Crataegus* (hawthorne)
15b.	Branches unarmed	17
16a.	Bark smooth and waxy, often separating into thin layers; leaf base symmetrical	*Betula* (birch)
16b.	Bark rough and furrowed, leaf base asymmetrical	*Ulmus* (elm)
17a.	Leaf base asymmetrical, strongly heart-shaped, at least on one side	*Tilia* (basswood or linden)
17b.	Leaf base acute, truncate, or slightly cordate	18
18a.	Leaf base asymmetrical; bark on older stems (trunk) often warty	*Celtis* (hackberry)
18b.	Leaf base symmetrical	19
19a.	Leaf blade usually about twice as long as broad, generally acute at the base; fruit fleshy	20
19b.	Leaf not much longer than broad, generally truncate at base; fruit a dry pod	*Populus* (poplar, popple, aspen)
20a.	Leaf tapering to a pointed tip, glandular at base	*Prunus* (cherry)
20b.	Leaf spoon-shaped with a rounded tip, no glands at base	*Crataegus* (hawthorne)
21a.	Leaf margins with lobes and points, fruit a schizocarp	*Acer* (maple)
21b.	Leaf margins without lobes or points; fruit a long capsule	*Catalpa* (catalpa)
22a.	Leaves needlelike, with 2 or more needles in a cluster	23
22b.	Leaves needlelike or scalelike, occurring singly	24
23a.	Leaves more than 5 in a cluster, soft, deciduous, borne at the ends of conspicuous stubby branches	*Larix* (larch, tamarack)
23b.	Leaves 2–5 in a cluster	*Pinus* (pines)
24a.	Leaves soft, not sharp to the touch	25
24b.	Leaves stiff or sharp and often unpleasant to touch	27
25a.	Leaves about 0.2 cm and scalelike, overlapping	*Thuja* (white cedar, arbor vitae)
25b.	Leaves needlelike, appear to form two ranks on twig	26
26a.	Leaves with distinct petioles, 0.8–1.5 cm long; twigs rough; female cones drooping from branches	*Tsuga* (hemlock)
26b.	Leaves without distinct petioles, 1–3 cm long; twigs smooth; female cones erect on branches	*Abies* (firs)
27a.	Leaves appear triangular-shaped, about 0.5 cm, and tightly pressed to twig; cone blue, berrylike	*Juniperus* (juniper, Eastern red cedar)
27b.	Leaves elongated and needlelike	28
28a.	Tree; leaves 4-sided, protrude stiffly from twig; female cones droop from branch	*Picea* (spruces)
28b.	Shrub; leaves flattened, pressed close to twig at base; seed partially covered by a fleshy coat, usually red	*Taxus* (yew)

Key to Some Common Genera of Trees of the Pacific Region of the United States and Canada

1a.	Leaves broad and flat; plants producing flowers and fruits (angiosperms)	2
1b.	Leaves needlelike or scalelike; plants producing cones, but no flowers or fruits (gymnosperms)	15
2a.	Leaves compound	3
2b.	Leaves simple	6
3a.	Leaves pinnately arranged	4
3b.	Leaves palmately arranged	5
4a.	Leaflets number 7, fruit a samara	*Fraxinus* (ash)
4b.	Leaflets 15–17, fruit a nut	*Juglans* (walnut)
5a.	Leaflets numbering 3, lobed; fruit a schizocarp	*Acer* (box elder)
5b.	Leaflets numbering more than 3; fruit a smooth or spiny capsule	*Aesculus* (buckeye)
6a.	Three or more equal-sized veins branching from leaf base	7
6b.	Leaf with single large central vein with other main veins branching from the central vein	9
7a.	Leaves opposite; fruit a schizocarp	*Acer* (maple)
7b.	Leaves alternate	8
8a.	Leaves nearly round in outline; fruit a pod	*Cercis* (redbud)
8b.	Leaves deeply lobed, very hairy beneath; fruit consisting of an aggregation of many 1-seeded nutlets surrounded by long hairs	*Platanus* (sycamore)
9a.	Leaf lobed; fruit a nut	*Quercus* (oak)
9b.	Leaf not lobed	10
10a.	Leaves opposite; fruit a drupe; halves of leaf remain attached by "threads" after blade has been creased and broken	*Cornus* (dogwood)
10b.	Leaves alternate	11
11a.	Upon crushing, blade gives off strong, penetrating odor	*Eucalyptus* (eucalyptus)
11b.	Blade not strongly odiferous upon crushing	12
12a.	Branch bark smooth, conspicuously red-brown; fruit a red ororange berry	*Arbutus* (madrone)
12b.	Branch rough, not colored red-brown	13
13a.	Undersurface of leaves golden-yellow; fruit a spiny, husked nut	*Catanopsis* (golden chinquapin)
13b.	Leaves green beneath	14
14a.	Petiole hairy; leathery blade with a stubby spine at end of each main vein; fruit a nut	*Lithocarpus* (tanoak)
14b.	Petiole and leaf lacking numerous hairs, leaves long and narrow, more than twice as long as wide	*Salix* (willow)

15a.	Leaves needlelike	16
15b.	Leaves scalelike	23
16a.	Leaves needlelike, with 2 or more needles in a cluster	17
16b.	Leaves needlelike, occurring singly	18
17a.	Needles 2–5 in a cluster	*Pinus* (pine)
17b.	Needles 6 or more per cluster, soft, deciduous, borne at the ends of stubby, conspicuous branches	*Larix* (larch)
18a.	Round scars on twigs where old needles have fallen off; twigs smooth; needles soft to the grasp; cones pointing upward with reference to stem	*Abies* (fir)
18b.	Twigs rough, with old needle petioles remaining	19
19a.	Needles angled, stiff, sharp, pointed, unpleasant to grasp; cones hanging downward from branch	*Picea* (spruce)
19b.	Needles soft, not sharp when grasped	20
20a.	Needles round in cross section, can be rolled easily between thumb and index finger; needles less than 1.3 cm long; cones small, less than 1.5 cm	*Tsuga* (hemlock)
20b.	Needles too flat to be rolled easily	21
21a.	Tips of needles blunt or rounded, undersurface with 2 white bands; cones with long, conspicuous, 3-lobed bracts	*Pseudotsuga* (Douglas fir)
21b.	Tips of needles pointed	22
22a.	Tops of needles grooved; woody seed cones broadly oblong in outline	*Sequoia* (redwood)
22b.	Tops of needles with ridges; lacking in cones, instead having a red, fleshy, cuplike seed covering	Taxus (yew)
23a.	Twig ends appear as if jointed	*Calocedrus* (incense cedar)
23b.	Tips of branches flattened, not jointed in appearance	24
24a.	Leaves glossy and fragrant	*Thuja* (Western red cedar)
24b.	Leaves awl-shaped, arranged spirally on twig	*Sequoiadendron* (giant sequoia)

Glossary to Tree Key

- *Acorn*—The fruit of an oak, consisting of a nut and its basally attached cup (Fig. 12-9d)
- *Acute*—Sharp-pointed (Fig. 12-2)
- *Alternate*—Describing the arrangement of leaves or other structures that occur singly at successive nodes or levels; not opposite or whorled (Fig. 12-5)
- *Angiosperm*—A flowering seed plant (e.g., bean plant, maple tree, grass)
- *Armed*—Possessing thorns or spines
- *Asymmetrical*—Not symmetrical
- *Axil*—The upper angle between a branch or leaf and the stem from which it grows
- *Axillary bud*—A bud occurring in the axil of a leaf (Figs. 12-3 through 12-7)
- *Basal*—At the base
- *Blade*—The expanded, more or less flat portion of a leaf (Fig. 12-2)
- *Bract*—A much reduced leaf
- *Capsule*—A dry fruit that splits open at maturity (e.g., buckeye; Fig. 12-9e)

- *Compound leaf*—Blade composed of 2 or more separate parts (leaflets) (Figs. 12-4, 12-7)
- *Cordate*—Heart-shaped (Fig. 12-2)
- *Deciduous*—Falling off at the end of a functional period (such as a growing season)
- *Drupe*—Fleshy fruit containing a single hard stone that encloses the seed (e.g., cherry, peach, or dogwood; Fig. 12-9g)
- *Fruit*—A ripened ovary, in some cases with associated floral parts (Figs. 12-9a–g)
- *Glandular*—Bearing secretory structures (glands)
- *Gymnosperm*—Seed plant lacking flowers and fruits (e.g., pine tree)
- *Lateral*—On or at the side (Fig. 12-4)
- *Leaflet*—One of the divisions of the blade of a compound leaf (Figs. 12-4, 12-7)
- *Lobed*—Separated by indentations (sinuses) into segments (lobes) larger than teeth (Fig. 12-3b)
- *Node*—Region on a stem where leaves or branches arise (Figs. 12-2 through 12-7)
- *Nut*—A hard, 1-seeded fruit that does not split open at maturity (e.g., acorn; Fig. 12-9d)
- *Obtuse*—Blunt (Fig. 12-6)
- *Opposite*—Describing the arrangement of leaves of other structures that occur 2 at a node, each separated from the other by half the circumference of the axis (Fig. 12-6)
- *Palmately compound*—With leaflets all arising at apex of petiole (Fig. 12-7)
- *Petiole*—Stalk of a leaf (Figs. 12-2, 12-3, 12-4, 12-7)
- *Pinnately compound*—A leaf constructed somewhat like a feather, with the leaflets arranged on both sides of the rachis (Fig. 12-4)
- *Pith*—Internally, the centermost region of a stem (Figs. 12-8a, b)
- *Pod*—A dehiscent, dry fruit; a rather general term sometimes used when no other more specific term is applicable (Fig. 12-9f)
- *Pome*—Fleshy fruit containing several seeds (e.g., apple or pear; Fig. 12-9a)
- *Rachis*—Central axis of a pinnately compound leaf (Fig. 12-4)
- *Samara*—Winged, 1-seeded, dry fruit (e.g., ash fruits; Fig. 12-9c)
- *Schizocarp*—Dry fruit that splits at maturity into two 1-seeded halves (Fig. 12-9b)
- *Simple leaf*—One with a single blade, not divided into leaflets (Figs. 12-3, 12-5, 12-6)
- *Spine*—Strong, stiff, sharp-pointed outgrowth on a stem or other organ (Fig. 12-6)
- *Symmetrical*—Capable of being divided longitudinally into similar halves
- *Terminal*—Last in a series (Fig. 12-4)
- *Thorn*—Sharp, woody, spinelike outgrowth from the wood of a stem; usually a reduced, modified branch
- *Tooth*—Small, sharp-pointed marginal lobe of a leaf (Fig. 12-3a)
- *Truncate*—Cut off squarely at end (Fig. 12-3a)
- *Unarmed*—Without thorns or spines
- *Whorl*—A group of 3 or more leaves or other structures at a node

12.3   What Species Is Your Christmas Tree? *(About 20 min.)*

Each year millions of "evergreen" trees become the center of attraction in human dwellings during the Christmas season. The process of selecting the all-important tree is the same whether you reside in the city where you buy your tree from a commercial grower, or whether you cut one off your "back forty." You ponder and evaluate each specimen until, with the utmost confidence, you bring home that perfect tree. Now that you have it, just what kind of tree stands in your home, looking somewhat like a cross between Old Glory and the Sistine Chapel? This key contains most of the trees that are used as Christmas trees; other gymnosperm trees are included, too. The common "Christmas trees" have an asterisk after their scientific name. Note that this key, unlike those in the preceding sections, indicates actual species designations.

1a.	Tree fragrant, boughs having supported (on clear moonlit nights) masses of glistening snow on their green needles; tree a product of nature	2
1b.	Tree not really a tree but rather a product of a cold and insensitive society; tree never giving life and never having life	17
2a.	Leaves persistent and green throughout the winter, needlelike, awl-shaped, or scalelike	3
2b.	Leaves deciduous; for this reason not a desirable Christmas tree	4
3a.	Leaves in clusters of 2–5, their bases within a sheath	5
3b.	Leaves borne singly, not in clusters	9
4a.	Cones 1.25–1.8 cm long, 12–15 scales making up cone	*Larix laricina* (tamarack)
4b.	Cones 1.8–3.5 cm long, 40–50 scales comprising cone	*Larix decidua* (larch)
5a.	Leaves 5 in a cluster, cones 10–25 cm long	*Pinus strobus** (white pine)
5b.	Leaves 2 in a cluster, cones less than 10 cm long	6
6a.	Leaves 2.5–7.5 cm long	7
6b.	Leaves 7.5–15 cm long	8
7a.	Leaves with a bluish cast; cones with a stout stalk, pointing away from the tip of the branch; bark orange in the upper part of the tree	*Pinus sylvestris** (scotch pine)
7b.	Leaves 1.25–3.75 cm long; cones stalkless, pointing forward toward the tip of branch	*Pinus banksiana* (jack pine)
8a.	Leaves slender, shiny; bark of trunk red-brown; cones 5–7.5 cm long; scales of cones without any spine at tip	*Pinus resinosa** (red pine)
8b.	Leaves thickened, dull; bark of trunk gray to nearly black; cones 5 to 7.5 cm long; scales of cone armed with short spine at tip	*Pinus nigra** (Austrian pine)
9a.	Leaves scalelike or awl-shaped	10
9b.	Leaves needlelike	11
10a.	Twigs flattened, leaves all of one kind, scalelike, extending down the twig below the point of attachment	*Thuja occidentalis* (white cedar, arbor vitae)
10b.	Twigs more or less circular in cross section; leaves of 2 kinds, either scalelike or awl-shaped, often both on same branch, not extending down the twig; coneless but may have a blue berrylike structure	*Juniperus virginiana* (red cedar)
11a.	Leaves with petioles	12
11b.	Leaves lacking petioles, leaf tip notched, needles longer than 1.25 cm	*Abies balsamea** (balsam fir)
12a.	Leaves angular, 4-sided in cross section, harsh to the touch; petiole adheres to twig	13
12b.	Leaves flattened	15
13a.	Leaves 3–10 mm long, blunt-pointed; twigs rusty and hairy	*Picea mariana** (black spruce)
13b.	Leaves 2 cm long, sharp-pointed; twigs smooth	14

14a.	Cones 2.5–5 cm long; leaves ill-scented when bruised or broken; smaller branches mostly horizontal	*Picea glauca** (white spruce)
14b.	Cones 7.5–15 cm long; scales comprising cone with finely toothed markings; leaves not ill-scented when bruised or broken; smaller branches drooping	*Picea abies** (Norway spruce)
15a.	Leaves pointed, over 1.25 cm long; red fleshy, berrylike structures present	16
15b.	Leaves rounded at tip, less than 1.25 cm long, with 2 white lines on underside	*Tsuga canadensis* (hemlock)
16a.	Leaves 2–2.5 cm long, dull dark green on top, with 2 broad yellow bands on undersurface; petiole yellowish	*Taxus cuspidata* (Japanese yew)
16b.	Leaves 1.25–2 cm long, without yellow bands on underside	*Taxus canadensis* (American yew)
17a.	Tree a glittering mass of structural aluminum, sometimes illuminated by multicolored floodlights	*Aluminous ersatzenbaum** (aluminum substitute)
17b.	Tree green, produced with petroleum products, increasing our dependence upon oil; used year after year; exactly like all others of its manufacture	*Plasticus perfectus** (plastic substitute)

_____ 1. The name "human" is an example of a
   (a) common name
   (b) scientific name
   (c) binomial
   (d) polynomial

_____ 2. Current scientific thought places organisms in one of ___ kingdoms.
   (a) two
   (b) four
   (c) five
   (d) six

_____ 3. The scientific name for the ruffed grouse is *Bonasa umbellus*. *Bonasa* is
   (a) the family name
   (b) the genus
   (c) the specific epithet
   (d) all of the above

_____ 4. A binomial is always a
   (a) genus
   (b) specific epithet
   (c) scientific name
   (d) two-part name

_____ 5. The science of classifying and naming organisms is known as
   (a) taxonomy
   (b) phylogeny
   (c) morphology
   (d) physiology

_____ 6. Which scientific name for the wolf is presented correctly?
   (a) Canis lupus
   (b) canis lupus
   (c) *Canis lupus*
   (d) Canis Lupus

_____ 7. A road that dichotomizes is
   (a) an intersection of two crossroads
   (b) a road that forks into two roads
   (c) a road that has numerous entrances and exits
   (d) a road that leads nowhere

_____ 8. Most scientific names are derived from
   (a) English
   (b) Latin
   (c) Italian
   (d) French

_____ 9. One objection to common names is that
   (a) many organisms may have the same common name
   (b) many common names may exist for the same organism
   (c) the common name may not be familiar to an individual not speaking the language of the common name
   (d) all of the above are true

_____ 10. Phylogeny is the apparent
   (a) name of an organism
   (b) ancestry of an organism
   (c) nomenclature
   (d) dichotomy of a system of classification

Name _____ Section Number _____

EXERCISE 12

Taxonomy: Classifying and Naming Organisms

POST-LAB QUESTIONS

Introduction

1. If you were to use a binomial system to identify the members of your family (mother, father, sisters, brothers), how would you write their names so that your system would most closely approximate that used to designate species?

2. Describe several advantages of using scientific names instead of common names.

3. Based on the following classification scheme, which two organisms are most closely phylogenetically related? Why?

	Organism 1	Organism 2	Organism 3	Organism 4
Kingdom	Animalia	Animalia	Animalia	Animalia
Phylum	Arthopoda	Arthropoda	Arthropoda	Arthropoda
Class	Insecta	Insecta	Insecta	Insecta
Order	Coleoptera	Coleoptera	Coleoptera	Coleoptera
Genus	*Caulophilus*	*Sitophilus*	*Latheticus*	*Sitophilus*
Specific epithet	*oryzae*	*oryzae*	*oryzae*	*zeamaize*
Common name	Broadnosed grain weevil	Rice weevil	Longheaded flour beetle	Maize weevil

12.2 Using a Taxonomic Key

Consider the drawing of plants A and B in answering questions 4–6.

fruit

plant A

cone

plant B

4. Using the taxonomic key in the exercise, identify the two plants as either angiosperms or gymnosperms.

   Plant A is a (an) _____.

   Plant B is a (an) _____.

5. To what genus does plant A belong? What is its common name?

   genus: _____

   common name: _____

6. To what genus does plant B belong? What is its common name?

   genus: _____

   common name: _____

Consider the drawing of plants C and D in answering questions 7–9.

plant C

plant D

7. As completely as possible, describe the leaf of plant C.

8. To what genus does plant C belong? What is its common name?

        genus: _____

  common name: _____

9. Using the taxonomic key in the exercise, identify the genus of the organism below.

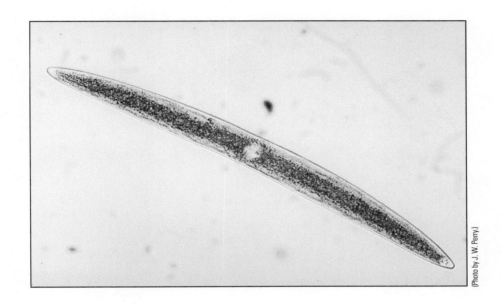

(Photo by J. W. Perry.)

        genus: _____

Food for Thought

10. If you owned a large, varied music collection, how might you devise a key to keep track of all your different kinds of music?

Bacteria and Protists

OBJECTIVES

After completing this exercise, you will be able to

1. define *prokaryotic, eukaryotic, pathogen, decomposer, coccus, bacillus, spirillum, Gram stain, antibiotic, symbiosis, parasitism, commensalism, mutualism, nitrogen fixation, monoecious, dioecious, plasmodium, obligate mutualism, gametangia, phagocytosis, vector; phytoplankton, phyt, phycobilin, agar, fucoxanthin, algin, kelp, gametangium, oogonia* and *antheridia;*

2. describe characteristics distinguishing bacteria from protists;

3. identify and classify the organisms studied in this exercise;

4. identify structures (those in **boldface** in the procedure sections) in the organisms studied;

5. distinguish Gram-positive and Gram-negative bacteria, indicating their susceptibility to certain antibiotics;

6. suggest measures that might be used to control malaria;

7. recognize and classify selected members of the seven phyla represented in this exercise;

8. distinguish among the structures associated with asexual and sexual reproduction described in this exercise;

9. identify the structures of the algae (those in **boldface** in the procedure sections).

INTRODUCTION

The bacteria (Domain Bacteria, Kingdom Bacteria) and archaea (Domain Archaea, Kingdom Archaea) and protists (Domain Eukarya, Kingdom Protista) are among the simplest of living organisms. These have unicellular organisms within them, but that's where the similarity ends.

Bacteria and archaea are **prokaryotic** organisms, meaning that their DNA is free in the cytoplasm, unbounded by a membrane. They lack organelles (cytoplasmic structures surrounded by membranes). By contrast, the protists are **eukaryotic** organisms: The genetic material contained within the nucleus and many of their cellular components are compartmentalized into membrane-bound organelles.

Both bacteria and archaea, and unicellular protists, are at the base of the food chain. From an ecological standpoint, these simple organisms are among the most important organisms on our planet. Ecologically, they're much more important than we are.

13.1 Domain Bacteria, Kingdom Bacteria *(About 40 min.)*

The Kingdom Bacteria consists of bacteria and cyanobacteria. Most bacteria are heterotrophic, dependent upon an outside source for nutrition, while cyanobacteria are autotrophic (photosynthetic), able to produce their own carbohydrates.

Some heterotrophic bacteria are **pathogens,** causing plant and animal diseases, but most are **decomposers,** breaking down and recycling the waste products of life. Others are nitrogen fixers, capturing the gaseous nitrogen in the atmosphere and making it available to plants via a symbiotic association with their roots.

MATERIALS

Per student:

- bacteria type slide
- microscope slide
- coverslip
- dissecting needle
- compound microscope

Per lab room:

- Gram-stained bacteria (3 demonstration slides)
- *Oscillatoria*—living culture; disposable pipet
- *Azolla*—living plants

A. Bacteria: Are Bacteria Present in the Lab? *(About 15 min.)*

MATERIALS

Per student group (4):

- dH₂O in dropping bottle
- 4 nutrient agar culture plates
- sterile cotton swabs
- china marker

- 2 bottles labeled A and B (A contains tap water, B contains 70% ethyl alcohol)
- transparent adhesive tape
- paper towels

PROCEDURE

Work in groups of four.

1. Obtain four petri dishes containing sterile nutrient agar. Using a china marker, label one dish "Dish 1: Control." Label the others "Dish 2: Dry Swab," "Dish 3: Treatment A," and "Dish 4: Treatment B." Also include the names of your group members.
2. Run a sterile cotton swab over a surface within the lab. Some examples of things you might wish to sample include the surface of your lab bench, the floor, and the sink. Be creative!
3. Lift the lid on Dish 2 as little as is necessary to run the swab over the surface of the agar.

   Note: Be careful that you don't break the agar surface.

4. Tape the lid securely to the bottom half of the dish.
5. Soak one paper towel with liquid A and a second paper towel with liquid B.
6. Wipe down one-half of the surface you just sampled with liquid A (tap water), the other half with liquid B (70% ethyl alcohol). After the areas have dried, using dishes 3 and 4, repeat the procedures described in step 2. Place the cultures in a desk drawer to incubate until the next lab period. At that time, examine your culture for bacterial colonies, noting the color and texture of the bacterial growth.
7. Make a prediction of what you will find in the culture plates after the next lab period.

   _____

   _____

8. Describe what you see.
   Source of sample: _____

   Dish 1: Control. _____

   _____

   _____

   Dish 2: Dry Swab. _____

   _____

   _____

   Dish 3: Treatment A. _____

   _____

   Dish 4: Treatment B. _____

   _____

   > ### Caution
   >
   > *Leave the lid on as you examine the cultures to prevent the spread of any potentially pathogenic (disease-causing) organisms. While the probability is small that pathogens are present, you should always err on the side of caution.*

9. Make a conclusion about the usefulness of tap water and 70% ethyl alcohol as disinfectants.

   _____

   _____

B. Bacteria: Bacterial Shape and Sensitivity to Antibiotics *(About 10 min.)*

MATERIALS

Per student:

- bacteria type slide
- compound microscope

Per lab room:

- Gram-stained bacteria (3 demonstration slides)

Work alone for this and the rest of these activities.

Bacteria exist in three shapes: **coccus** (plural, *cocci;* spherical), **bacillus** (plural, *bacilli;* rods), and **spirillum** (plural, *spirilla;* spirals).

PROCEDURE

1. Study a bacteria type slide illustrating these three shapes. You'll need to use the highest magnification available on your compound microscope. In Figure 13-1, draw the bacteria you are observing.

In addition to being differentiated by shape, bacteria can be separated according to how they react to a staining procedure called **Gram stain,** named in honor of a nineteenth-century microbiologist, Hans Gram. *Gram-positive* bacteria are purple after being stained by the Gram stain procedure, while *Gram-negative* bacteria appear pink. The Gram stain reaction is important to bacteriologists because it is one of the first steps in identifying an unknown bacterium. Furthermore, the Gram stain reaction indicates a bacterium's susceptibility or resistance to certain **antibiotics,** substances that inhibit the growth of bacteria.

2. Examine the *demonstration slides* illustrating Gram-stained bacteria. Gram-positive bacteria are susceptible to penicillin, while Gram-negative bacteria are not. In Table 13-1, list the species of bacteria that you have examined and their staining characteristics.

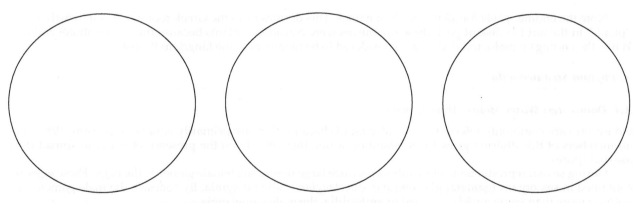

Figure 13-1 Drawings of the three bacterial shapes (_____×).

TABLE 13-1 Gram Stain Reaction of Various Bacteria	
Bacterial Species	**Gram Reactions (+ or −)**

13.2   Domain Eukarya, Kingdom Protista *(About 2 hr.)*

The protists are a diverse assemblage of organisms, both green (photoautotrophic) and nongreen (heterotrophic). They are so diverse that different protists have previously been classified as fungi, animals, and plants!

The protists make an enormous impact on the biosphere, both positively and negatively. Among their greatest contribution is the production of oxygen, because these are the photosynthetic protistans. Many are given the common name "algae."

Pond scum, frog spittle, seaweed, the stuff that clogs your aquarium if it's not cleaned routinely, the debris on an ocean beach after a storm at sea, the nuisance organisms of a lake—these are the images that pop into our mind when we first think about the organisms called algae. But many algae are also **phytoplankton**, the weakly swimming or floating algae, at the base of the aquatic food chain.

The following organisms are examined in this exercise:

Phylum	Common Name
Euglenozoa	Euglenoids
Chrysophyta	Yellow-green algae and diatoms
Dinoflagellata	Dinoflagellates
Rhodophyta	Red algae
Phaeophyta	Brown algae
Chlorophyta	Green algae
Oomycotes	Water molds
Amoebozoa	Slime molds
Alveolata	Apicomplexans

Note the ending -*phyta* for all the phylum names. This derives from the Greek root word *phyt,* which means "plant." In the not too distant past, these organisms were considered plants because they were photosynthetic. While the endings remain, today they are considered to be members of the kingdom Protista.

A. Phylum Stramenopila

A.1. Oomycotes: Water Molds *(About 15 min.)*

Oomycotes are commonly referred to as water molds because they are primarily aquatic organisms. While not all members of this division grow in freestanding water, they all rely on the presence of water to spread their asexual spores.

During sexual reproduction, all members produce large nonmotile female gametes, the eggs. These eggs are contained in sex organs (**gametangia;** singular, *gametangium*) called **oogonia.** By contrast, the male gametes are nothing more than *sperm nuclei* contained in **antheridia,** the male gametangia.

MATERIALS

Per student:

- culture of *Saprolegnia* or *Achlya*
- glass microscope slide
- compound microscope

A.1.a. Phytophthora

Some of the most notorious and historically important plant pathogens known to humans are water molds. Included in this group is *Phytophthora infestans,* the fungus that causes the disease known as late blight of potato. This disease spread through the potato fields of Ireland between 1845 and 1847. Most of the potato plants died, and 1 million Irish working-class citizens who had depended on potatoes as their primary food source starved to death. Another 2 million emigrated, many to the United States.

Perhaps no other plant pathogen so poignantly illustrates the importance of environmental factors in causing disease. While *Phytophthora infestans* had been present previous to 1845 in the potato-growing fields of Ireland, it was not until the region experienced several consecutive years of wet and especially cool growing seasons that late blight became a major problem. We can easily observe the importance of these climate-associated factors by studying another *Phytophthora* species, *P. cactorum.*

MATERIALS

Per student:

- culture of *Phytophthora cactorum*
- glass microscope slide
- dissecting needle
- compound microscope

Per lab room:

- refrigerator

or

Per student group (4):

- ice bath

PROCEDURE

1. Obtain a culture of *P. cactorum* that has been flooded with distilled water. Note that the agar has been removed from the edges of the petri dish and that the mycelium has grown from the agar edge into the water.

2. Place a glass slide on the stage of your compound microscope. This slide will serve as a platform for the culture, allowing you to use the mechanical stage of the microscope to move the culture (if the microscope is so equipped).

3. Remove the lid from the culture, carefully place the culture dish on the platform, and examine the culture with the low-power objective.

4. Search the surface of the mycelium, especially at the edges, until you find the rather *pear-shaped* **zoosporangia.** Switch to the medium-power objective for closer observation and then draw in Figure 13-2 a single zoosporangium.

5. Return your microscope to the low-power objective, remove the culture, replace the cover, and place it in a refrigerator or on ice for 15–30 minutes.

6. After the incubation time, again observe the zoosporangia microscopically. Find one in which the **zoospores** are escaping from the zoosporangium. Each zoospore has the potential to grow into an entirely new mycelium! Draw the zoospores in Figure 13-2.

Figure 13-2 Drawing of zoosporangium and zoospores of *Phytophthora cactorum.*

(_____×).

Labels: zoosporangium, zoospores

Like the other water molds, *Phytophthora* reproduces sexually. Your cultures contain the sexual structures as well as asexual zoosporangia.

7. Using a dissecting needle, cut a section about 1 cm square from the agar colony and *invert* it on a glass slide (so that the bottom side of the agar is now uppermost).

8. Place a coverslip on the agar block and observe with your compound microscope, first with the low-power objective, then with the medium-power, and finally with the high-dry objective.

9. Identify the spherical **oogonia** that contain **eggs** or thick-walled **zygotes** (depending on the stage of development). If present, the **antheridia** are club shaped and plastered to the wall of the oogonium.

10. In Figure 13-3, draw an oogonium, eggs (zygotes), and antheridia.

B. Phylum Amoebozoa: Slime Molds

The slime molds have both plantlike and animal-like characteristics. Because they engulf their food and lack a cell wall in their vegetative (nonreproductive) state, they are placed in the kingdom Amoebozoa. However, when they reproduce, they produce spores with a rigid cell wall, similar to plants.

B.1. Amoeba *(About 20 min.)*

Amoebas continually change shape by forming projections called *pseudopodia* (singular, *pseudopodium,* "false foot"). One notorious human pathogen is *Entamoeba histolytica,* the cause of amoebic dysentery.

Figure 13-3 Drawing of the gametangia of *Phytophthora cactorum.*

(_____×).

Labels: oogonium, eggs (zygotes), antheridium

MATERIALS

Per student:

- depression slide
- coverslip
- dissecting needle
- compound microscope

Per group (table):

- carmine, in 2 screw-cap bottles
- tissue paper

Per lab room:

- *Amoeba*—living culture on demonstration at dissecting microscope; disposable pipet

PROCEDURE

1. Observe the *Amoeba*-containing culture on the stage of a demonstration dissecting microscope. (One species of amoeba has the scientific name *Amoeba*.) The microscope has been focused on the bottom of the culture dish, where the amoebas are located. Look for gray, irregularly shaped masses moving among the food particles in the culture.
2. Using a clean pipette, remove an amoeba and place it, along with some of the culture medium, in a depression slide.
3. Examine it with your compound microscope using the medium-power objective. You will need to adjust the diaphragm to increase the contrast (see Exercise 1) because *Amoeba* is nearly transparent.
4. Refer to Figure 13-4. Locate the **pseudopodia.** At the periphery of the cell, identify the **ectoplasm,** a thin, clear layer that surrounds the inner, granular **endoplasm.**

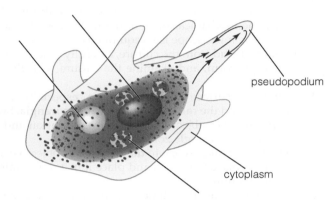

Figure 13-4 Artist's rendering of *Amoeba*.
Labels: ectoplasm, endoplasm, nucleus, contractile vacuole, food vacuole

Watch the organism as it changes shape. Which region of the endoplasm appears to stream, the outer or the inner? _____

This region, called the *plasmasol,* consists of a fluid matrix that can undergo phase changes with the semisolid *plasmagel,* the outer layer of the endoplasm. Pseudopodium formation occurs as the plasmasol flows into new environmental frontiers and then changes to plasmagel.

Numerous granules will be found within the endoplasm. Some of these are organelles; others are food granules.

5. Within the endoplasm, try to locate the **nucleus,** a densely granular, spherical structure around which the cytoplasm is streaming.
6. Find the clear, spherical **contractile vacuoles,** which regulate water balance within the cell. Watch for a minute or two to observe the action of contractile vacuoles. Label Figure 13-4.

Amoeba feeds by a process called **phagocytosis,** engulfing its food. Pseudopodia form around food particles, and then the pseudopodia fuse, creating a **food vacuole** within the cytoplasm. Enzymes are then emptied into the food vacuole, where the food particle is digested into a soluble form that can pass through the vacuolar membrane. You can stimulate feeding behavior by drawing carmine under the coverslip:

7. Place a drop of distilled water against one edge of the coverslip.
8. Pick up some carmine crystals by dipping a dissecting needle into the bottle; and deposit them into the water droplet.
9. Draw the suspension beneath the coverslip by holding a piece of absorbent tissue against the coverslip on the side *opposite* the carmine suspension.
10. Observe the *Amoeba* with your microscope again—you may catch it in the act of feeding.

C. Phylum Alveolata: Apicomplexans *(About 20 min.)*

All apicomplexans are parasites, infecting a wide range of animals, including humans. *Plasmodium vivax* causes one type of malaria in humans. In this section, you will study its life cycle with demonstration slides. Refer to Figure 13-3 as you proceed.

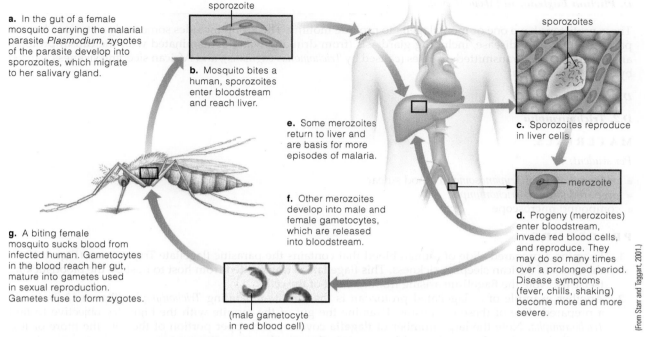

a. In the gut of a female mosquito carrying the malarial parasite *Plasmodium*, zygotes of the parasite develop into sporozoites, which migrate to her salivary gland.

sporozoite

b. Mosquito bites a human, sporozoites enter bloodstream and reach liver.

e. Some merozoites return to liver and are basis for more episodes of malaria.

f. Other merozoites develop into male and female gametocytes, which are released into bloodstream.

g. A biting female mosquito sucks blood from infected human. Gametocytes in the blood reach her gut, mature into gametes used in sexual reproduction. Gametes fuse to form zygotes.

(male gametocyte in red blood cell)

sporozoites

c. Sporozoites reproduce in liver cells.

merozoite

d. Progeny (merozoites) enter bloodstream, invade red blood cells, and reproduce. They may do so many times over a prolonged period. Disease symptoms (fever, chills, shaking) become more and more severe.

(From Starr and Taggart, 2001.)

Figure 13-5 Life cycle of *Plasmodium vivax*, causal agent of malaria.

Plasmodium vivax

MATERIALS

Per lab room:

- demonstration slide of *Plasmodium vivax*, sporozoites
- demonstration slide of *P. vivax*, merozoites
- demonstration slide of *P. vivax*, immature gametocytes

PROCEDURE

1. Examine Figure 13-5a. *P. vivax* is transmitted to humans through the bite of an infected female *Anopheles* mosquito. The mosquito serves as a **vector,** a means of transmitting the organism from one host to another. Male mosquitos cannot serve as vectors, because they lack the mouth parts for piercing skin and sucking blood. If the mosquito carries the pathogen, **sporozoites** enter the host's bloodstream with the saliva of the mosquito.
2. Examine the demonstration slide of sporozoites (Figure 13-5b).
3. The sporozoites travel through the bloodstream to the liver, where they penetrate certain cells, grow, and multiply. When released from the liver cells, the parasite is in the form of a **merozoite** and infects the red blood cells. Figures 13-5c and 13-5d show this process.

(There are two intervening stages between sporozoites and merozoites. These are the *trophozoites* and *schizonts*, both developmental stages in red blood cells.)

4. Now examine the demonstration slide illustrating merozoites in red blood cells (Figure 13-5d).
5. Within the red blood cells, merozoites divide, increasing the merozoite population. At intervals of 48 or 72 hours, the infected red blood cells break down, releasing the merozoites. At this time, the infected individual has disease symptoms, including fever, chills, and shaking caused by the release of merozoites and metabolic wastes from the red blood cells. Some of these merozoites return to the liver cells, where they repeat the cycle and are responsible for recurrent episodes of malaria.
6. Merozoites within the bloodstream can develop into **gametocytes.** For development of a gametocyte to be completed, the gametocyte must enter the gut of the mosquito. This occurs when a mosquito feeds upon an infected (diseased) human.
7. Observe the demonstration slide of an **immature gametocyte** in a red blood cell (Figure 13-5f).
8. Within the gut of the mosquito, the gametocyte matures into a gamete (Figure 13-5g). When gametes fuse, they form a zygote that matures into an **oocyst.** Within each oocyst, sporozoites form, completing the life cycle of *Plasmodium vivax*. These sporozoites migrate to the mosquito's salivary glands to be injected into a new host.

D. Phylum Euglenozoa *(About 10 min.)*

These protistans have one or more flagella to provide motility. The group includes some fairly notorious human parasites that cause disease, including giardiasis (from drinking water contaminated with the causal protozoans), some sexually transmitted diseases (caused by *Trichomonas vaginalis*), and African sleeping sickness, caused by *Trypanosoma brucei*.

D.1. Trypanosoma

D.2. Trichonympha

MATERIALS

Per student:

- prepared slide of *Trypanosoma* in blood smear
- prepared slide of *Trichonympha*
- compound microscope

PROCEDURE

1. Examine a prepared slide of human blood that contains the parasitic flagellate *Trypanosoma* (Figure 13-6), the cause of African sleeping sickness. This flagellate is transmitted from host to host by the bloodsucking tsetse fly. Note the **flagellum** arising from one end of the cell.
2. Another example of a flagellated protozoan is the termite-inhabiting *Trichonympha* (Figure 13-7). Study a prepared slide of these organisms. Examine the gut of the termite with the high-dry objective to find *Trichonympha*. Note the large number of **flagella** covering the upper portion of the cell, the more or less centrally located **nucleus** and wood fragments in the cytoplasm.

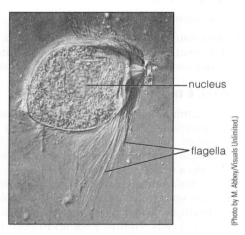

Figure 13-6 *Trypanosoma.*

Figure 13-7 *Trichonympha* (900×).

The association of the termite and *Trichonympha* is an example of **obligate mutualism,** in which neither organism is capable of surviving without the other. Termites lack the enzymes to metabolize cellulose, a major component of wood. Wood particles ingested by termites are engulfed by *Trichonympha,* whose enzymes break the cellulose into soluble carbohydrates that are released for use by the termite.

| 13.3 | **Phylum Chrysophyta: Diatoms** *(About 10 min.)* |

The phylum Chrysophyta includes yellow green algae, and diatoms. You will examine only the diatoms here.

Diatoms are called the organisms that live in glass houses because their cell walls are composed largely of opaline *silica* ($SiO_2 \cdot nH_2O$). Diatoms are important as primary producers in the food chain of aquatic environments, and their cell walls are used for a wide variety of industrial purposes, ranging from the polishing agent in toothpaste to a reflective roadway paint additive. Massive deposits of cell walls of long-dead diatoms make up diatomaceous earth (Figure 13-8).

MATERIALS

Per student:

- microscope slide
- coverslip
- prepared slide of freshwater diatom
- compound microscope

Per group (table):

- diatomaceous earth
- dH₂O in 2 dropping bottles

Per lab room:

- diatoms—living culture; disposable pipet

(Photo courtesy Dan Williams.)

Figure 13-8 Diatomaceous earth quarry near Quincy, Washington.

PROCEDURE

1. Prepare a wet mount of living diatoms. Use the high-dry objective to note the golden brown chloroplasts within the cytoplasm and the numerous holes in the cell walls (shells).
2. In Figure 13-9, sketch several of the diatoms you are observing.
3. Now obtain a prepared slide of diatoms. These cells have been "cleaned," making the perforations in the cell wall especially obvious if you close the iris diaphragm on your microscope's condenser to increase the contrast. Study with the high-dry objective.

The pattern of the holes in the walls are characteristic of a given species. Before the advent of electronic techniques, microscopists observed diatom walls to assess the quality of microscope lenses. The resolving power (see discussion of resolving power in Exercise 1) could be determined if one knew the diameter of the holes under observation.

Figure 13-9 Drawing of diatoms (_____×).

| 13.4 | **Phylum Dinoflagellata: Dinoflagellates** *(About 10 min.)* |

Dinoflagellates spin as they move through the water due to the position of their flagellum. On occasion, populations of certain dinoflagellates may increase dramatically, causing the seas to turn red or brown. These are the **red tides,** which can devastate fish populations because neurotoxins produced by the dinoflagellates poison fish.

MATERIALS

Per student:

- prepared slide of a dinoflagellate (for example, *Gymnodinium, Ceratium,* or *Peridinium*)
- compound microscope

Per lab room:

- dinoflagellate—living culture; disposable pipet (optional)

PROCEDURE

1. With the high-dry objective of your compound microscope, examine a prepared slide or living representative.
2. Compare what you are observing with Figures 13-10a and b.
3. Attempt to identify the stiff cellulosic plates encasing the cytoplasm.
4. Locate the two grooves formed by the junction of the plates. This is where the flagella are located. If you are examining living specimens, chloroplasts may be visible beneath the cellulose plates.
5. Examine the scanning electron micrograph of a dinoflagellate in Figure 13-11.

flagellar groove

flagellar groove

(Photos by J. W. Perry.)

a   b

Figure 13-10   Two representative dinoflagellates. (**a**) *Ceratium* (240×). (**b**) *Peridinium* (640×).

(Photo by S. Carty, Heidelberg College.)

Figure 13-11   Scanning electron micrograph of a dinoflagellate (1000×).

13.5   Phylum Rhodophyta: Red Algae *(About 10 min.)*

Although commonly called red algae, members of the Rhodophyta vary in color from red to green to purple to greenish-black. The color depends on the quantity of their photosynthetic accessory pigments, the **phycobilins,** which are blue and red. These accessory pigments allow capture of light energy across the entire visible spectrum. This energy is passed on to chlorophyll for photosynthesis. One phycobilin, the red phycoerythrin, allows some red algae to live at great depths where red wavelengths, those of primary importance for green and brown algae, fail to penetrate.

Which wavelengths (colors) would be absorbed by a red pigment?

_____

Most abundant in warm marine waters, red algae are the source of **agar** and carageenan substances extracted from their cell walls. Agar is the solidifying agent in microbiological media and carageenan is a thickener used in ice cream and bean.

MATERIALS

Per lab room:

- culture dish containing dried agar and petri dish of hydrated agar
- demonstration slide of *Porphyridium*
- demonstration specimen and slide of *Porphyra* (nori)

PROCEDURE

1. Observe the dried agar that is on demonstration.
2. Now observe the petri dish containing agar that has been hydrated, heated, and poured into the dish.

3. Examine these cells of the unicellular *Porphyridium* at the demonstration microscope, noting the reddish chloroplast.
4. In Figure 13-12, sketch a cell of *Porphyridium*.
5. Examine a portion of the multicellular membranous *Porphyra* specimen on demonstration. Draw what you see in Figure 13-13.
6. Compare the specimen with the photo of live *Porphyra* (Figure 13-14).
7. In the adjacent demonstration microscope, note the microscopic appearance of *Porphyra* (Figure 13-15). Note that the clear areas are actually the cell walls.

Porphyra is used extensively as a food substance in Asia, where it's commonly sold under the name *nori*. In Japan, nori production is valued at $20 million annually.

Figure 13-12 Drawing of *Porphyridium* (_____×).

Figure 13-13 Drawing of the macroscopic appearance of *Porphyra* (nori) (_____×).

(Photo by J. W. Perry.)

Figure 13-14 Living *Porphyra* (0.5×).

cell wall

(Photo by J. W. Perry.)

Figure 13-15 Microscopic appearance of *Porphyra* (nori) (278×).

The vast majority of the brown algae are found in cold, marine environments. All members are multicellular, and most are macroscopic. Their color is due to the accessory pigment fucoxanthin, which is so abundant that it masks the green chlorophylls. Some species are used as food, while others are harvested for fertilizers. Of primary economic importance is **algin,** a cell wall component of brown algae that makes ice cream smooth, cosmetics soft, and paint uniform in consistency, among other uses.

A. *Kelps*—Laminaria and Macrocystis

Kelps are large (up to 100 m long), complex brown algae. They are common along the seashores in cold waters.

MATERIALS

Per lab room:

- demonstration specimen of *Laminaria*
- demonstration specimen of *Macrocystis*

PROCEDURE

Examine specimens of *Laminaria* (Figure 13-16) and *Macrocystis* (Figure 13-17). On each, identify the rootlike **holdfast** that anchors the alga to the substrate; the **stipe,** a stemlike structure; and the leaflike **blades.**

B. *Rockweed*—Fucus

Fucus is a common brown alga of the coastal shore, especially abundant attached to rocks where the plants are periodically wetted by splashing waves and the tides.

MATERIALS

Per lab room:

- demonstration specimen of *Fucus*

PROCEDURE

1. Examine demonstration specimens of *Fucus* (Figure 13-18), noting the branching nature of the body.
2. Locate the short **stipe** and **blade.**

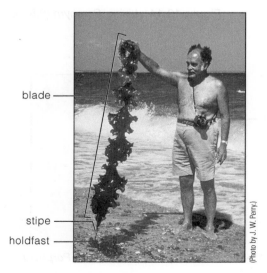

blade —

stipe —

holdfast —

(Photo by J. W. Perry.)

Figure 13-16 *Laminaria.*

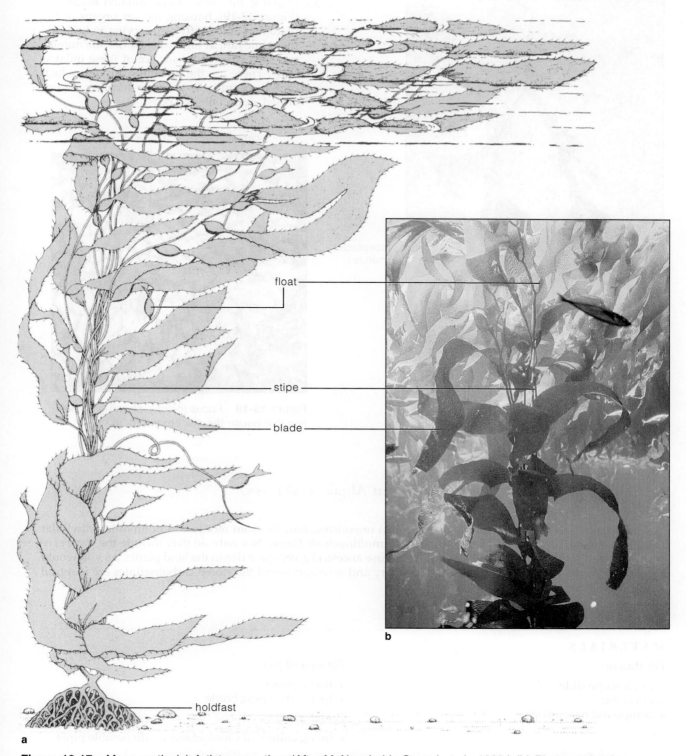

float

stipe

blade

holdfast

a

b

Figure 13-17 *Macrocystis*. (**a**) Artist conception. (After M. Neushul in Scagel et al., 1982.) (**b**) Photograph taken at Monterey Bay Aquarium, Monterey, CA. (Photo by J. W. Perry.) (Both 0.01×)

3. Examine the swollen and inflated blade tips (Figure 13-19), housing the sex organs of the plant and apparently also serving to keep the plant buoyant at high tide. Notice the numerous tiny dots on the surface of these inflated ends. These are the openings through which motile sperm cells swim to fertilize the enclosed, nonmotile egg cells.

Figure 13-18 The rockweed, *Fucus* (0.60×). (Photo by J. W. Perry.)

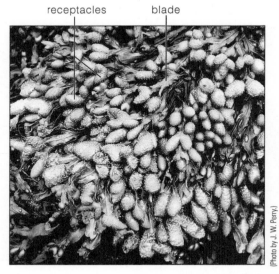

Figure 13-19 *Fucus* (colony, showing swollen tips that house the sex organs (0.35×).

13.7 Phylum Chlorophyta: Green Algae *(About 15 min.)*

The Chlorophyta is a diverse assemblage of green organisms, ranging from motile and nonmotile unicellular forms to colonial, filamentous, membranous, and multinucleate forms. Not only do they include the most species, they are also important phylogenetically because ancestral green gave rise to the land plants. As you would expect, the photosynthetic pigments—both primary and accessory—and the stored carbohydrates are identical in the green algae and land plants.

A. Chlamydomonas—A Motile Unicell

MATERIALS

Per student:

- microscope slide
- coverslip
- compound microscope

Per student pair:

- tissue paper
- I₂KI in dropping bottle

Per lab room:

- living culture of *Chlamydomonas*, disposable pipet

PROCEDURE

1. Prepare a wet mount of *Chlamydomonas* cells from the culture provided.
2. First examine with the low-power objective of your compound microscope. Notice the numerous small cells swimming across the field of view.
3. It will be difficult to study the fast-swimming cells, so kill the cells by adding a drop of I₂KI to the edge of the coverslip; draw the I₂KI under the coverslip by touching a folded tissue to the opposite edge. To observe the cells, switch to the highest power objective available.
4. Identify the large, green cup-shaped **chloroplast** filling most of the cytoplasm.

5. *Chlamydomonas* stores its excess photosynthate as *starch grains,* which appear dark blue or black when stained with I_2KI. Locate the starch grains.
6. If the orientation of the cell is just right, you may be able to detect an orange **stigma** (eyespot) that serves as a light receptor.
7. Close the iris diaphragm to increase the contrast and find the two **flagella** at the anterior end of the cell.
8. Examine Figure 13-20, a transmission electron micrograph of *Chlamydomonas.* The electron microscope makes much more obvious the structures you can barely see with your light microscope. Notice the magnification.
9. The green algae have a specialized center for starch synthesis located within their chloroplast, the **pyrenoid.** Find the pyrenoid.

flagellum
(only one of two
flagella is shown)

chloroplast

cell wall

nucleolus

nucleus

mitochondrion

chloroplast

strach

pyrenoid

(Photo courtesy H. Hoops.)

Figure 13-20 Transmission electron micrograph of *Chlamydomonas* (9750×).

B. Ulva—A Membranous Form

The second representative of the green algae illustrates the morphological form of a membranous (tissuelike) body.

MATERIALS

Per lab room:

- demonstration specimen of *Ulva*

PROCEDURE

Examine living or preserved specimens of *Ulva,* commonly known as sea lettuce (Figure 13-21). The broad, leaflike body is called a *thallus,* a general term describing a vegetative body with relatively little cell differentiation. The *Ulva* body is only two cells thick!

(Photo by J. W. Perry.)

Figure 13-21 The sea lettuce, *Ulva* (0.5×).

_____ 1. Some members of the Domain Bacteria have
(a) a nucleus
(b) membrane-bound organelles
(c) chloroplasts
(d) photosynthetic ability

_____ 2. A pathogen is
(a) a disease
(b) an organism that causes a disease
(c) a substance that kills bacteria
(d) the same as a heterocyst

_____ 3. Which of the following is true?
(a) All bacteria are autotrophic
(b) All protists are heterotrophic
(c) *Oscillatoria* is photoautotrophic
(d) *Trypanosoma* is photoautotrophic

_____ 4. Which organisms are characterized as decomposers?
(a) bacteria
(b) protozoans
(c) amoebas
(d) sporozoans

_____ 5. Organisms capable of nitrogen fixation
(a) include some bacteria
(b) include some cyanobacteria
(c) may live as symbionts with other organisms
(d) all of the above

_____ 6. A spherical bacterium is called a
(a) bacillus
(b) coccus
(c) spirillum
(d) none of the above

_____ 7. Gram stain is used to distinguish between different
(a) bacteria
(b) protistans
(c) dinoflagellates
(d) all of the above

_____ 8. Those organisms that are covered by numerous, tiny locomotory structures belong to the phylum
(a) Euglenozoa
(b) Stramenopila
(c) Amoebozoa
(d) Ciliata

_____ 9. A vector is
(a) an organism that causes disease
(b) a disease
(c) a substance that prevents disease
(d) an organism that transmits a disease causing organism

_____ 10. The organism that causes malaria is
(a) a pathogen
(b) *Plasmodium vivax*
(c) carried by a mosquito
(d) all of the above

_____ 11. Which of these organisms (or parts of the organisms) might you find as an ingredient in toothpaste?
(a) euglenoids
(b) diatoms
(c) dinoflagellates
(d) stoneworts

_____ 12. Red tides are caused by
   (a) dinoflagellates
   (b) red algae
   (c) brown algae
   (d) diatoms

_____ 13. Agar is derived from
   (a) red algae
   (b) brown algae
   (c) green algae
   (d) all of the above

_____ 14. Which is the correct plural form of the word for the organisms studied in this exercise?
   (a) alga
   (b) algae
   (c) algas
   (d) algaes

_____ 15. Phycobilins are
   (a) photosynthetic pigments
   (b) found in the red algae
   (c) blue and red pigments
   (d) all of the above

_____ 16. The cell wall component algin is
   (a) found in the brown algae
   (b) used in the production of ice cream
   (c) used as a medium on which microorganisms are grown
   (d) both a and b

_____ 17. Specifically, female sex organs are known as
   (a) oogonia
   (b) gametangia
   (c) antheridia
   (d) zygotes

_____ 18. A reagent that stains the stored food of a green alga black is
   (a) India ink
   (b) I_2KI
   (c) methylene blue
   (d) both a and b

_____ 19. The starch production center within many algal cells is the
   (a) nucleus
   (b) cytoplasm
   (c) stipe
   (d) pyrenoid

_____ 20. The phylum of organisms _most_ closely linked to the evolution of land plants is the
   (a) Chlorophyta
   (b) Charophyta
   (c) Phaeophyta
   (d) Euglenozoa

Name _____ Section Number _____

EXERCISE 13

Bacteria and Protists

POST-LAB QUESTIONS

Introduction

1. What major characteristic distinguishes bacteria from protists?

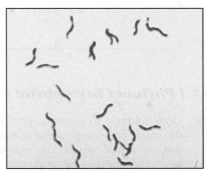

(1100×).

13.1A Bacteria

2. What form of bacterium is shown in this photomicrograph?

13.2A Phylum Stramenopila

3. While the organism that resulted in the Irish potato famine of 1845–1847 had long been present, environmental conditions that occurred during this period resulted in the destructive explosion of disease. Indicate what those environmental conditions were and why they resulted in a major disease outbreak.

13.2B Phylum Amoebozoa

4. This photomicrograph was taken from a prepared slide of a stained specimen. You observed unstained living specimens in lab. Describe the mechanism by which it moves from place to place.

(425×).

5. What is phagocytosis? What function does it serve?

Food for Thought

6. If you were to travel to a region where rice is grown in paddies, you would see lots of the water fern *Azolla* growing in the water. A farmer would tell you this is done because *Azolla* is considered a "natural fertilizer." Explain why this is the case.

7. Based on your knowledge of the life history of *Plasmodium vivax*, suggest two methods for controlling malaria. Explain why each method would work.

   a. _____

   b. _____

13.3 Phylum Chrysophyta: Diatoms

8. On a field trip to a stream, you collect a leaf that has fallen into the water and scrape some of the material from its surface, and prepare a wet mount. You examine your preparation with the high-dry objective of your compound microscope, finding the organism pictured at the right. What substance makes up a significant portion of the cell wall?

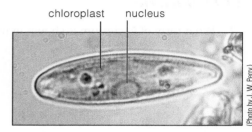
chloroplast   nucleus

(235×).

13.5 Phylum Rhodophyta: Red Algae

9. While wading in the warm salt water off the beaches of the Florida Keys on spring break, you stoop down to look at the feathery alga shown here.

   a. What pigment gives this organism its coloration?

   b. What commercial products are derived from this phylum?

(0.25×).

13.6 Phylum Phaeophyta: Brown Algae

10. While walking along the beach at Point Lobos, California, the fellow pictured walks up to you with alga in hand. Figuring you to be a college student who has probably had a good introductory biology course, he asks if you know what it is.

    a. What is the cell wall component of the organism that has commercial value?

    b. Name three uses for that cell wall component.

Food for Thought

11. Some botanists consider the stoneworts to be a link between the higher plants and the algae. As you will learn in future exercises, higher plants, such as the mosses, have both haploid and diploid stages that are *multicellular*.

   a. Describe the multicellular organism in the charophytes.

   b. Is this organism haploid or diploid?

   c. Is the zygote haploid or diploid?

   d. Is the zygote unicellular or multicellular?

12. a. What color are the marker lights at the edge of an airport taxiway?

   _____

   b. Are the wavelengths of this color long or short, relative to the other visible wavelengths?

   _____

   c. Which wavelengths penetrate deepest into water, long or short?

   _____

   d. Make a statement regarding why phycobilin pigments are present in deep-growing red algae.

   e. What benefit is there to the color of airport taxiway lights for a pilot attempting to taxi during foggy weather?

13. a. How is an algal holdfast similar to a root?

   b. How is it different?

14. Why do you suppose the Swedish automobile manufacturer Volvo chose this company name?

15. List three reasons why algae are useful and important to life.

   a.

   b.

   c.

Fungi

After completing this exercise, you will be able to

1. define *parasite, saprobe, mutualist, gametangium, hypha, mycelium, multinucleate, sporangium, rhizoid, zygosporangium, ascus, conidium, ascospore, ascocarp, basidium, basidiospore, basidiocarp, lichen, mycorrhiza;*

2. recognize representatives of the major phyla of fungi;

3. distinguish structures that are used to place various representatives of the fungi in their proper phyla;

4. list reasons why fungi are important;

5. distinguish between the structures associated with asexual and sexual reproduction described in this exercise;

6. identify the structures (in **boldface**) of the fungi examined;

7. determine the effect of light on certain species of fungi.

INTRODUCTION

As you walk in the woods following a warm rain, you are likely to be met by a vast assemblage of colorful fungi. Some of them grow on dead or diseased trees, some on the surface of the soil, others in pools of water. Some are edible, some deadly poisonous.

Fungi (kingdom Fungi) are *heterotrophic* organisms; that is, they are incapable of producing their own food material. They secrete enzymes from their bodies that digest their food externally. The digested materials are then absorbed into the body.

Depending on the relationship between the fungus and its food source, fungi can be characterized in one of three ways:

1. Parasitic fungi (**parasites**) obtain their nutrients from the organic material of another living organism, and in doing so adversely affect the food source, often causing death.
2. Saprotrophic fungi (**saprobes**) grow on nonliving organic (carbon-containing) matter. Some are even **mutualists.**
3. Mutualistic fungi (**mutualists**) form a partnership beneficial to both the fungus and its host.

Fungi, along with the bacteria, are essential components of the ecosystem as decomposers. These organisms recycle the products of life, making the products of death available so that life may continue. Without them we would be hopelessly lost in our own refuse. Fungi and fungal metabolism are responsible for some of the food products that enrich our lives—the mushrooms of the field, the blue cheese of the dairy case, even the citric acid used in making soft drinks.

The kingdom Fungi is divided into four separate phyla, based on structures formed during sexual reproduction (Table 14.1). Certain fungi (the "imperfect fungi") do not reproduce sexually; hence they are considered an informal "group."

TABLE 14-1 Classification of the Fungi

Phylum	Common Name
Chytridiomycota	Chytrids
Zygomycota	Zygosporangium-forming fungi
Ascomycota	Sac fungi
Basidiomycota	Club fungi
"Imperfect Fungi"	Fungi without sexual reproduction

14.1   Phylum Chytridiomycota *(About 5 min.)*

Commonly known as chytrids, these fungi are among the most simple in body form. While most live on dead organic matter, some are parasitic on economically important plants, resulting in damage and/or death of the host plant. Parasitic organisms that cause disease are called **pathogens.**

MATERIALS

Per lab room:

- preserved specimen of potato tuber with black wart disease

PROCEDURE

1. Examine the preserved specimen (if available) and Figure 14-1 of the potato tuber that exhibits the disease known as black wart. Notice the warty eruptions on the surface of the tuber. The warts are caused by the presence of numerous cells of a chytrid infecting the tuber.
2. Now look at Figure 14-2, a photomicrograph of a chytrid similar to that which causes black wart disease.

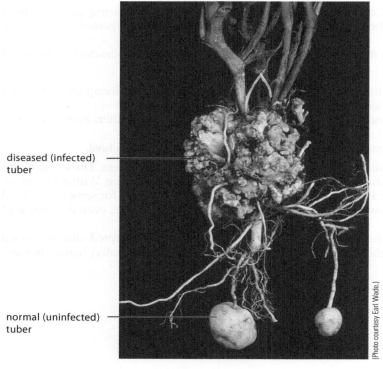

diseased (infected) tuber

normal (uninfected) tuber

(Photo courtesy Earl Wade.)

Figure 14-1   Potato tuber infected by black wart pathogen (0.5×).

rhizoids

Figure 14-2   Chytrid. (71×). (Photo by M. S. Fuller, *Zoosporic Fungi in Teaching and Research*, Fuller and A. Jaworski (eds.), 1987, Southeastern Publishing Company, Athens, GA.)

Commonly called "zygomycetes," all members of this phylum produce a thick-walled zygote called a **zygosporangium.** Most zygomycetes are saprobes. The common black bread mold, *Rhizopus*, is a representative zygomycete. Before the introduction of chemical preservatives into bread, *Rhizopus* was an almost certain invader, especially in high humidity.

MATERIALS

Per student:

- culture of *Rhizopus*
- prepared slide of *Rhizopus*
- dissecting needle
- glass microscope slide
- coverslip
- compound microscope

Per student pair:

- dH$_2$O in dropping bottle

Per lab room:

- demonstration culture of *Rhizopus* zygosporangia, on dissecting microscope

PROCEDURE

Examine Figure 14-7, the life cycle of *Rhizopus*, as you study this organism.

1. Obtain a petri dish culture of *Rhizopus*.
2. Observe the culture, noting that the body of the organism consists of many fine strands. These are called **hyphae** (Figure 14-3). All of the hyphae together are called the **mycelium**. Biologists use the term *mycelium* instead of saying "the fungal body."
3. Now note that the culture contains numerous black "dots." These are the **sporangia** (singular, *sporangium*; Figures 14-7a and b). Sporangia contain **spores** (Figures 14-7c–d) by which *Rhizopus* reproduces asexually.
4. Using a dissecting needle, remove a small portion of the mycelium and prepare a wet mount. Examine your preparation with the high-dry objective of your compound microscope.
5. It's likely that when you added the coverslip, you crushed the sporangia, liberating the spores. Are there many or few spores within a single sporangium? _____
6. Identify the **rhizoids** (Figure 14-7a) at the base of a sporangium-bearing hypha. Rhizoids anchor the mycelium to the substrate.
7. Now observe the demonstration culture of sexual reproduction in *Rhizopus* (Figure 14-4). Two different mycelia must grow in close proximity before sexual reproduction can occur. (The difference in the mycelia is genetic rather than structural. Because they are impossible to distinguish, the mycelia are simply referred to as + and − mating types, as indicated in Figure 14-7.)
8. Note the black "line" running down the center of the culture plate. These are the numerous **zygosporangia,** the products of sexual reproduction. Here's how the zygosporangia are formed:

Figure 14-3   Bread mold culture (0.5×).

Figure 14-4   Sexual reproduction in the bread mold. Black line consists of zygosporangia (0.5×).

   (a)   As the hyphae from each mating type grow close together, chemical messengers produced within the hyphae signal them to produce protuberances (Figure 14-7f).

   (b)   When the protuberances make contact, gametangia (Figures 14-5, 14-7g) are produced at their tips. Each gametangium contains many haploid nuclei of a single mating type.

   (c)   The wall between the two gametangia then dissolves, and the cytoplasms of the gametangia mix.

   (d)   Eventually the many haploid nuclei from each gametangium fuse (Figure 14-7h). The resulting cell contains many diploid nuclei resulting from the fusion of gamete nuclei of opposite mating types. Each diploid nucleus is considered a *zygote*. This multinucleate cell is called a zygospore.

(e) Eventually a thick, bumpy wall forms around this zygospore. Because germination of the zygospore results in the production of a sporangium, the thick-walled zygospore-containing structure is called a zygosporangium. Meiosis takes place inside the zygopsporangium so that the spores formed are haploid, some of one mating type, some of the opposite type (Figures 14-6, 14-7i).

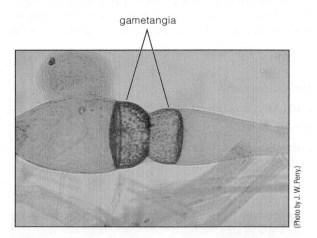

gametangia

Figure 14-5 Gametangia of a bread mold (230×).

(Photo by J. W. Perry.)

zygosporangium   zygospore

Figure 14-6 Zygospore and zygosporangium of the bread mold (230×).

(Photo by J. W. Perry.)

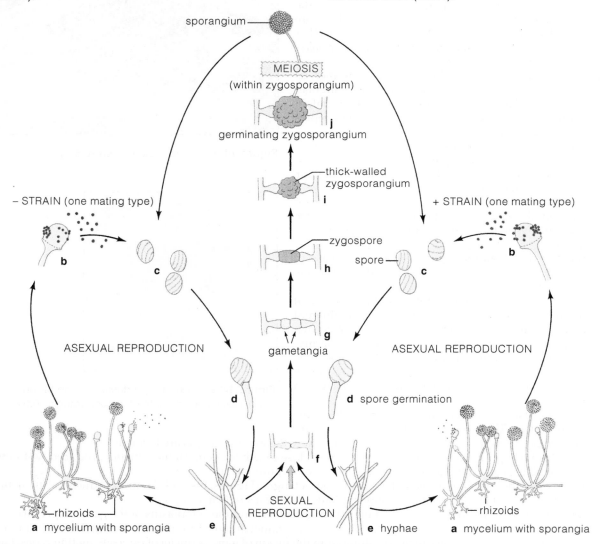

Figure 14-7 Life cycle of *Rhizopus*, black bread mold. (Green structures are 2n.)

9. Obtain a prepared slide of *Rhizopus*. Examine it with the medium- and high-power objective of your compound microscope.
10. Find the stages of sexual reproduction in *Rhizopus*, including gametangia, zygospores, and zygosporangia.

14.3 Experiment: Bread Mold and Food Preservatives *(Setup: about 10 min.)*

Knowing that fungal spores are all around us, why don't we have fungi covering everything we own? Well, given the proper environmental conditions just such a situation can occur. This is particularly true of food products. That's one reason we refrigerate many of our foodstuffs. Manufacturers often incorporate chemicals into some of our foods to retard spoilage, which includes preventing the growth of fungi.

This experiment addresses the hypothesis that *the chemicals placed in bread retard the growth of Rhizopus.*

MATERIALS

Per student group:

- one slice of bread without preservatives
- one slice of bread with preservatives
- suspension culture of bread mold fungus
- sterile dH₂O
- 2 large culture bowls

- plastic film
- pipet and bulb
- china marker
- metric ruler

PROCEDURE

1. With the china marker, label the side of one culture bowl "NO PRESERVATIVES," the other "WITH PRESERVATIVES." Place the appropriate slice of bread in its respective bowl.
2. Add a small amount of dH₂O to the bottom of each culture bowl. This provides humidity during incubation.
3. Add 5 drops of the spore suspension of the bread mold fungus to the center of each slice of bread.
4. Cover the bowls with plastic film and place them in a warm place designated by your instructor.
5. In Table 14-2, list the ingredients of both types of bread.
6. Make a prediction of what you think will be the outcome of the experiment, writing it in Table 14-2.
7. Check your cultures over the next three days, looking for evidence of fungal growth. Measure the diameter of the mycelium present in each culture, using a metric ruler.
8. Record your measurements and conclusion in Table 14-2, accepting or rejecting the hypothesis.

TABLE 14-2 Growth of Bread Mold			
Ingredients			
Bread without preservatives:			
Bread with preservatives:			
Prediction:			
		Mycelial Diameter (cm)	
Culture	Day 1	Day 2	Day 3
With preservatives			
No preservatives			
Conclusion:			

Design an experiment that would allow you to identify the substance that has the effect you observed.

_____

_____

14.4   Phylum Ascomycota: Sac Fungi *(About 30 min.)*

Members of the ascomycetes produce spores in a sac, the **ascus** (plural, *asci*), which develops as a result of sexual reproduction. Asexual reproduction takes place when the fungus produces asexual spores called **conidia** (singular, *conidium*). The phylum includes organisms of considerable importance, such as the yeasts crucial to the baking and brewing industries, as well as numerous plant pathogens. A few are highly prized as food, including morels and truffles. Truffles cost in excess of $400 per pound!

MATERIALS

Per student:

- glass microscope slide
- coverslip
- dissecting needle
- prepared slide of *Peziza*
- compound microscope

Per student pair:

- culture of *Eurotium*
- dH$_2$O in dropping bottle
- large preserved specimen of *Peziza* or another cup fungus

A. Eurotium: *A Blue Mold*

The blue mold *Eurotium* gets its common name from the production of blue-walled asexual conidia.

PROCEDURE

1. Use a dissecting needle to scrape some **conidia** from the agar surface of the culture provided, then prepare a wet mount. (Try to avoid the yellow bodies—more about them in a bit.)
2. Refer to Figure 14-8 as you observe your preparation with the high-dry objective of your compound microscope.
3. Note that the conidia are produced at the end of a specialized hypha that has a swollen tip.

This arrangement has been named *Aspergillus*. This structure, the *conidiophore,* somewhat resembles an aspergillum used in the Roman Catholic Church to sprinkle holy water, from which its name is derived.

These tiny conidia are carried by air currents to new environments, where they germinate to form new mycelia.

(You may be confused about why we italicize *Aspergillus*. The reason is that this is a scientific name. Fungi other than *Eurotium* produce the same type of asexual structure; hence the asexual structure itself is given a scientific name.)

4. Note the yellow bodies on the culture medium. These are the *fruiting bodies,* known as **ascocarps,** which are the products of sexual reproduction (Figure 14-9).
5. With your dissecting needle, remove an ascocarp from the culture and prepare a wet mount.

conidiophore without conidia   conidia

(Photo courtesy Biodisc, Inc.)

Figure 14-8 Conidiophore and conidia of the blue mold, *Eurotium* (138×).

ascus containing ascospores   ascocarp

(Photo by J. W. Perry.)

Figure 14-9 Crushed asocarp of *Eurotium* (287×).

6. Using your thumb, carefully press down on the coverslip to rupture the ascocarp.
7. Observe your preparation with the medium-power and high-dry objectives of your compound microscope. Identify the **asci,** which contain dark-colored, spherical **ascospores** (Figure 14-9).

The sexual cycle of the sac fungi is somewhat complex and is summarized in Figure 14-10.

The female gametangium, the **ascogonium** (Figure 14-10a; plural, *ascogonia*) is fertilized by male nuclei from antheridia (Figure 14-10a).

The male nuclei (darkened circles in Figure 14-10a) pair with the female nuclei (open circles) but do not fuse immediately.

Papillae grow from the ascogonium, and the paired nuclei flow into these papillae (Figure 14-10b).

Now cell walls form between each pair of sexually compatible nuclei (Figure 14-10c).

Subsequently, the two nuclei fuse; the resultant cell is the diploid ascus (Figure 14-10d). (Consequently, the ascus is a zygote.)

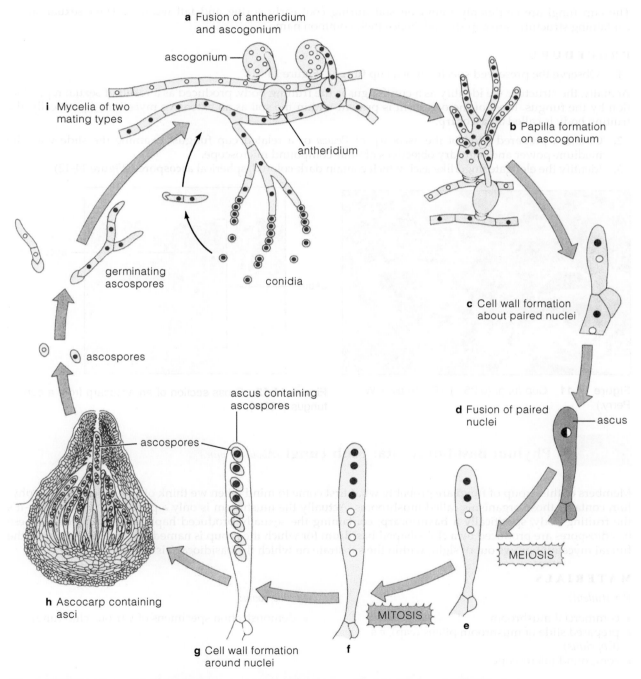

a Fusion of antheridium and ascogonium

ascogonium

i Mycelia of two mating types

antheridium

b Papilla formation on ascogonium

germinating ascospores

conidia

c Cell wall formation about paired nuclei

ascospores

ascus containing ascospores

ascospores

d Fusion of paired nuclei

ascus

MEIOSIS

h Ascocarp containing asci

MITOSIS

e

g Cell wall formation around nuclei

f

Figure 14-10 Life cycle of a sac fungus, such as *Eurotium* or *Peziza*. (Green structure is 2n.)

The nucleus of the ascus undergoes meiosis to form four nuclei (Figure 14-10e).

Mitosis then produces eight nuclei from these four (Figure 14-10f). (Notice that cytokinesis—cytoplasmic division—does not follow meiosis.)

Next, a cell wall forms about each nucleus, some of the cytoplasm of the ascus being included within the cell wall (Figure 14-10g).

Thus, eight haploid uninucleate ascospores (Figure 14-10g) have been formed.

While asci and ascospores are forming, surrounding hyphae proliferate to form the ascocarp (Figure 14-10h) around the asci.

As you see, two different types of ascospores are produced during meiosis. Each ascospore gives rise to a mycelium having only one mating type (Figure 14-10i).

B. Peziza: *A Cup Fungus*

The cup fungi are commonly found on soil during cool early spring and fall weather. Their sexual spore-containing structures are cup shaped, hence their common name.

PROCEDURE

1. Observe the preserved specimen of a cup fungus (Figure 14-11).

Actually, the structure we identify as a cup fungus is the fruiting body, produced as a result of sexual reproduction by the fungus. Most of the organism is present within the soil as an extensive mycelium. Specifically, the fruiting body is called an **ascocarp.**

2. Obtain a prepared slide of the ascocarp of *Peziza* or a related cup fungus. Examine the slide with the medium-power and high-dry objectives of your compound microscope.
3. Identify the elongate fingerlike **asci,** which contain dark-colored, spherical **ascospores** (Figure 14-12).

Figure 14-11 Cup fungi (0.25×). (Photo by J. W. Perry.)

Figure 14-12 Cross section of an ascocarp from a cup fungus (186×).

| 14.5 | **Phylum Basidiomycota: Club Fungi** *(About 30 min.)* |

Members of this group of fungi are probably what first come to mind when we think of fungi, because this phylum contains those organisms called mushrooms. Actually the mushroom is only a portion of the fungus—it's the fruiting body, specifically a **basidiocarp,** containing the sexually produced haploid **basidiospores.** These basidiospores are produced by a club-shaped **basidium** for which the group is named. Much (if not most) of the fungal mycelium grows out of sight, within the substrate on which the basidiocarp is found.

MATERIALS

Per student:

- commercial mushroom
- prepared slide of mushroom pileus (cap), c.s. (*Coprinus*)
- compound microscope

Per lab room:

- demonstration specimens of various club fungi

Mushrooms called gill fungi have their sexual spores produced on sheets of hyphae that look like the gills of fish.

PROCEDURE

1. Obtain a fresh fruiting body, more properly called a **basidiocarp** (Figure 14-13). Identify the **stalk** and **cap.**

2. Look at the bottom surface of the cap, noting the numerous gills. It is on the surface of these gills that the haploid basidiospores are produced. Remember that all the structures you are examining are composed of aggregations of fungal hyphae.

3. Obtain a prepared slide of a cross section of the cap of a mushroom (Figure 14-14). Observe the slide first with the low-power objective of your compound microscope.

4. In the center of the cap, identify the **stalk.** The **gills** radiate from the stalk to the edge of the cap, much as spokes of a bicycle wheel radiate from the hub to the rim.

5. Switch to the high-dry objective to study a single gill (Figure 14-15). Note that the component hyphae produce club-shaped structures at the edge. These are the **basidia** (singular, *basidium*).

6. Each basidium produces four haploid **basidiospores.** Find them. (All four may not be in the same plane of section.)

Each basidiospore is attached to the basidium by a tiny hornlike projection. As the basidiospore matures, it is shot off the projection due to a buildup of turgor pressure within the basidium.

The life cycle of a typical mushroom is shown in Figure 14-16.

Because of genetic differences, basidiospores are of two different types. Mycelia produced by the two types of basidiospores are of two mating strains. Figure 14-16 shows these two different nuclei as open and closed (darkened) circles.

When a haploid basidiospore (Figure 14-16a) germinates, it produces a haploid *primary mycelium* (Figure 14-16b). The primary mycelium is incapable of producing a fruiting body.

Fusion between two sexually compatible mycelia (Figure 14-16b) must occur to continue the life cycle.

Surprisingly, the nuclei of the two mycelia don't fuse immediately; thus, each cell of this so-called *secondary mycelium* (Figure 14-16c) contains two genetically *different* nuclei. This condition is called "dikaryotic."

The secondary mycelium forms an extensive network within the substrate. An environmental or genetic trigger eventually stimulates the formation of the aerial basidiocarp (Figure 14-16d).

Each cell of the basidiocarp has two genetically different nuclei, including the basidia (Figure 14-16e) on the gills.

Within the basidia, the two nuclei fuse; the basidia are now diploid (Figure 14-16f).

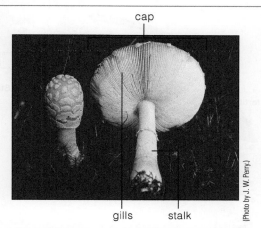

Figure 14-13 Mushroom basidiocarps. The one on the left is younger than that on the right (0.25×).

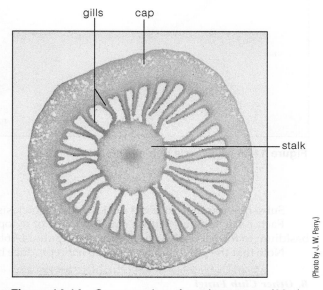

Figure 14-14 Cross section of mushroom cap (23×).

Figure 14-15 High magnification of a mushroom gill (287×).

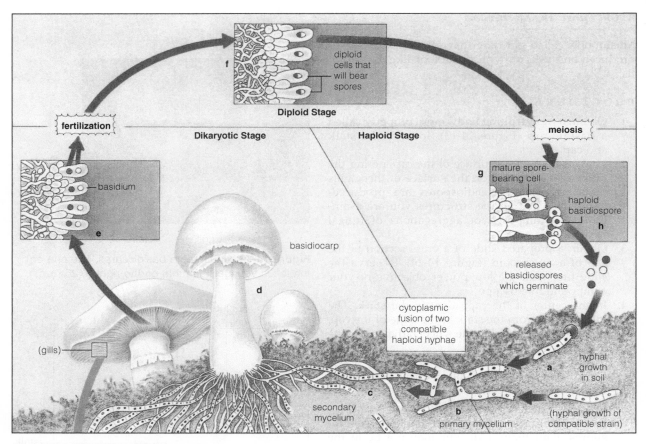

Figure 14-16 Life cycle of a mushroom.

Subsequently, these diploid nuclei undergo meiosis, forming genetically distinct nuclei (Figure 14-16g).

Each nucleus flows with a small amount of cytoplasm through the hornlike projections at the tip of the basidium to form a haploid basidiospore (Figure 14-16h).

Note that the gilled mushrooms do *not* reproduce by means of asexual conidia.

B. Other Club Fungi

A wide variety of basidiomycetes are not mushrooms. Let's examine a few representatives that you're likely to see in the field.

PROCEDURE

1. Examine the representatives of fruiting bodies of other members of the club fungi available in the laboratory.
2. Observe "puffballs" (Figure 14-17).The basidiospores of puffballs are contained within a spherical basidiocarp that develops a pore at the apex. Basidiospores are released when the puffball is crushed or hit by driving rain.
3. Examine "shelf fungi" (Figure 14-18). What you are looking at is actually the basidiocarp of the fungus that has been removed from the surface of a tree.

The presence of a basidiocarp of the familiar shelf fungi indicates that an extensive network of fungal hyphae is growing within a tree, digesting the cells of the wood. As a forester assesses a woodlot to determine the potential yield of usable wood, one of the things noted is the presence of shelf fungi, which indicates low-value (diseased) trees.

The most common shelf fungi are called polypores because of the numerous holes ("pores") on the lower surface of the fruiting body. These pores are lined with basidia bearing basidiospores.

4. Observe the undersurface of the basidiocarp that is on demonstration at a dissecting microscope and note the pores.

(Photo by J. W. Perry.)

Figure 14-17 Puffballs. Note pore for spore escape (0.31×).

(Photo by J. W. Perry.)

Figure 14-18 Shelf fungus (0.12×).

14.6 "Imperfect Fungi" *(About 15 min.)*

This group consists of fungi for which no sexual stage is known. Someone once decided that in order for a life to be complete—to be "perfect"—sex was necessary. Thus, these fungi are "imperfect." Reproduction takes place primarily by means of asexual conidia.

These fungi are among the most economically important, producing antibiotics (for example, one species of *Penicillium* produces penicillin). Others produce the citric acid used in the soft-drink industry; still others are used in the manufacture of cheese. Some are important pathogens of both plants and animals.

MATERIALS

Per student:

- dissecting needle
- glass microscope slide
- coverslip
- prepared slide of *Penicillium* conidia (optional)
- compound microscope

Per student pair:

- dH₂O in dropping bottle
- culture of *Alternaria*

Per lab room:

- demonstration of *Penicillium*-covered food *and/or* plate cultures

A. Penicillium*

The genus *Penicillium* has numerous species. The common feature of all species in this genus is the distinctive shape of the hypha that produce the conidia (Figure 14-19).

PROCEDURE

1. Examine demonstration specimens of moldy oranges or other foods. The blue color is attributable to a pigment in the numerous conidia produced by this fungus, *Penicillium*.
2. With a dissecting needle, scrape some of the conidia from the surface of the moldy specimen (or from a petri dish culture plate containing *Penicillium*) and

*Some species of Penicillium reproduce sexually, forming ascocarps. These species are classified in the phylum Ascomycota. However, not all fungi producing the conidiophore form called Penicillium reproduce sexually. Those that reproduce only by asexual means are considered "imperfect fungi."

conidia

conidiophore

(Photo courtesy G. L. Barron, University of Guelph.)

Figure 14-19 *Penicillium* (300×).

prepare a wet mount. Observe your preparation using the high-dry objective. (Prepared slides may also be available.)

3. Identify the **conidiophore** and the numerous tiny, spherical **conidia** (Figure 14-19). The name *Penicillium* comes from the Latin word *penicillus*, meaning "a brush." (Appropriate, isn't it?)

B. Alternaria

Perhaps no other fungus causes more widespread human irritation than *Alternaria*, an allergy-causing organism. During the summer, many weather programs announce the daily pollen (from flowering plants, Exercise 17) and *Alternaria* spore counts as an index of air quality for allergy sufferers.

PROCEDURE

1. From the petri dish culture plate provided, remove a small portion of the mycelium and prepare a wet mount.

2. Examine with the high-dry objective of your compound microscope to find the **conidia** (Figure 14-20). Produced in chains, *Alternaria* conidia are multicellular, unlike those of *Penicillium* or *Aspergillus*. This makes identification very easy, since the conidia are quite distinct from all others produced by the fungi.

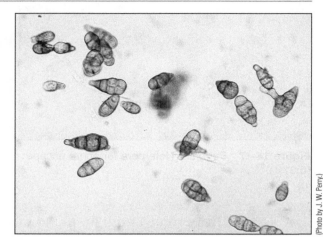

Figure 14-20 Conidia of *Alternaria* (332×).

14.7   Mutualistic Fungi *(About 20 min.)*

Fungi team up with plants or members of the bacterial or protist kingdoms to produce some remarkable mutualistic relationships. The best way to envision such relationships is to think of them as good interpersonal relationships, in which both members benefit and are made richer than would be possible for each individual on its own.

MATERIALS

Per lab room:

- demonstration specimens of crustose, foliose, and fruticose lichens
- demonstration slide of lichen, c.s. on compound microscope
- demonstration slide of mycorrhizal root, c.s. on compound microscope

A. Lichens

Lichens are organisms made up of fungi and either green algae (kingdom Protista) or cyanobacteria (kingdom Eubacteria). The algal or cyanobacterial cells photosynthesize, and the fungus absorbs a portion of the carbohydrates produced. The fungal mycelium provides a protective, moist shelter for the photosynthesizing cells. Hence, both partners benefit from the relationship.

granite (rock) substrate

crustose lichen

Figure 14-21 Crustose lichen (0.5×).

PROCEDURE

1. Examine the demonstration specimen of a **crustose lichen** (Figure 14-21).

2. What is it growing on?

_____

_____

3. Write a sentence describing the crustose lichen.

_____

_____

4. Observe the demonstration specimen of a **foliose lichen** (Figure 14-22).

5. What is it growing on? _____

6. Write a sentence describing the foliose lichen.

_____

_____

_____

_____

7. Examine the demonstration specimen of a **fruticose lichen** (Figure 14-23).

8. What is it growing on?

_____

_____

Figure 14-22 Foliose lichen (0.5×).

(Photo by J. W. Perry.)

9. Write a sentence describing the fruticose lichen.

_____

_____

_____

apothecia (spore containers)

moss

(Photo by J. W. Perry.)

Figure 14-23 Fruticose lichen (1×).

10. Observe the cross section of a lichen at the demonstration microscope. This particular lichen is composed of fungal and green algae cells (Figure 14-24).
11. Locate the **fungal mycelium** and then the **algae cells.**
12. It's likely that this slide has a cup-shaped fruiting body. To which fungal phylum does this fungus belong?

_____

Figure 14-24 Section of lichen (84×).

B. Mycorrhizae

Mycorrhiza literally means "fungus root." A mycorrhiza is a mutualistic association between plant roots and certain species of fungi. In fact, many of the mushroom species (see Section 14-5A) you find in forests (especially those that appear to grow right from the ground) are part of a mycorrhizal association.

The fungus absorbs carbohydrates from the plant roots. The fungal hyphae penetrate much farther into the soil than plant root hairs can reach, absorbing water and dissolved mineral ions that are then released to the plant. Again, both partners benefit. In fact, many plants don't grow well in the absence of mycorrhizal associations.

There are two different types of mycorrhizal roots, **ectomycorrhizae** and **endomycorrhizae.** "Ectos" produce a fungal sheath around the root, and the hyphae penetrate between the cell walls of the root's cortex, but not into the root cells themselves. By contrast, "endos" do not form a covering sheath, and the fungi are found within the cells. We'll look at both types.

MATERIALS

Per student:

- ectomyccorhizal pine root, prep. slide, c.s.
- endomyccorhizal root, prep. slide, c.s.
- compound microscope

PROCEDURE

1. Obtain a prepared slide of an ectomycorrhizal pine root. Examine it with the medium- and high-power objective of your compound microscope.
2. Identify the sheath of fungal hyphae that surround the root.
3. Now look for hyphae between the cell walls within the cortex of the root.
4. Draw what you see in Figure 14-25.
5. Obtain a prepared slide of an endomycorrhizal root (Figure 14-26) and examine it as you did above.
6. Identify the hyphae within the plant root cells.

Figure 14-25 Drawing of ectomycorrhizal pine root (_____×).

highly branched hypha in root cell

hyphae in root cell

(Photo by J. W. Perry.)

Figure 14-26 Cross section of endomycorrhizal root (110×).

| 14.8 | **Experiment: Environmental Factors and Fungal Growth** |

(About 45 min. to set up)

Like all living organisms, environmental cues are instrumental in causing growth responses in fungi. Intuitively, we know that light is important for plant growth. Light also affects animals in a myriad of ways, from triggering reproductive events in deer to affecting the complex psyche of humans. What effect might light have on fungi? These experiments enable you to determine whether this environmental factor has any effect on fungal growth.

A. Light and Darkness

This experiment addresses the hypothesis that *light triggers spore production of certain fungi.*

MATERIALS

Per experimental group (student pair):

- transfer loop
- bunsen burner (or alcohol lamp)
- matches or striker
- 3 petri plates containing potato dextrose agar (PDA)
- grease pencil or other marker

Per lab bench:

- test tubes with spore suspensions of *Trichoderma viride, Penicillium claviforme*, and *Aspergillus ornatus*

PROCEDURE

Work in pairs, and refer to Figure 14-27, which shows how to inoculate the cultures.

1. Receive instructions from your lab instructor as to which fungal culture you should use.

   Note: Do not open the petri plates until step 3.

2. Use a grease pencil or other lab marker to label each cover with your name and the name of the fungus you have been assigned. Write "CONTINUOUS LIGHT" on one petri plate, "CONTINUOUS DARKNESS" on a second plate, and "ALTERNATING LIGHT AND DARKNESS" on the third one.

3. Following the directions in Figure 14-27, inoculate each plate by touching the loop gently on the agar surface approximately in the middle of the plate.

a Sterilize the loop by holding the wire in a flame until it is red hot. Allow it to cool before proceeding.

b While holding the sterile loop and the bacterial culture, remove the cap as shown.

c Briefly heat the mouth of the tube in a burner flame before inserting the loop for an inoculum.

d Get a loopful of culture, withdraw the loop, heat the mouth of the tube, and replace the cap.

e To inoculate a solid medium in a petri plate, place the plate on a table and lift one edge of the cover.

Figure 14-27   Procedure for inoculating a culture plate. (After Case and Johnson, 1984.)

4. Place one plate in each condition:
   - continuous light
   - continuous darkness
   - alternating light and dark
5. In Table 14-3, write your prediction of what will occur in the different environmental conditions.
6. Check the results after 5–7 days and make conclusions concerning the effect of light on the growth of the cultures. Record your results in Table 14-3. Draw what you observe in Figure 14-28.
7. Compare the results you obtained with the results of other experimenters who used different species. Record your conclusions in Table 14-3.

TABLE 14-3 Effect of Light on Fungal Sporulation in _____ (insert the fungus name)

Prediction:

Conditions:

    Continuous light

    Continuous darkness

    Alternating light and darkness

Conclusions:

    Trichoderma viride

    Penicillium claviforme

    Aspergillus ornatus

continuous light   continuous darkness   alternating light/dark

Figure 14-28 Drawing of effect of alternating light and darkness on sporulation of _____ (insert name of fungus).

B. Directional Illumination

This experiment addresses the hypothesis that *light from one direction causes the spore-bearing hyphae of certain fungi to grow in the direction of the light*.

MATERIALS

Per experimental group (student pair):

- transfer loop
- bunsen burner (or alcohol lamp)
- matches or striker
- 2 petri plates containing either potato dextrose agar (PDA) or cornmeal (CM) agar
- grease pencil or other marker

Per lab bench:

- test tubes with spore suspensions of
  Phycomyces blakesleeanus (inoculate onto PDA)
  Penicillium isariforme (inoculate onto PDA)
  Aspergillus giganteus (inoculate onto CM)

PROCEDURE

Work in pairs and refer to Figure 14-27, which shows how to inoculate cultures.

1. Receive instructions from your lab instructor as to which fungal culture you should use.

   Note: Do not open the petri plates until step 3.

2. Use a grease pencil or other lab marker to label each cover with your name and the name of the fungus you have been assigned. Without removing the lid, turn the petri plate upside down and place a line across its center from edge to edge.
3. Following the directions in Figure 14-27, inoculate each petri plate by dragging a loop full of spore suspension over the agar surface above the line you marked on the bottom of the plate.
4. Place one plate in each condition:
   - continuous unilateral illumination
   - continuous illumination from above the plate
5. In Table 14-4, write your prediction of what will occur in the two environmental conditions.
6. Check the results after 5–7 days and make conclusions concerning the effect of light on the growth of the cultures. Record your results in Table 14-4. Draw what you see in Figure 14-29.
7. Compare the results you obtained with the results of other experimenters who used different species. Record your conclusions in Table 14-4.

TABLE 14-4	Effect of Directional Illumination on Growth of the Fungus _____ (insert fungus name)
Prediction:	
Conditions:	
Unilateral illumination	
Illumination from above	
Conclusions:	
Phycomyces blakesleeanus	
Penicillium isariforme	
Aspergillus giganteus	

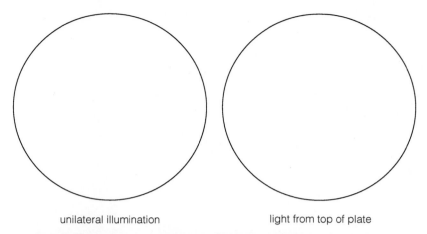

unilateral illumination   light from top of plate

Figure 14-29   Drawing of effect of unilateral illumination on growth of ____
_____ (insert name of fungus).

PRE-LAB QUESTIONS

_____ 1. An organism that grows specifically on nonliving organic material is called
   (a) an autotroph
   (b) a heterotroph
   (c) a parasite
   (d) a saprophyte

_____ 2. Taxonomic separation into fungal phyla is based on
   (a) sexual reproduction, or lack thereof
   (b) whether the fungus is a parasite or saprophyte
   (c) the production of certain metabolites, like citric acid
   (d) the edibility of the fungus

_____ 3. Fungi is to fungus as _____ is to
   _____.

   (a) mycelium, mycelia
   (b) hypha, hyphae
   (c) sporangia, sporangium
   (d) ascus, asci

_____ 4. Which statement is not true of the zygospore-forming fungi?
   (a) They are in the phylum Zygomycota
   (b) Ascospores are found in an ascus
   (c) *Rhizopus* is a representative genus
   (d) A zygospore is formed after fertilization

_____ 5. Which structures would you find in a sac fungus?
   (a) ascogonium, antheridium, zygospores
   (b) ascospores, oogonia, asci, ascocarps
   (c) basidia, basidiospores, basidiocarps
   (d) ascogonia, asci, ascocarps, ascospores

_____ 6. The club fungi are placed in the phylum Basidiomycota
   (a) because of their social nature
   (b) because they form basidia
   (c) because of the presence of an ascocarp
   (d) because they are dikaryotic

_____ 7. Which statement is *not* true of the imperfect fungi?
   (a) They reproduce sexually by means of conidia
   (b) They form an ascocarp
   (c) Sex organs are present in the form of oogonia and antheridia
   (d) All of the above are false

_____ 8. A relationship between two organisms in which both members benefit is said to be
   (a) parasitic
   (b) saprotrophic
   (c) mutualistic
   (d) heterotrophic

_____ 9. An organism that is made up of a fungus and an associated green alga or cyanobacterium is known as a
   (a) sac fungus
   (b) lichen
   (c) mycorrhizal root
   (d) club fungus

_____ 10. A mutualistic association between a plant root and a fungus is known as a
   (a) sac fungus
   (b) lichen
   (c) mycorrhizal root
   (d) club fungus

EXERCISE 14

Fungi

POST-LAB QUESTIONS

14.1 Phylum Zygomycota: Zygosporangium-Forming Fungi

1. Observe this photo at the right of a portion of a fungus you examined in lab.

    a. What is structure a?

    b. Are the contents of structure a haploid or diploid?

2. Distinguish between a *hypha* and a *mycelium*.

3. Examine the below photomicrographs of a fungal structure you studied in lab. Is this structure labeled **b** in the photomicrograph below the product of sexual or asexual reproduction?

(130×).

(120×).

14.3 Phylum Ascomycota: Sac Fungi

4. Distinguish among an *ascus*, an *ascospore*, and an *ascocarp*.

5. Walking in the woods, you find a cup-shaped fungus. Back in the lab, you remove a small portion from what appears to be its fertile surface and crush it on a microscope slide, preparing the wet mount that appears at the right. Identify the fingerlike structures present on the slide.

(287×).

14.4 Phylum Basidiomycota: Club Fungi

6. What type of spores are produced by the fungus pictured at the right?

7. The photo below shows a fungus growing on a dead hemlock tree. What is the common name of a fungus of this sort? Be specific.

14.5 "Imperfect Fungi"

8. Explain the name "imperfect fungi."

Food for Thought

9. Give the correct singular or plural form of the following words in the blanks provided.

	Singular	Plural
a.	hypha	
b.		mycelia
c.	zygospore	
d.		asci
e.	basidium	
f.		conidia

10. Lichens are frequently the first colonizers of hostile growing sites, including sunbaked or frozen rock, recently hardened lava, and even gravestones. How can lichens survive in habitats so seemingly devoid of nutrients and under such harsh physical conditions?

Bryophytes and Seedless Vascular Plants

After completing this exercise, you will be able to

1. define *alternation of generations, isomorphic, heteromorphic, dioecious, antheridium, archegonium, hygroscopic, protonema, tracheophyte, rhizome, mutualism, sporophyte, sporangium, gametophyte, gametangium, antheridium, archegonium, epiphyte, strobilus, node, internode, frond, sorus, annulus, hygroscopic,* and *chemotaxis;*

2. diagram the plant life cycle to show alternation of generations;

3. distinguish between alternation of isomorphic and heteromorphic generations;

4. list evidence supporting the evolution of land plants from green algae;

5. recognize charophytes, mosses, and liverworts;

6. identify the sporophytes, gametophytes, and associated structures of liverworts and mosses (those in **boldface** in the procedure sections);

7. describe the function of the sporophyte and the gametophyte;

8. postulate why bryophytes live only in environments where free water is often available;

9. recognize whisk ferns, club mosses, horsetails, and ferns when you see them, placing them in the proper taxonomic phylum;

10. identify the structures of the fern allies and ferns in **boldface;**

11. describe the life cycle of ferns;

12. explain the mechanism by which spore dispersal occurs from a fern sporangium;

13. describe the significant differences between the life cycles of the bryophytes, and the club mosses and ferns.

INTRODUCTION

This is the first in a series of exercises that addresses true plants—the kingdom Plantae.

Plants evolved from the green algae, specifically now extinct relatives of living green algae called **charophytes.** Evidence for this includes identical food reserves (starch), the same photosynthetic pigments (chlorophylls a and b, carotenes, and xanthophylls), similarities in structure of their flagella, and the way cell division takes place. Some biologists have gone so far as to suggest that the land plants are nothing more than highly evolved green algae.

One major mystery is the origin of a feature common to *all* true plants (but *not* charophytes), **alternation of generations.** In alternation of generations, two distinct phases exist: A diploid **sporophyte** alternates with a haploid **gametophyte,** as summarized in Figure 15-1.

As animals, we find the concept of alternation of generations difficult to envision. But think of it as the existence of two body forms of the same organism. The primary reproductive function of one

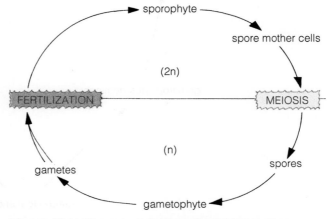

Figure 15-1 Summary of alternation of generations.

body form, the gametophyte, is to produce gametes (eggs and/or sperm) by *mitosis*. The primary reproductive function of the other, the sporophyte, is to produce spores by *meiosis*.

A fundamental distinction exists between the green algae and land plants with respect to alternation of generations. Although some green algae have alternation of generations, the sporophyte and gametophyte look *identical*. To the naked eye, they are indistinguishable. This is called alternation of **isomorphic** generations. (*Iso-* comes from a Greek word meaning "equal"; *morph-* is Greek for "form.")

By contrast, the alternation of generations in land plants is **heteromorphic** (*hetero-* is Greek for "different"). The sporophytes and gametophytes of land plants, including the bryophytes, are distinctly different from one another. The contrast between isomorphic and heteromorphic alternation of generations is modeled in Figure 15-2.

During the course of evolution, two major lines of divergence took place in the plant kingdom. The plants in one line had as their dominant phase the gametophytic generation, meaning that the sporophyte was never free living but was permanently attached to and dependent on the gametophyte for nutrition. Today these plants are represented by the bryophytes, mosses and their relatives. It seems that this line exemplifies *dead-end evolution*— no other group of plants present today arises from it.

In the other line of evolution, the sporophyte led an independent existence, the gametophyte being quite small and inconspicuous. Figure 15-3 summarizes these two evolutionary lines.

As you will see in this exercise, the land plants known as liverworts and mosses are often fairly dissimilar in appearance. They do share similarities, including the following:

1. Both exhibit alternation of heteromorphic generations in which the gametophyte is the dominant organism. The sporophyte remains attached to the gametophyte, deriving most of its nutrition from the gametophyte.
2. Both are dependent on water for fertilization, since their sperm must swim to a nonmotile egg.
3. Both lack true vascular tissues, xylem and phloem, and hence are relatively small organisms.

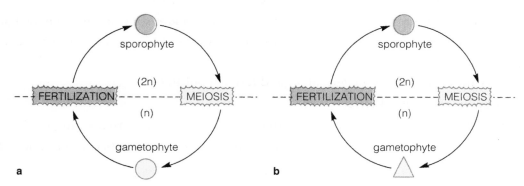

Figure 15-2 Types of alternation of generations. (**a**) Isomorphic. (**b**) Heteromorphic.

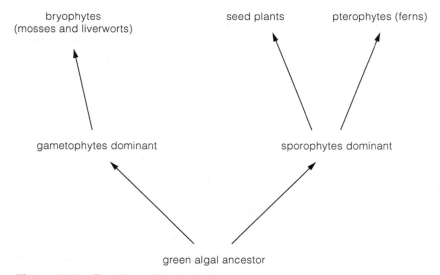

Figure 15-3 Evolution of land plants.

A major distinction exists between the bryophytes (liverworts and mosses) and the fern allies, ferns, gymnosperms, and flowering plants: Whereas the dominant and conspicuous portion of the life cycle in the bryophytes is the **gametophyte** (the gamete-producing part of the life cycle), in all other plants that you will examine in this and subsequent exercises, it is the **sporophyte** (that portion of the life cycle producing spores).

A second, and perhaps more important, distinction also exists between bryophytes and the fern allies, ferns, gymnosperms, and flowering plants: The latter group contains *vascular tissue*. Vascular tissues include *phloem*, the tissue that conducts the products of photosynthesis, and *xylem*, the tissue that conducts water and minerals. As a result of the presence of xylem and phloem, fern allies, ferns, gymnosperms, and flowering plants are sometimes called **tracheophytes.**

Push gently on the region of your throat at the base of your larynx (voicebox or Adam's apple). If you move your fingers up and down, you should be able to feel the cartilage rings in your *trachea* (windpipe). To visualize its structure, imagine that your trachea is a pipe with donuts inside of it (Figure 15-4). This same arrangement exists in some cell types within the xylem of plants. Thus, early botanical microscopists called plants having such an arrangement *tracheophytes*.

In this exercise, you will study the tracheophytes that lack seeds. Two phyla of plants make up the seedless vascular plants:

Phylum	Common Names
Lycophyta	Club mosses
Moniliophyta	Whisk ferns, horsetails, and ferns

Figure 15-4 Three-dimensional representation of the cartilage in your trachea and some xylem cells of vascular plants.

Whisk ferns and horsetails are very unlike what we often think of as ferns, but molecular evidence confirms their relationship to more typical ferns. We will study most closely the life cycle of the ferns, since they are common in our environment and have gametophytes and sporophytes that beautifully illustrate the concept of alternation of generations.

15.1   Phylum Charophyta—Ancestors of True Plants *(About 10 min.)*

Before beginning study of true plants (kingdom Plantae), let's look at their closest algal relatives. Charophytes (kingdom Protista) called stoneworts, are within a lineage that millions of years ago gave rise to the land plants.

Stoneworts are interesting organisms found "rooted" in brackish and fresh waters, particularly those high in calcium. (Two of your lab manual authors—the Perrys—have ponds that are delightfully full of stoneworts.) They get their common names by virtue of being able to precipitate calcium carbonate over their surfaces, encrusting them and rendering them somewhat stony and brittle. (The suffix *-wort* is from a Greek word meaning "herb.")

MATERIALS

Per student:

- small culture dish
- dissecting microscope

Per lab room:

- living culture (or preserved) *Chara* or *Nitella*
- demonstration slide of *Chara* with sex organs

PROCEDURE

1. From the classroom culture provided, obtain some of the specimen and place it in a small culture dish partially filled with water.

2. Observe the specimen with a dissecting microscope. Note that the stoneworts resemble what we would think of as a plant. They are divided into "stems" and "branches" (Figure 15-5).

3. Search for flask-shaped and spherical structures along the stem. These are the sex organs. If none is present on the specimen, observe the demonstration slide (Figure 15-6) that has been selected to show these structures.

4. The flask-shaped structures are **oogonia,** each of which contains a single, large egg (Figure 15-7). Notice that the oogonium is covered with cells that twist over the surface of the gametangium. Because of the presence of these cells, the oogonium is considered to be a *multicellular* sex organ. Multicellular sex organs are present in all land plants.

Based on your study of previously examined specimens, would you say the egg is motile or nonmotile?

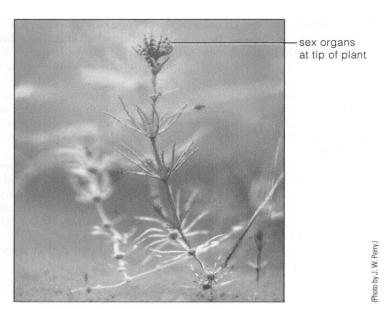

sex organs at tip of plant

Figure 15-5 The stonewort, *Chara*, with sex organs (2×).

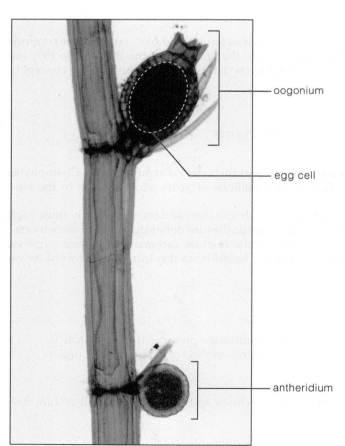

oogonium

egg cell

antheridium

Figure 15-6 *Chara*, showing sex organs (30×). (Photo by J. W. Perry.)

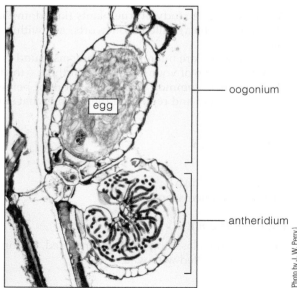

egg

oogonium

antheridium

Figure 15-7 Antheridia and oogonia of *Chara* (80×).

5. Now find a spherical **antheridium** (Figure 15-7). Like the oogonium, the antheridium is covered by cells and is also considered to be multicellular. Cells within the interior of the antheridium produce numerous flagellated sperm cells.

Fertilization of eggs by sperm produces a *zygote* within the oogonium. The zygote-containing oogonium eventually falls off from the parent plant. The zygote can remain dormant for some time before the nucleus undergoes meiosis in preparation for germination. Apparently, three of the four nuclei produced during meiosis disintegrate.

15.2   Phylum Hepatophyta: Liverworts *(About 10 min.)*

Liverworts!? What in the world is a liverwort? Knowing why these plants are called liverworts is a start to knowing them.

The Greek suffix *-wort* means "herb," a nonwoody plant. The "liver" portion of the common name comes about because the plants look a little like a lobed human liver. These are small plants that you have likely overlooked (until now!) because they're inconspicuous and don't look like anything important. You'll find them growing on rocks that are periodically wetted along clean freshwater streams.

MATERIALS

Per student:

- living or preserved *Marchantia* thalli, with gemma cups, antheridiophores, archegoniophores, and mature sporophytes
- dissecting microscope

PROCEDURE

1. Examine the living or preserved plants of the liverwort, *Marchantia*, that are on demonstration. The body of this plant is called a **thallus** (the plural is *thalli*), because it is flattened and has little internal tissue differentiation (Figure 15-8).
2. The thallus is the gametophyte portion of the life cycle.

Is it haploid or diploid? _____

3. Obtain and examine one thallus of the liverwort. Notice that the thallus is lobed. Centuries ago, herbalists believed that plants that looked like portions of the human anatomy could be used to treat ailments of that part of the body. This plant reminded them of the liver, and hence the plant was called a liverwort.
4. Now place the thallus on the stage of a dissecting microscope. Looking first at the top surface, find the *pores* that lead to the interior of the plant and serve as avenues of exchange for atmospheric gases (CO_2 and O_2; Figure 15-8).
5. Identify **gemma cups** (Figure 15-8) on the upper surface. Look closely within a gemma cup to find the **gemmae** inside (the singular is *gemma*). Gemmae are produced by *mitotic* divisions of the thallus. They are dislodged by splashing water. If they land on a suitable substrate, they grow into new thalli; hence they are a means of asexual reproduction.
6. Are gemmae haploid or diploid? _____
7. Turn the plant over to find the hairlike **rhizoids** that anchor the organism to the substrate.

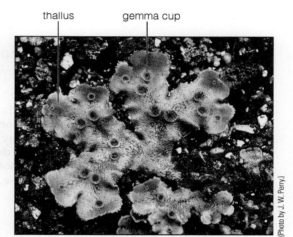

thallus   gemma cup

(Photo by J. W. Perry.)

Figure 15-8 Thallus of a liverwort with gemma cups (1×).

As noted above, the thalli are the gametophyte generation. Similar to higher animals (humans, as an example), gametes are produced in special organs on the plant. In this liverwort, the organs are contained within elevated branches. The general name for these elevated branches is *gametangiophores*. (The suffix *-phore* is derived from a Greek word meaning "branch.") There are male and female gametangiophores.

8. On a male thallus, find the male **antheridiophores.** They look like umbrellas (Figure 15-9a). The sperm-producing male sex organs called **antheridia** (the singular is *antheridium*) are within the flattened splash platform of the umbrella.
9. On female plants, find the female **archegoniophores** (Figure 15-9b); these look somewhat like an umbrella that has lost its fabric and has only ribs remaining. Underneath these ribs are borne the female gametangia, **archegonia** (singular, *archegonium*).

antheridiophore

a

archegoniophore

thallus

b

(Photos by J. W. Perry.)

Figure 15-9 Liverwort thalli with gametangiophores. (**a**) Male thalli with antheridiophores. (**b**) Female thalli with archegoniophores (0.5×).

15.3   Experiment: Effect of Photoperiod
(About 10 min. to set up; requires 6 weeks to complete)

Photoperiod, the length of light and dark periods, exerts a significant effect upon most living things. Flowering in many plants is dependent on photoperiod, some plants being classified as "long day (short night)," others as "short day (long night)," and still others as "day neutral." Flowering is a reproductive event. The reproductive behavior of many animals, such as deer, is also dependent on day length.

    This experiment examines the effect of photoperiod on the production of gametangiophores and gemma cups in the liverwort, *Marchantia.* One possible experimental hypothesis is that *reproduction of* Marchantia *is stimulated by long days (short nights).*

MATERIALS

Per student group:

- vigorously growing colony of the liverwort *Marchantia polymorpha*
- pot label
- china or other marker

Per lab room:

- growth chambers set to long day (16 hr light, 8 hr darkness) and short day (8 hr light, 16 hr darkness) conditions

PROCEDURE

1. In Table 15-1, write a prediction about the effect of day length on *Marchantia* reproduction.
2. Obtain a colony of the liverwort, *Marchantia polymorpha.* On the pot label, write your name, date, and the experimental condition (long day or short day) to which you are going to subject the colony.
3. Place the colony in the growth chamber that is designated as "short day" or "long day," depending on which condition has been assigned to your experimental group. You will be responsible for watering the colonies on a regular basis. Failure to do so will result in unreliable experimental results and/or death of the plants.
4. Observe the colonies weekly over a period of six weeks, recording your observations in Table 15-1.
5. After six weeks of experimental treatment, compare observations with other experimental groups using the same and different independent variables.
6. List the results and make conclusions, writing them in Table 15-2.

Did the experimental results support your hypothesis? _____

    Can you suggest any reasons why it might be beneficial to the liverwort to display the results that the different experimental groups found?

_____

_____

TABLE 15-1 The Effect of Photoperiod on the Reproduction of the Liverwort, *Marchantia polymorpha*

Prediction:

Week	Observations of the Effect of _____ (Long or Short) Day Illumination
1	
2	
3	
4	
5	
6	

TABLE 15-2 Summary of Results: The Effect of Photoperiod on the Reproduction of the Liverwort *Marchantia polymorpha*

Photoperiod	Results
Long day	
Short day	
Conclusions:	

15.4 Phylum Bryophyta: Mosses *(About 40 min.)*

Mosses are plants that you've probably noticed before. They grow on trees, rocks, and soil. Mosses have a wide variety of human uses, the most common ones being as a soil additive to potting soil and as a major component of peat, which is used for fuel in some parts of the world.

MATERIALS

Per student:

- *Polytrichum*, male and female gametophytes, the latter with attached sporophytes
- prepared slide of moss antheridial head, l.s.
- prepared slide of moss archegonial head, l.s.
- prepared slide of moss sporangium (capsule), l.s.
- glass microscope slide
- coverslip

- compound microscope
- dissecting microscope
- dissecting needle

Per student pair:

- dH₂O in dropping bottle

Per student group (table):

- moss protenemata growing on culture medium

PROCEDURE

Refer to Figure 15-16 as you study the life cycle of the mosses.

1. Obtain a living or preserved specimen of a moss that grows in your area. The hairy-cap moss, *Polytrichum*, is a good choice because one of the ten species in this genus is certain to be found near wherever you live in North America.

Lacking vascular tissues, the mosses do not have true roots, stems, or leaves, although they do have structures that are rootlike, stemlike, and leaflike and perform the same functions as the true organs.

2. Identify the rootlike **rhizoids** at the base of the plant. What function do you think rhizoids perform?

_____

_____

3. Notice that the leaflike organs are arranged more or less radially about the stemlike *axis*. You are examining the **gametophyte generation** of the moss. In terms of the life cycle of the organism, what function does the gametophyte serve?

_____

_____

Figure 15-10   Colony of male gametophytes (0.5×).

Polytrichum is **dioecious**, meaning that there are separate male and female plants. (Some other mosses are monoecious.) The male gametophyte can usually be distinguished by the flattened rosette of leaflike structures at its tip.

4. Examine a male gametophyte (Figures 15-10, 15-16a), noting this feature. Embedded within the rosette are the male sex organs, **antheridia** (singular, *antheridium*).

5. With the low- and medium-power objectives of your compound microscope, examine a prepared slide with the antheridia of a moss (Figure 15-16c). Identify the *antheridia* (Figure 15-11).

6. Study a single antheridium (Figure 15-11), using the high-dry objective. Locate the jacket layer surrounding the sperm-forming tissue that, with maturity, gives rise to numerous biflagellate *sperm*. Scattered among the antheridia, find the numerous sterile *paraphyses*. These do not have a reproductive role (and hence are called sterile) but instead function to hold capillary water, preventing the sex organs from drying out.

7. Examine a female gametophyte of *Polytrichum* (Figure 15-16b). Before the development of the sporophyte, the female gametophyte can usually be distinguished by the absence of the rosette at its tip. Nonetheless, the apex of the female gametophyte contains the female sex organs, **archegonia** (singular, *archegonium*).

8. Obtain a prepared slide of the archegonial tip of a moss (Figures 15-12a, 15-16d). Start with the low-power objective of your compound microscope to gain an impression of the overall organization. Find the sterile *paraphyses* and the *archegonia*.

9. Switch to the medium-power objective to study a single archegonium, identifying the long **neck** and the slightly swollen base. Within the base, locate the **egg cell** (Figure 15-16d).

paraphyses

antheridia

a

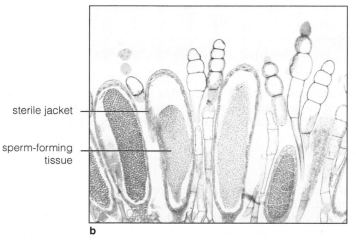

sterile jacket

sperm-forming tissue

b

Figure 15-11   Longitudinal section of antheridial head of a moss (**a**) 8×. (**b**) 93×.

Figure 15-12 (a) Longitudinal section of archegonial head of a moss (22×). (b) Detail of archegonium (88×).

Remember, you are looking at a *section* of a three-dimensional object. The archegonium is very much like a long-necked vase, except that it's solid. The egg cell is like a marble suspended in the middle of the base.

The central core of the archegonial neck contains cells that break down when the egg is mature, liberating a fluid that is rich in sucrose and that attracts sperm that are swimming in dew or rainwater. (Sperm are capable of swimming only short distances and so male plants must be close by.) Fertilization of the egg produces the diploid zygote (Figure 15-16e), the first cell of the **sporophyte generation.**

Numerous mitotic divisions produce an **embryo** (embryo sporophyte, Figure 15-16f), which differentiates into the **mature sporophyte** (Figure 15-16g) that protrudes from the tip of the gametophyte. What is the function of the sporophyte (that is, what does it do, or what reproductive structures does it produce)?

_____

_____

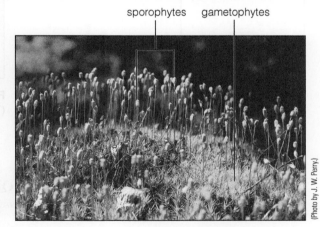

Figure 15-13 Colony of female gametophytes with attached sporophytes (0.25×).

10. Grasp the stalk of the sporophyte and detach it from the gametophyte. The base of the stalk absorbs water and nutrients from the gametophyte.

11. At the tip of the sporophyte, locate the **sporangium** covered by a papery hood. The cover is a remnant of the tissue that surrounded the archegonium and is covered with tiny hairs—hence the common name, hairy-cap moss, for *Polytrichum.*

12. Remove the hood to expose the sporangium (Figure 15-16h). Notice the small cap at the top of the sporangium.

13. Remove the cap and observe the interior of the sporangium with a dissecting microscope. Find the *peristomal teeth* that point inward from the margin of the opening.

The peristomal teeth are **hygroscopic,** meaning that they change shape as they absorb water. As the teeth dry, they arch upward, loosening the cap over the spore mass. The teeth may subsequently shrink or swell, thus regulating how readily the spores inside may escape.

Bryophytes and Seedless Vascular Plants **271**

14. Study a prepared slide of a longitudinal section of a sporangium (Figure 15-14). At the top, you will find sections of the peristomal teeth. Internally, locate the **sporogenous tissue,** which differentiates into *spores* when mature. The sporogenous tissue of the sporangium is diploid, but the spores are haploid and are the first cells of the gametophyte generation.

What type of nuclear division must take place for the sporogenous tissue to become spores?

_____

When the spores are shed from the sporangium, they are carried by wind and water currents to new sites. If conditions are favorable, the spore germinates to produce a filamentous **protonema** (Figures 15-15, 15-16j; plural, *protonemata*) that looks much like a filamentous green alga.

Is the protonema part of the gametophyte or sporophyte generation?

_____

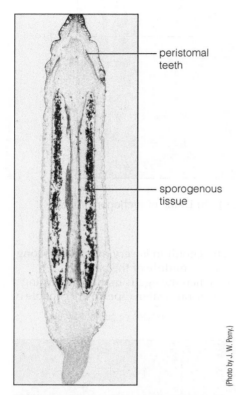

(Photo by J. W. Perry.)

Figure 15-14 Longitudinal section of sporangium of a moss (12×).

(Photo courtesy Biodisc, Inc.)

Figure 15-15 Moss protonema, whole mount (70×).

15.5 Experiment: Effect of Light Quality on Moss Spore Germination and Growth *(About 20 min. to set up; requires 8 weeks to complete)*

What causes plants to grow and reproduce? One significant environmental trigger is light. Both light *quantity* (the length of illumination) and light *quality* (the wavelengths or color of light) trigger growth and reproduction in organisms. In this experiment, you will grow moss protonemata from spores and examine the effect of different wavelengths of light on germination of spores and subsequent growth of the protonema. One hypothesis this simple experiment might address is that *moss spores germinate and protonemata grow best in short (blue) wavelength light.*

antheridial head
archegonial head

a male gametophyte

b female gametophyte

rhizoids

paraphyses

antheridium

c longitudinal section of antheridial head

egg cell

paraphyses

archegonium

d longitudinal section of archegonial head

FERTILIZATION

sperm

calyptra

neck

young sporophyte

zygote

tip of female gametophyte

e archegonium after fertilization

f developing sporophyte

rhizoid

l young gametophyte

bud

k old protonemata with bud

protonemata

peristomal teeth

germinating spore

j spore germination

i spores

cap

h sporangium

hood (removed from sporangium)

MEIOSIS

mature sporophyte

female gametophyte

g gametophyte with attached sporophyte

Figure 15-16 Life cycle of representative moss. (Green structures are 2n.) (Modified from Carolina Biological Supply Company diagrams.)

MATERIALS

Per student group:

- culture plate with moss agar
- water suspension containing moss spores
- china or other marker
- Pi-pump (1 mL or 10 mL)
- 1-mL pipet
- 8-cm strip of parafilm

- compound microscope
- glass microscope slide
- coverslip

Per lab room:

- 4 incubation chambers (one each for white, blue, green, and red light)

PROCEDURE

1. Obtain the following: 1 culture plate containing moss agar, china or other marker, a Pi-pump, a 1-mL pipet, and an 8-cm strip of parafilm.
2. Prepare a wet mount of the moss spore suspension provided by your instructor. Examine the spores with all magnifications available with your compound microscope.
3. Draw the spores in Figure 15-17, noting color.
4. Examine Figure 15-18, which shows you how to open the culture plate.
5. Pipet 1 mL of the spore suspension onto the culture plate.
6. Seal the culture plate with the strip of parafilm to prevent drying: Remove the paper backing, place one end of the parafilm on the edge of the culture plate, hold the edge down with index finger pressure of the hand that is holding the culture plate, and stretch the parafilm around the circumference of the plate with a rolling motion.
7. With the marker, write your name, the date, and the light regime you will be using on the cover of the culture plate. Place the culture in the incubator with the proper light regime. Your instructor will designate the light regime (white, blue, green, or red) under which you should incubate your culture. This is the independent variable.
8. Formulate a prediction regarding this experiment. Write it in the proper space in Table 15-3.
9. Observe your cultures weekly: Remove the lid (if necessary), place the culture on the stage of a dissecting microscope, and observe the spores. Record your observations in Table 15-3. Suggested dependent variables include percent germination, abundance of growth, color of protonemal cells, and formation of buds.
10. After eight weeks, compare your results with other students using the same and different light regimes.
11. Summarize your observations and make conclusions in Table 15-4.

Was your hypothesis supported by the experimental results? _____

Figure 15-17 Drawing of ungerminated moss spores (_____×).

Figure 15-18 Method for inoculating petri plate culture so as to avoid contamination.

TABLE 15-3   Effect of Light Quality on Moss Spore Germination and the Growth of Protonemata

Prediction:

Week	Observations of Dependent Variables (list them here)
1	
2	
3	
4	
5	
6	
7	
8	

TABLE 15-4   Summary of Results on the Effect of Light Quality on the Germination of Moss Spores and Growth of Protonemata

Color of Light	Results
White	
Blue	
Green	
Red	
Conclusions	

Lycopodium and *Selaginella* are the most commonly found genera in the phylum Lycophyta, the club mosses. The common name of this phylum comes from the presence of the so-called **strobilus** (plural, *strobili*), a region of the stem specialized for the production of spores. The strobilus looks like a very small club. Strobili are sometimes called cones.

MATERIALS

Per lab room:

- *Lycopodium,* living, preserved, or herbarium specimens with strobili
- *Lycopodium* gametophyte, preserved (optional)
- *Selaginella,* living, preserved, or herbarium specimens

- *Selaginella lepidophylla,* resurrection plant, 2 dried specimens
- culture bowl containing water

A. Lycopodium

The club moss *Lycopodium* is a small, forest-dwelling plant. These plants are often called ground pines or trailing evergreens. The scientific name comes from the appearance of the rhizome—it looked like a wolf's paw to early botanists. *Lycos* is Greek for "wolf," and *podium* means "foot."

PROCEDURE

1. Observe the living, preserved, or herbarium specimens of *Lycopodium* (Figure 15-19).
2. On your specimen, identify the true **roots, stems,** and **leaves.**
3. The adjective *true* is used to indicate that the organs contain vascular tissue—xylem and phloem.
4. Identify the **rhizome** to which the upright stems are connected. In the case of *Lycopodium,* the rhizome may be either beneath or on the soil surface, depending on the species. Notice that leaves cover the rhizome, as are the upright stems.
5. At the tip of an upright stem, find the **strobilus** (Figure 15-19). Look closely at the strobilus. As you see, it too is made up of leaves, but these leaves are much more tightly aggregated than the sterile (nonreproductive) leaves on the rest of the stem.

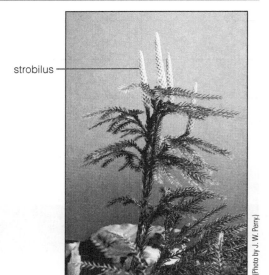

strobilus

Figure 15-19   Sporophyte of *Lycopodium* (0.6×).

The leaves of the strobilus produce *spores* within a *sporangium,* the spore container. As was pointed out in the introduction, the plant you are looking at is a diploid sporophyte.

Is the sporophyte haploid (n) or diploid (2n)? _____

Since the spores are haploid, what process must have taken place within the sporangium?

_____

As maturation occurs, the internodes between the sporangium-bearing leaves elongate slightly, the sporangium opens, and the spores are carried away from the parent plant by wind. If they land in a suitable habitat, the spores germinate to produce small and inconspicuous subterranean gametophytes, which bear sex organs—antheridia and archegonia. For fertilization and the development of a new sporophyte to take place, free water must be available, since the sperm are flagellated structures that must swim to the archegonium.

6. If available, examine a preserved *Lycopodium* gametophyte (Figure 15-20).

B. Selaginella

Selaginella is another genus in the phylum Lycophyta. These plants are usually called spike mosses. (This points out the problem with common names—the common name for the phylum is club mosses, but individual genera have their own common names.) Some species are grown ornamentally for use in terraria.

PROCEDURE

1. Examine living representatives of *Selaginella* (Figure 15-21).
2. Look closely at the tips of the branches and identify the rather inconspicuous **strobili.**
3. Examine the specimens of the resurrection plant (yet another common name!), a species of *Selaginella* sold as a novelty, often in grocery stores. A native of the southwestern United States, this plant grows in environments that are subjected to long periods without moisture. It becomes dormant during these periods.
4. Describe the color and appearance of the dried specimen.

   _____

   _____

5. Now place a dried specimen in a culture bowl containing water. Observe what happens in the next hour or so, and describe the change in appearance of the plant.

   _____

   _____

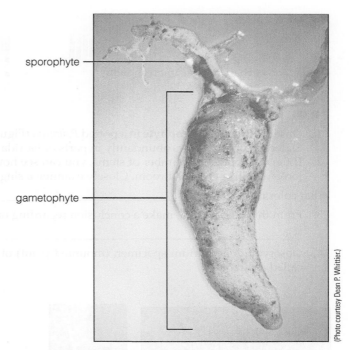

Figure 15-20 Gametophyte with young sporophyte of *Lycopodium* (2×).

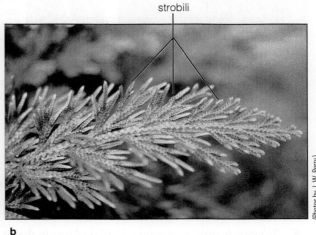

Figure 15-21 (a) Sporophyte of *Selaginella* (0.4×). (b) Higher magnification showing strobili at branch tips (0.9×).

15.7 Phylum Moniliophyta, Subphylum Psilophyta: Whisk Ferns *(About 10 min.)*

The whisk ferns consist of only two genera of plants, *Psilotum* (the *P* is silent) and *Tmesipteris* (the *T* is silent). Neither has any economic importance, but they have intrigued botanists for a long time, especially because *Psilotum* resembles the first vascular plants that colonized the earth. Current evidence indicates that the psilophytes are not directly related to those very early land plants, but instead are ferns. We'll examine only *Psilotum*.

MATERIALS

Per lab room:

- *Psilotum,* living plant
- *Psilotum,* herbarium specimen showing sporangia and rhizome
- *Psilotum* gametophyte
- dissecting microscope

PROCEDURE

1. Observe first the **sporophyte** in a potted *Psilotum* (Figure 15-22). Within the natural landscapes of the United States, this plant grows abundantly in parts of Florida and Hawaii.
2. If the pot contains a number of stems, you can see how it got its common name, the whisk fern, because it looks a bit like a whisk broom. Closely examine a single aerial stem.

What color is it? _____

3. From this observation, make a conclusion regarding one function of this stem.

_____

4. Observe the herbarium specimen (mounted plant) of *Psilotum.* Identify the nongreen underground stem, called a **rhizome.**

Figure 15-22 Sporophytes of *Psilotum.* (**a**) Single stem without sporangia. (**b**) Portion of stem with sporangia (0.3×). (**c**) Sporangia (10×).

5. *Psilotum* is unique among vascular plants in that it lacks roots. Absorption of water and minerals takes place through small rhizoids attached to the rhizome. Additionally, a fungus surrounds and penetrates into the outer cell layers of the rhizome. The fungus absorbs water and minerals from the soil and transfers them to the rhizome. This beneficial association is similar to the mycorrhizal association between plant roots and fungi described in the fungi exercise. A beneficial relationship like that between the fungus and *Psilotum* is called a **mutualistic symbiosis** or, more simply, **mutualism.**
6. On either the herbarium specimen or the living plant, identify the tiny scalelike outgrowths that are found on the aerial stems. Because these lack vascular tissue, they are not considered true leaves. Their size precludes any major role in photosynthesis.
7. The plant you are observing is a sporophyte. Thus, it must produce spores. Find the three-lobed structures on the stem (Figure 15-22b). Each lobe is a single **sporangium** containing spores.
8. If these spores germinate after being shed from the sporangium, they produce a small and infrequently found gametophyte that grows beneath the soil surface. The gametophyte survives beneath the soil thanks to a symbiotic relationship similar to that for the sporophyte's rhizome.
9. If a gametophyte is available, observe it with the aid of a dissecting microscope (Figure 15-23). Note the numerous **rhizoids.** If you look very carefully, you may be able to distinguish **gametangia** (sex organs; singular, *gametangium*).

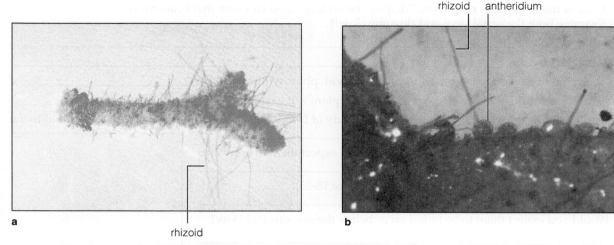

a

b

rhizoid

rhizoid   antheridium

(Photos by J. W. Perry.)

Figure 15-23   (a) *Psilotum* gametophyte (7.5×). (b) Higher magnification showing antheridia (23×).

10. The male sex organs are **antheridia** (Figure 15-23b; singular, *antheridium*); the female sex organs are **archegonia** (singular, *archegonium*). Both antheridia and archegonia are on the same gametophyte. Is the gametophyte dioecious or monoecious? _____

11. Fertilization of an egg within an archegonium results in the production of a new sporophyte.

| 15.8 | **Phylum Moniliophyta, Subphylum Sphenophyta: Horsetails** *(About 10 min.)* |

During the age of the dinosaurs, tree-sized representatives of this phylum flourished. But like the dinosaurs, they too became extinct. Only one genus remains. However, the remnants of these plants, along with others that were growing at that time, remain in the form of massive coal deposits. *Speno-*, a Greek prefix meaning "wedge," gives the phylum its name, presumably because the leaves of these plants are wedge shaped.

A single genus, *Equisetum*, is the only living representative of this subphylum. Different species of *Equisetum* are common throughout North America. Many are highly branched, giving the appearance of a horse's tail, and hence the common name. (*Equus* is Latin for "horse"; *saeta* means "bristle.")

MATERIALS

Per lab room:

- *Equisetum*, living, preserved, or herbarium specimens with strobili
- *Equisetum* gametophytes, living or preserved

PROCEDURE

1. Examine the available specimens of *Equisetum* (Figure 15-24). Depending on the species, it will be more or less branched.
2. Note that the plant is divided into **nodes** (places on the stem where the leaves arise) and **internodes** (regions on the stem between nodes). Identify the small leaves at the node.

If the specimen you are examining is a highly branched species, don't confuse the branches with leaves. The leaves are small, scalelike structures, often brown. (They *do* have vascular tissue, so they are true leaves.) Distinguish the leaves.

strobilius

leaves at node

branches

(Photo by J. W. Perry.)

Figure 15-24   Sporophyte of the horsetail, *Equisetum* (0.2×).

3. Look at the herbarium mount and identify the underground **rhizome** that bears **roots.**
4. Examine both the aerial stem and rhizome closely.

Do both have nodes? _____

Do both have leaves? _____

Which portion of *Equisetum* is primarily concerned with photosynthesis? _____

5. Find the **strobilus** (Figure 15-24). Where on the plant is it located? _____

Based on the knowledge you've acquired in your study of *Lycopodium,* what would you expect to find within the strobilus? _____

When spores fall to the ground, what would you expect them to grow into after germination? _____

6. Now observe the horsetail gametophytes (Figure 15-25).
What color are they? _____

Would you expect them to be found on or below the soil surface? Why?

_____

_____

Figure 15-25 Horsetail gametophyte (5×).

(Photo courtesy Dean Whittier.)

15.9   Phylum Moniliophyta, Subphylum Pterophyta: Ferns *(About 45 min.)*

The variation in form of ferns is enormous, as is their distribution and ecology. We typically think of ferns as inhabitants of moist environments, but some species are also found in very dry locations. Tropical species are often grown as houseplants.

This subphylum gets its name from the Greek word *pteri,* meaning "fern."

MATERIALS

Per student:

- fern sporophytes, fresh, preserved, or herbarium specimens
- prepared slide of fern rhizome, c.s.
- fern gametophytes, living, preserved, or whole mount prepared slides
- fern gametophyte with young sporophyte, living or preserved
- microscope slide

- compound microscope
- dissecting microscope

Per lab room:

- squares of fern sori, in moist chamber (*Polypodium aureum* recommended)
- demonstration slide of fern archegonium, median l.s.
- other fern sporophytes, as available

PROCEDURE

1. Obtain a fresh or herbarium specimen of a typical fern **sporophyte.** As you examine the structures described in this experiment, refer to Figure 15-33, a diagram of the life cycle of a fern.

The sporophyte of many ferns (Figures 15-26, 15-33a) consists of *true* roots, stems, and leaves; that is, they contain vascular tissue.

2. Identify the horizontal stem, the **rhizome** (which produces true **roots**), and upright leaves. The leaves of ferns are called **fronds** and are often highly divided.

Ferns, unlike bryophytes, are vascular plants, their sporophytes containing xylem and phloem. Let's examine this vascular tissue.

3. Obtain a prepared slide of a cross section of a fern stem (rhizome). Study it using the low-power objective of your compound microscope. Use Figure 15-27 as a reference.
   (a) Find the **epidermis, cortex,** and **vascular tissue.**
   (b) Within the vascular tissue, distinguish between the **phloem** (of which there are outer and inner layers) and the thick-walled **xylem** sandwiched between the phloem layers.
4. Now examine the undersurface of the frond. Locate the dotlike **sori** (singular, *sorus;* Figure 15-26).

Figure 15-26 (a) Morphology of a typical fern (0.25×). (b) Enlargement showing the sori (0.5×).

(Photos by J. W. Perry.)

Figure 15-27 Cross section of a fern rhizome (29×). Inset shows higher magnification of vascular tissue (80×).

5. Each sorus is a cluster of **sporangia.** Using a dissecting microscope, study an individual sorus. Identify the sporangia (Figures 15-28, 15-33b).

Each sporangium contains *spores* (Figure 15-33c). Although the sporangium is part of the diploid (sporophytic) generation, spores are the first cells of the haploid (gametophytic) generation.

What process occurred within the sporangium to produce the haploid spores? _____

6. Obtain a single sorus-containing square of the hare's foot fern (*Polypodium aureum*).
   (a) Place it sorus-side up on a glass slide (DON'T ADD A COVER-SLIP), and examine it with the low-power objective of your compound microscope.
   (b) Note the row of brown, thick-walled cells running over the top of the sporangium, the **annulus** (Figures 15-28, 15-33b).

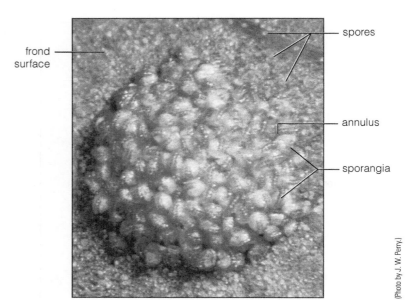

Figure 15-28 Sorus containing sporangia (30×).

(Photo by J. W. Perry.)

The annulus is **hygroscopic.** Changes in moisture content within the cells of the annulus cause the sporangium to crack open. Watch what happens as the sporangium dries out.

As the water evaporates from the cells of the annulus, a tension develops that pulls the sporangium apart. Separation of the halves of the sporangium begins at the thin-walled lip cells. As the water continues to evaporate, the annulus pulls back the top half of the sporangium, exposing the spores. The sporangium continues to be pulled back until the tension on the water molecules within the annulus exceeds the strength of the hydrogen bonds holding the water molecules together. When this happens, the top half of the sporangium flies forward, throwing the spores out. The fern sporangium is a biological catapult!

If spores land in a suitable environment, one that is generally moist and shaded, they germinate (Figures 15-33d and e), eventually growing into the heart-shaped adult **gametophyte** (15-33f).

7. Using your dissecting microscope, examine a living, preserved, or prepared slide whole mount of the gametophyte (Figures 15-29, 15-33f).

What color is the gametophyte? _____

What does the color indicate relative to the ability of the gametophyte to produce its own carbohydrates?

   (a) Examine the undersurface of the gametophyte. Find the **rhizoids,** which anchor the gametophyte and perhaps absorb water.
   (b) Locate the gametangia (sex organs) clustered among the rhizoids (Figure 15-33f). There are two types of gametangia: **antheridia** (Figure 15-33g), which produce the flagellated *sperm,* and **archegonia** (Figures 15-30, 15-33h), which produce *egg cells.*

8. Study the demonstration slide of an archegonium (Figure 15-31). Identify the **egg** within the swollen basal portion of the archegonium. Note that the *neck* of the archegonium protrudes from the surface of the gametophyte.

The archegonia secrete chemicals that attract the flagellated sperm, which swim in a water film down a canal within the neck of the archegonium. One sperm fuses with the egg to produce the first cell of the sporophyte generation, the *zygote* (Figure 15-33i). With subsequent cell divisions, the zygote

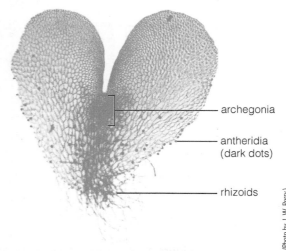

Figure 15-29 Whole mount of fern gametophyte, undersurface (10×).

(Photo by J. W. Perry.)

develops into an embryo (embryo sporophyte). As the embryo grows, it pushes out of the gametophyte and develops into a young sporophyte (Figure 15-33j).

9. Obtain a specimen of a young sporophyte that is attached to the gametophyte (Figures 15-32, 15-33j). Identify the **gametophyte** and then the *primary leaf* and *primary root* of the young sporophyte. As the sporophyte continues to develop, the gametophyte withers away.

10. Examine any other specimens of ferns that may be on demonstration, noting the incredible diversity in form. Look for sori on each specimen.

archegonium

antheridium

(Photo by J. W. Perry.)

Figure 15-30 Gametangia (antheridia and archegonia) on undersurface of fern gametophyte (57×).

egg cell

archegonium

(Photo by J. W. Perry.)

Figure 15-31 Longitudinal section of a fern archegonium (218×).

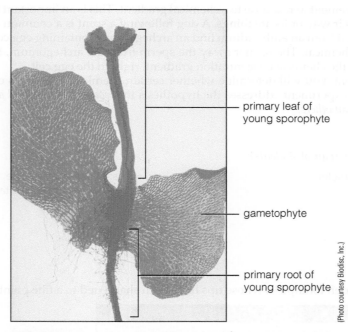

primary leaf of young sporophyte

gametophyte

primary root of young sporophyte

(Photo courtesy Biodisc, Inc.)

Figure 15-32 Fern gametophyte with attached sporophyte (12×).

Figure 15-33 Life cycle of a typical fern.

Experiment: Fern Sperm Chemotaxis *(About 60 min.)*

Chemotaxis is a movement in response to a chemical gradient. This is an important biological process as it allows organisms to find their way or locate things. A dog following a scent is a common example of chemotaxis. How does a sperm cell shed from an antheridium find an archegonium-containing egg cell? The archegonium secretes a sperm-attracting chemical. The farther away the sperm from the archegonium, the more dilute the chemical. The sperm swim up the chemical concentration gradient, right to the egg cell.

In this experiment, you will determine whether certain chemical substances evoke a chemotactic response by fern sperm. This experiment addresses the hypothesis that *some chemicals will attract sperm more strongly and for greater duration than others.*

MATERIALS

Per experimental group (pair of students):

- 6 sharpened toothpicks
- 5 test solutions
- dissecting needle
- depression slide

- dissecting microscope
- petri dish culture containing *C-Fern*™ gametophytes

PROCEDURE

Work in pairs.

1. Obtain six wooden toothpicks whose tips have been sharpened to a fine point.

> **Caution**
>
> *Do not touch the sharpened end with your fingers!*

2. To identify the toothpicks, place one to five small dots along the side of the toothpicks near the unsharpened end so that each toothpick has a unique marking (one dot, two dots, and so on). One toothpick remains unmarked.

3. Dip the sharpened end of the toothpick with one dot into test solution 1. Insert it with the sharpened end up in the foam block toothpick holder.

4. Repeat step 3 with the four remaining toothpicks and four other test solutions. Leave the unmarked toothpick dry.

Which toothpick serves as the control? _____

5. Obtain a depression slide and pipet one drop of Sperm Release Buffer (SRB) into the depression.

6. Obtain a 12- to 18-day-old culture of *C-Fern*™ gametophytes. Remove the cover, place it on the stage of a dissecting microscope, and observe the gametophytes using transmitted light.

7. Identify the two types of gametophytes present—the smaller thumb-shaped male gametophytes that have many bumps on them and the larger, heart-shaped bisexual gametophytes (Figure 15-34).

8. Using a dissecting needle, pick up 7–10 male gametophytes and place them into the SRB in the depression slide well. They don't need to be completely submerged.

Caution

If you wound or damage a gametophyte, discard it.

9. Place the petri dish cover on the stage of the dissecting microscope, edges up, and then place the gametophyte-containing depression slide on the cover. (This keeps the gametophytes cooler, particularly important if your dissecting microscope has an incandescent light.) Adjust the magnification so it is at least 12×.

10. Within 5 minutes, you should be able to observe sperm being released from the antheridia.

11. Wait another 5 minutes to ensure that a sufficient number of sperm have been released, and then begin testing for chemotactic response by following steps 12–15.

12. While using 12–20× magnification, focus on the TOP surface of the sperm suspension droplet in an area devoid of male gametophytes.

Caution

As you make the tests, do not insert the toothpick fully into the drop—just touch the surface briefly (Figure 15-35).

13. Remove one test toothpick from the block and, while looking through the oculars of the dissecting microscope, gently and briefly touch the sharpened end of the toothpick to the surface of the drop (Figure 15-35).

14. Observe whether any chemotactic response takes place. Record your observation in Table 15-5.

15. Repeat the procedure with the remaining toothpicks, stirring the sperm suspension (if necessary) with a dissecting needle after each test to redistribute the sperm.

16. Place your data on the lab chalk or marker board. Your instructor will pool the data for all experimental groups.

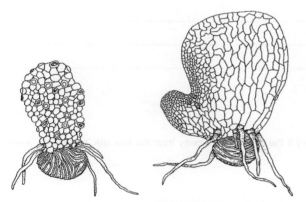

Figure 15-34 Mature male (left) and bisexual (right) *C-Fern*™ gametophytes.

Figure 15-35 Method for applying test substances. Proper technique is important. Gently and briefly touch the end of the toothpick to the surface of the sperm suspension. *Note:* The size of the drop of suspension is exaggerated to show detail.

17. Make a conclusion about the chemotactic properties of the various chemical test substances, and note it in Table 15-5.

Examine the chemical structures of each test solution (Figure 15-36). Relate the biological (chemotactic) response you observed to any of the chemical structural differences of the test substances. _____

_____

_____

_____

What is the advantage to using the pooled data to draw your conclusion? _____

_____

_____

What do you hypothesize the naturally occurring chemical produced by mature archegonia to be? _____

_____

_____

_____

1 succinic acid   2 L-malic acid   3 D-malic acid

4 fumaric acid   5 maleic acid

Figure 15-36 Chemical structures of test substance.

TABLE 15-5 My Data: Chemotactic Response of *C-Fern*™ Sperm				
Prediction:				
	Swarming Response[b]			
	Intensity (low, medium, high)		Duration (short, medium, long)	
Test Substance[a]	My Data	Pooled Data	My Data	Pooled Data
0				
1				
2				
3				
4				
5				
Conclusion:				

[a] Identified by number of dots on toothpick.
[b] Quantify the response by using the symbols (0) for no response, (–) if the sperm move away from the test site, and (+, ++, +++) for varying degrees of attraction to the test site.

_____ 1. Land plants are believed to have evolved from
   (a) mosses
   (b) ferns
   (c) charophytes
   (d) fungi

_____ 2. In the bryophytes, the sporophyte is
   (a) the dominant generation
   (b) dependent on the gametophyte generation
   (c) able to produce all of its own nutritional requirements
   (d) both a and c

_____ 3. Liverworts and mosses utilize which of the following pigments for photosynthesis?
   (a) chlorophylls a and b
   (b) carotenes
   (c) xanthophylls
   (d) all of the above

_____ 4. Which statement _best_ describes the concept of alternation of generations?
   (a) One generation of plants is skipped every other year
   (b) There are two phases, a sporophyte and a gametophyte
   (c) The parental generation alternates with a juvenile generation
   (d) A green sporophyte phase produces food for a nongreen gametophyte

_____ 5. Alternation of heteromorphic generations
   (a) is found only in the bryophytes
   (b) is common to all land plants
   (c) is typical of most green algae
   (d) occurs in the liverworts but not mosses

_____ 6. An organ that is hygroscopic
   (a) is sensitive to changes in moisture
   (b) is exemplified by the peristomal teeth in the sporophyte of mosses
   (c) may aid in spore dispersal in mosses
   (d) is all of the above

_____ 7. Gemmae function for
   (a) sexual reproduction
   (b) water retention
   (c) anchorage of a liverwort thallus to the substrate
   (d) asexual reproduction

_____ 8. Sperm find their way to the archegonium
   (a) by swimming
   (b) due to a chemical gradient diffusing from the archegonium
   (c) as a result of sucrose being released during the breakdown of the neck canal cells of the archegonium
   (d) by all of the above

_____ 9. A protonema
   (a) is part of the sporophyte generation of a moss
   (b) is the product of spore germination of a moss
   (c) looks very much like a filamentous brown alga
   (d) produces the sporophyte when a bud grows from it

_____ 10. The suffix _-phore_ is derived from a Greek word meaning
   (a) branch
   (b) moss
   (c) liverwort
   (d) male

_____ 11. The sporophyte is the dominant and conspicuous generation in
   (a) the fern allies and ferns
   (b) gymnosperms
   (c) flowering plants
   (d) all of the above

_____ 12. A tracheophyte is a plant that has
   (a) xylem and phloem
   (b) a windpipe
   (c) a trachea
   (d) the gametophyte as its dominant generation

_____ 13. _Psilotum_ lacks
   (a) roots
   (b) a mechanism to take up water and minerals
   (c) vascular tissue
   (d) alternation of generations

_____ 14. Spore germination followed by cell divisions results in the production of
   (a) a sporophyte
   (b) an antheridium
   (c) a zygote
   (d) a gametophyte

_____ 15. Which phrase *best* describes a plant that is an epiphyte?
  (a) a plant that grows upon another plant
  (b) a parasite
  (c) a plant with the gametophyte generation dominant and conspicuous
  (d) a plant that has a mutually beneficial relationship with another plant

_____ 16. Club mosses
  (a) are placed in the subphylum Pterophyta
  (b) are so called because of the social nature of the plants
  (c) do not produce gametophytes
  (d) are so called because most produce strobili

_____ 17. The resurrection plant
  (a) is a species of *Selaginella*
  (b) grows in the desert Southwest of the United States
  (c) is a member of the phylum Lycophyta
  (d) all of the above

_____ 18. Which statement is *not* true?
  (a) Nodes are present on horsetails
  (b) The rhizome on horsetails bears roots
  (c) The internode of a horsetail is the region where the leaves are attached
  (d) Horsetails are members of the subphylum Sphenophyta

_____ 19. In ferns
  (a) xylem and phloem are present in the sporophyte
  (b) the sporophyte is the dominant generation
  (c) the leaf is called a frond
  (d) all of the above are true

_____ 20. The spores of a fern are
  (a) produced by mitosis within the sporangium
  (b) diploid cells
  (c) the first cells of the gametophyte generation
  (d) both a and b

EXERCISE 15

Bryophytes and Seedless Vascular Plants

POST-LAB QUESTIONS

Introduction

1. Explain why water must be present for the bryophytes to complete the sexual portion of their life cycle.

2. Green algae are believed to be the ancestors of the bryophytes. Cite four distinct lines of evidence to support this belief.

   a.

   b.

   c.

   d.

3. Complete this diagram of a "generic" alternation of generations.

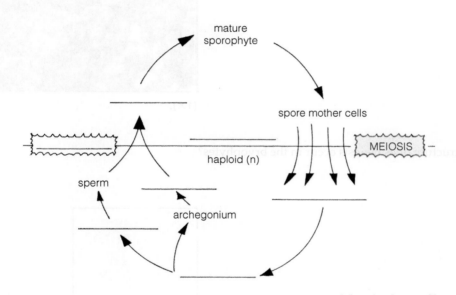

4. Describe in your own words the difference between a sporophyte and a gametophyte.

5. List two features that distinguish the seedless vascular plants from the bryophytes.

   a.

   b.

6. After consulting a biological or scientific dictionary, explain the derivation from the Greek of the word *symbiosis*.

15.2 Phylum Hepatophyta: Liverworts

7. While the plant shown here is one that you didn't study specifically in lab, you should be able to identify it. Is this the gametophyte or the sporophyte of the plant?

(1×).

8. In what structure does meiosis occur in the bryophytes?

15.4 Phylum Bryophyta: Mosses

9. Identify the type of gametangium shown here.

(150×).

10. Walking along a stream in a damp forest, you see the plants shown at the right. Is this the sporophyte or the gametophyte?

(0.38×).

11. a. What are the golden stalks seen in this photo?

   b. Are they the products of meiosis or fertilization?

(0.25×).

12. Identify the plants in the photo at the right as male or female, gametophyte or sporophyte, moss or liverwort.

(0.25×).

15.6 Phylum Lycophyta: Club Mosses

13. Both *Lycopodium* and *Equisetum* have strobili, roots, and rhizomes. What did you learn in this exercise that enables you to distinguish these two plants?

Examine the photo at the right.

a. Give the genus of this plant.

_____

b. Label the structure indicated.

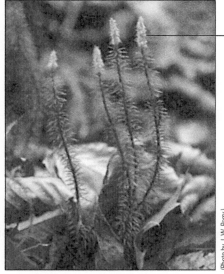

14. Some species of *Lycopodium* produce gametophytes that grow beneath the surface of the soil, while others grow on the soil surface. Basing your answer on what you've learned from other plants in this exercise, predict how each respective type of *Lycopodium* gametophyte might obtain its nutritional needs.

(0.3×).

(Photo by J. W. Perry.)

15.7 Phylum Moniliophyta, Subphylum Psilophyta: Whisk Ferns

15. Using a biological or scientific dictionary, or a reference in your textbook, determine the meaning of the root word *psilo,* and relate it to the appearance of *Psilotum.*

15.8 Phylum Moniliophyta, Subphylum Sphenophyta: Horsetails

16. Examine the photo on the right. You studied this genus in lab, but this is a different species. This species has two separate stems produced at different times in the growing season. The stem on the left is a reproductive branch, while that on the right is strictly vegetative. Based on the characteristics obvious in this photo, identify the plant, give its scientific name, and then identify the labeled structures.

Scientific name

_____

A

_____

B

_____

C

_____

(0.75×).

(Photo by J. W. Perry.)

17. Explain the distinction between a *node* and an *internode*.

15.9 Phylum Moniliophyta, Subphylum Pterophyta: Ferns

18. While rock climbing, you encounter the plant shown in the photo on the right growing out of a crevice.

    a. Is this the sporophyte or the gametophyte?

    b. What special name is given to the leaf of this plant?

(0.5×).

19. The environments in which ferns grow range from standing water to very dry areas. Nonetheless, all ferns are dependent upon free water in order to complete their life cycles. Explain why this is the case.

12. Explain the distinction between a node and an internode.

78. While rock climbing, you encounter the plant shown in the photo on the right growing out of a crevice.

   a. Is this the sporophyte or the gametophyte?

   b. What special name is given to the leaf of this plant?

[0.5x]

79. The environments in which ferns grow range from standing water to very dry areas. Nonetheless, all ferns are dependent upon free water in order to complete their life cycles. Explain why this is the case.

Seed Plants I: Gymnosperms

OBJECTIVES

After completing this exercise, you will be able to

1. define *gymnosperm, pulp, heterosporous, homosporous, pollination, fertilization, dioecious, monoecious;*

2. describe the characteristics that distinguish seed plants from other vascular plants;

3. produce a cycle diagram of heterosporous alternation of generations;

4. list uses for conifers;

5. recognize the structures in **boldface** and describe the life cycle of a pine;

6. distinguish between a male and a female pine cone;

7. describe the method by which pollination occurs in pines;

8. describe the process of fertilization in pines;

9. recognize members of the four phyla: Coniferophyta, Cycadophyta, Ginkgophyta, and Gnetophyta.

INTRODUCTION

The development of the seed was a significant event in the evolution of vascular plants. Seeds have remarkable ability to survive under adverse conditions. This is one reason for the dominance of seed plants today.

Let's examine the characteristics of seeds and seed plants.

1. All seed plants produce **pollen grains.** Pollen grains serve as carriers for sperm. This characteristic is one factor accounting for the widespread distribution of seed plants. As a benefit of pollen production, the sperm of seed plants do *not* need free water to swim to the egg. Thus, seed plants can reproduce in harsh climates where nonseed plants are much less successful.

2. Almost all seeds have some type of **stored food** for the embryo to use as it emerges from the seed during germination. (The sole exception is orchid seeds, which rely on symbiotic association with a fungus to obtain nutrients.)

3. All seeds have a **seed coat,** a protective covering enclosing the embryo and its stored food.

A seed coat and stored food are particularly important for survival. An embryo within a seed is protected from an inhospitable environment. Consider a seed produced during a severe drought. Water is necessary for the embryo to grow. If none is available, the seed can remain dormant until growing conditions are favorable. When germination occurs, a ready food source is present to get things underway, providing nutrients until the developing plant can produce its own carbohydrates by photosynthesis.

4. Like the bryophytes, fern allies, and ferns, seed plants exhibit **alternation of generations.**

5. All seed plants are **heterosporous;** that is, they produce *two* types of spores. Bryophytes and most fern allies and ferns are **homosporous,** producing only *one* spore type.

Examine Figure 16-1, a diagram of the heterosporous alternation of generations.

Gymnosperms are one of two groups of seed plants. *Gymnosperm* translates literally as "naked seed," referring to the production of seeds on the *surface* of reproductive structures. This contrasts with the situation in the angiosperms (see Exercise 17), whose seeds are contained within a fruit.

The general assemblage of plants known as gymnosperms contains plants in four separate phyla:

Phylum	Common Name
Coniferophyta	Conifers
Cycadophyta	Cycads
Ginkgophyta	Ginkgos
Gnetophyta	Gnetophytes or vessel-containing gymnosperms

16.1   Phylum Coniferophyta: Conifers *(About 90 min.)*

By far the most commonly recognized gymnosperms are the conifers. Among the conifers, perhaps the most common is the pine (*Pinus*). Many people think of conifers and pines as one and the same. However, while all members of the genus *Pinus* are conifers, not all conifers are pines. Examples of other conifers include spruce (*Picea*), fir (*Abies*), and even some trees that lose their leaves in the fall such as larch.

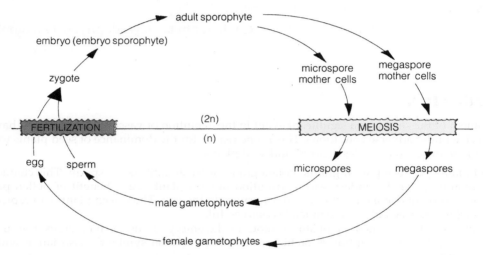

Figure 16-1   Heterosporous alternation of generations.

The conifers are among the most important plants economically, because their wood is used in building construction. Millions of hectares (1 hectare = 2.47 acres) are devoted to growing conifers for this purpose, not to mention the numerous plantations that grow Christmas trees. In many areas conifers are used for **pulp,** the moistened cell wall–derived cellulose used to manufacture paper.

The structures and events associated with reproduction in pine (*Pinus*) will be studied here as a representative conifer.

MATERIALS

Per student:

- cluster of male cones
- prepared slide of male strobilus, l.s., with microspores
- young female cone
- prepared slide of female strobilus, l.s., with megaspore mother cell
- prepared slide of pine seed, l.s.
- compound microscope
- dissecting microscope
- single-edged razor blade

Per student group (table):

- young sporophyte, living or herbarium specimen

Per lab room:

- demonstration slide of female strobilus with archegonium
- demonstration slide of fertilization
- pine seeds, soaking in water
- pine seedlings, 12 weeks old
- pine seedlings, 36 weeks old

(Photo by J. W. Perry.)

Figure 16-2 Cluster of male cones shedding pollen (0.75×).

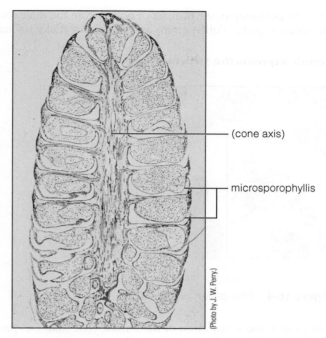

(cone axis)

microsporophyllis

(Photo by J. W. Perry.)

Figure 16-3   Male pine cone, l.s. (12×).

PROCEDURE

As you do this activity, examine Figure 16-12, representing the life cycle of a pine tree. To refresh your memory, look at a specimen of a small pine tree. This is the adult **sporophyte** (Figure 16-12a). Identify the stem and leaves. You probably know the main stem of a woody plant as the trunk. The leaves of conifers are often called needles because most are shaped like needles.

A. Male Reproductive Structures and Events

1. Obtain a cluster of **male cones** (Figures 16-2, 16-12b). The function of male cones is to produce **pollen;** consequently, male cones are typically produced at the ends of branches, where the wind currents can catch the pollen as it is being shed.
2. Note all the tiny scalelike structures that make up the male cones. These are *microsporophylls.*

Translated literally, a sporophyll would be a "spore-bearing leaf." The prefix *micro-* refers to "small." But the literal interpretation "small, spore-bearing leaf" does not convey the full definition; biologists use *microsporophyll* to mean a leaf that produces *male* spores, called *microspores.* These develop into winged, immature male *gametophytes* called **pollen grains.** (Why they are immature is a logical question. The male gametophyte is not mature until it produces sperm.)

3. Remove a single microsporophyll and examine its lower surface with a dissecting microscope. Identify the two **microsporangia,** also called **pollen sacs** (Figure 16-12c).
4. Study a prepared slide of a longitudinal section of a male cone (also called a male *strobilus*), first with a dissecting microscope to gain an impression of the cone's overall organization and then with the low-power objective of your compound microscope. Identify the *cone axis* bearing numerous **microsporophylls** (Figures 16-3).
5. Switch to the medium-power objective to observe a single microsporophyll more closely. Note that it contains a cavity; this is the **microsporangium** (also called a *pollen sac*), which contains numerous *pollen grains.*

As the male cone grows, several events occur in the microsporophylls that lead to the production of pollen grains. Microspore mother cells within the microsporangia undergo meiosis to form *microspores.* Cell division within the microspore wall and subsequent differentiation result in the formation of the pollen grain.

6. Examine a single **pollen grain** with the high-dry objective (Figures 16-4, 16-12d). Identify the earlike *wings* on either side of the body.
7. Identify the four cells that make up the body: The two most obvious are the **tube cell** and smaller **generative cell.** (The nucleus of the tube cell is almost as large as the entire generative cell.) Note that this male gametophyte is made up of only four cells!

In conifers, **pollination,** the transfer of pollen from the male cone to the female cone, is accomplished by wind and occurs during spring. Pollen grains are caught in a sticky *pollination droplet* produced by the female cone.

B. Female Reproductive Structures and Events

wing   tube cell   generative cell

(Photo courtesy Biodisc, Inc.)

Figure 16-4   Pine pollen grains (400×).

Figure 16-5   Female cones of pine (1×).

(Photo by J. W. Perry.)

Development and maturation of the female cone take 2–3 years; the exact time depends on the species. Female cones are typically produced on higher branches of the tree. Because the individual tree's pollen is generally shed downward, this arrangement favors crossing between *different* individuals.

1. Obtain a young **female cone** (Figures 16-5, 16-12e), and note the arrangement of the cone scales. Unlike the male cone, the female cone is a complex structure, each scale consisting of an **ovuliferous** scale fused atop a *sterile bract.*

2. Remove a single scale-bract complex (Figure 16-12f). On the top surface of the complex find the two **ovules,** the structures that eventually will develop into the **seeds.**

3. Examine a prepared slide of a longitudinal section of a female cone (Figures 16-6, 16-12g) first with the dissecting microscope. Note the spiral arrangement of the scales on the cone axis. Distinguish the smaller *sterile bract* from the *ovuliferous scale.*

4. Now examine the slide with the low-power objective of your compound microscope. Look for a section through an ovuliferous scale containing a very large cell; this is the **megaspore mother cell** (Figures 16-7, 16-12g). The tissue surrounding the megaspore mother cell is the **megasporangium.** Protruding inward toward the cone axis are "flaps" of tissue surrounding the megasporangium, the **integument.** Find the integuments and the opening between them, the **micropyle.**

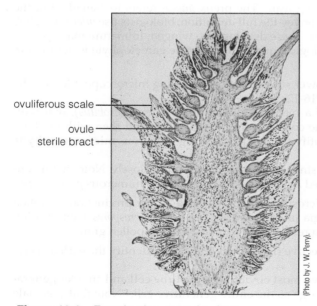

ovuliferous scale —
ovule —
sterile bract —

(Photo by J. W. Perry.)

Figure 16-6   Female pine cone, l.s. (5×).

integument   megaspore mother cell

ovuliferous scale

microphyte   megasporangium   (sterile bract)

(Photo by J. W. Perry.)

Figure 16-7   Portion of female cone showing megaspore mother cell (75×).

Think for a moment about the three-dimensional nature of the ovule: It's much like a short vase lying on its side on the ovuliferous scale. The neck of the vase is the integument, the opening the micropyle. The integument extends around the base of the vase. If you poured liquid rubber inside the base of a vase, suspended a marble in the middle, and allowed the rubber to harden, you'd have a model of the megasporangium and the megaspore mother cell. Figure 16-8 gives you an idea of the three-dimensional structure.

The megaspore mother cell undergoes meiosis to produce four haploid *megaspores* (Figure 16-12h), but only one survives; the other three degenerate. The functional megaspore repeatedly divides mitotically to produce the multicellular **female gametophyte** (Figure 16-12i). At the same time, the female cone is continually increasing in size to accommodate the developing female gametophytes. (Remember, there are numerous ovuliferous scale/sterile bract complexes on each cone.)

The female gametophyte of pine is produced _____ (within *or* outside of) the megasporangium.

5. Examine the demonstration slide of **archegonia** (Figures 16-9, 16-12i) that have developed within the female gametophyte. Identify the single large **egg cell** that fills the entire archegonium. (The nucleus of the egg cell may be visible as well. The other generally spherical structures are protein bodies within the egg.)

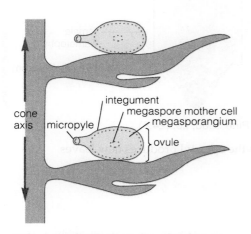

Figure 16-8 Ovule and ovuliferous scale/sterile bract complex.

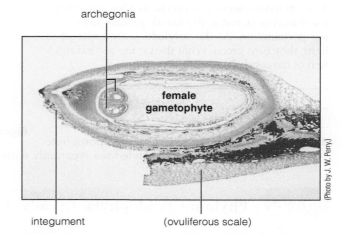

Figure 16-9 Pine ovule with female gametophyte and archegonia, l.s. (12×).

Recall that the pollen grains produced within male cones are caught in a sticky pollination droplet produced by the female cone. As the pollination droplet dries, the pollen grain is drawn through the micropyle and into a cavity called the *pollen chamber*.

Fertilization—the fusion of egg and sperm—occurs after the *pollen tube,* an outgrowth of the pollen grain's tube cell, penetrates the megasporangium and enters the archegonium. The generative cell of the pollen grain has divided to produce two sperm, one of which fuses with the egg. (The second sperm nucleus degenerates.)

6. Examine the demonstration slide of fertilization in *Pinus.* Identify the **zygote,** the product of fusion of egg and sperm (Figures 16-10, 16-12j).

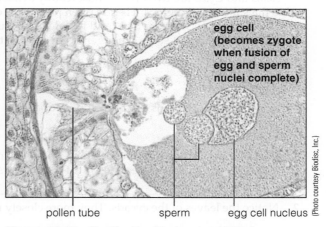

Figure 16-10 Fertilization in pine, l.s. (175×).

After fertilization, numerous mitotic divisions of the zygote take place, eventually producing an **embryo** (*embryo sporophyte*). Fertilization also triggers changes in the integument, causing it to harden and become the seed coat.

7. With the low-power objective of your compound microscope, study a prepared slide of a longitudinal section through a pine seed (Figures 16-11, 16-12k). Starting from the outside, identify the **seed coat, megasporangium** (a very thin, papery remnant), the female gametophyte, and **embryo** (embryo sporophyte).

8. Within the embryo, identify the **hypocotyl-root axis** and numerous **cotyledons,** in the center of which is the **epicotyl.** (*Hypo-* and *epi-* are derived from Greek, meaning "under" and "over," respectively. Thus, these terms refer to orientation with reference to the cotyledons.) The female gametophyte will serve as a food source for the embryo sporophyte when germination takes place.

9. Obtain a pine seed that has been soaked in water to soften the seed coat. Remove it and make a freehand longitudinal section with a sharp razor blade.

10. Identify the papery remnant of the **megasporangium,** the white **female gametophyte,** and **embryo** (embryo sporophyte).

How many cotyledons are present? _____

_____

11. Examine the culture of pine seeds that were planted in sand 12 weeks ago. Note the germinating seeds (Figure 16-12l).

12. Identify the **hypocotyl-root axis, cotyledons, female gametophyte,** and **seed coat.**

The cotyledons serve two functions. One is to absorb the nutrients stored in the female gametophyte during germination. As the cotyledons are exposed to light, they turn green. What then is the second function of the cotyledons?

_____

_____

_____

13. Finally, examine the 36-week-old sporophyte seedlings. Notice that the cotyledons eventually wither away as the epicotyl produces new leaves.

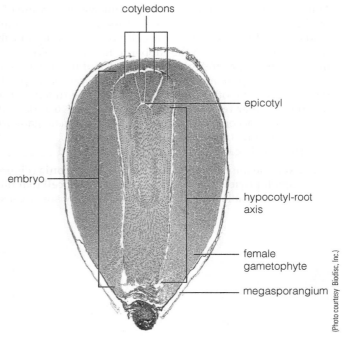

Figure 16-11   Pine seed, l.s. (24×).

(Photo courtesy Biodisc, Inc.)

16.2 Phylum Cycadophyta: Cycads *(About 10 min.)*

During the age of the dinosaurs (240 million years ago), cycads were extremely abundant in the flora. In fact, botanists often call this "the age of the cycads."

Zamia and *Cycas* are two cycads most readily available in North America. In nature, these two species are limited to the subtropical regions. They're often planted as ornamentals in Florida, Gulf Coast states, and California.

All cycads have separate male and female plants, unlike pine.

The female cones of some other genera become extremely large, weighing as much as 30 kg!

MATERIALS

Per lab room:

■ demonstration specimens of *Zamia* and/or *Cycas*

PROCEDURE

1. Examine the demonstration specimen of *Zamia* and/or *Cycas* (Figure 16-13). Both have the common name *cycad.* Do these plants resemble any of the conifers you know? _____

_____

2. Notice the leaves of the cycads. They more closely resemble the leaves of the ferns than those of the conifers.

16.3 Phylum Ginkgophyta: Ginkgo *(About 10 min.)*

A single species of this phylum is all that remains of what was once a much more diverse assemblage of plants. *Ginkgo biloba* is sometimes called a living fossil because it has changed little in the last 80 million years. In fact, at one time it was believed to be extinct; the Western world knew it from the fossil record before living trees were discovered in the Buddhist temple courtyards of remote China. Today *Ginkgo* is a highly prized ornamental tree that is commonly planted in our urban areas. The tree has a reputation for being resistant to most insect pests and atmospheric pollution. The seeds are ground up and sold as a memory-enhancing dietary supplement, although the supplement's ability to do that is in dispute.

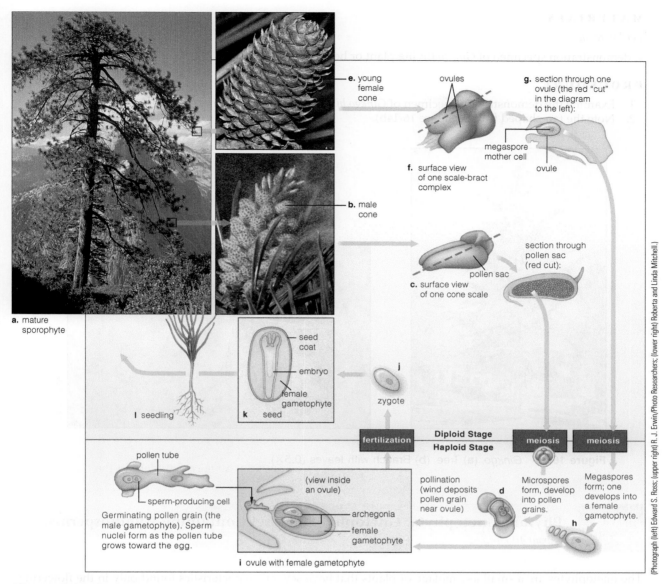

Figure 16-12 Pine life cycle.

(Photograph (left) Edward S. Ross; (upper right) R. J. Erwin/Photo Researchers; (lower right) Roberta and Linda Mitchell.)

a. mature sporophyte

e. young female cone

g. section through one ovule (the red "cut" in the diagram to the left):

ovules

megaspore mother cell

ovule

f. surface view of one scale-bract complex

b. male cone

section through pollen sac (red cut):

pollen sac

c. surface view of one cone scale

seed coat

embryo

female gametophyte

j zygote

k seed

l seedling

fertilization

Diploid Stage

Haploid Stage

meiosis

meiosis

pollen tube

sperm-producing cell

Germinating pollen grain (the male gametophyte). Sperm nuclei form as the pollen tube grows toward the egg.

(view inside an ovule)

archegonia

female gametophyte

i ovule with female gametophyte

pollination (wind deposits pollen grain near ovule)

d

h

Microspores form, develop into pollen grains.

Megaspores form; one develops into a female gametophyte.

a

b

Figure 16-13 Cycads. (a) *Cycas* (0.01×). (b) *Zamia* (0.1×).

(Photos by J. W. Perry.)

MATERIALS

Per lab room:

■ demonstration specimen of *Ginkgo* (living plant or herbarium specimen)

PROCEDURE

1. Examine the demonstration specimen of *Ginkgo biloba,* the maidenhair tree (Figure 16-14a).
2. Note the fan-shaped leaves (Figure 16-14b).

a   b

Figure 16-14 *Ginkgo.* (**a**) Tree. (**b**) Branch with leaves (0.5×).

16.4	Phylum Gnetophyta: Gnetophytes (Vessel-Containing Gymnosperms)

(About 10 min.)

The gnetophytes are a small assemblage of plants that have several characteristics found only in the flowering plants (angiosperms). Their reproductive structures look much more like flowers than cones. "Double fertilization", a feature thought to be unique to the flowering plants, has been reported in one gnetophyte species. And the water-conducting xylem tissue contains vessels in all species. Consequently, many scientists now believe these plants are very closely related to the flowering plants. Most species are found in desert or arid regions of the world. In the desert Southwest of the United States, *Ephedra* is a common shrub known as Mormon tea, because its stems were once harvested by Mormon settlers in Utah and used to make a tea.

MATERIALS

Per lab room:

■ demonstration specimen of *Ephedra* and/or *Gnetum* (living plant or herbarium specimen)

PROCEDURE

1. Examine the demonstration specimen of *Ephedra* (Figure 16-15).
2. A second representative gnetophyte is the genus *Gnetum* (pronounced "neat-um"). A few North American college and university greenhouses—and some tropical gardens—keep these specimens. *Gnetum* is native to Brazil, tropical west Africa, India, and Southeast Asia. Different species vary in form from vines to trees (Figures 16-16a, b). Examine the living specimen if one is on display, noting particularly the broad, flat leaves (Figure 16-16c).

Figure 16-15 *Ephedra.* (**a**) Several plants (1×). (**b**) Close-up of stems (0.5×).

Figure 16-16 *Gnetum.* (**a**) A species that is a vine (0.02×). (**b**) A species that is a tree (0.02×). (**c**) Leaves (0.38×).

_____ 1. Which statement is *not* true about conifers?
   (a) Conifers are gymnosperms
   (b) All conifers belong to the genus *Pinus*
   (c) All conifers have naked seeds
   (d) Conifers are heterosporous

_____ 2. Seed plants
   (a) have alternation of generations
   (b) are heterosporous
   (c) develop a seed coat
   (d) are all of the above

_____ 3. A pine tree is
   (a) a sporophyte
   (b) a gametophyte
   (c) diploid
   (d) both a and c

_____ 4. The male pine cone
   (a) produces pollen
   (b) contains a female gametophyte
   (c) bears a megasporangium containing a megaspore mother cell
   (d) gives rise to a seed

_____ 5. The male gametophyte of a pine tree
   (a) is produced within a pollen grain
   (b) produces sperm
   (c) is diploid
   (d) is both a and b

_____ 6. Which of these are produced directly by meiosis in pine?
   (a) sperm cells
   (b) pollen grains
   (c) microspores
   (d) microspore mother cells

_____ 7. An ovule
   (a) is the structure that develops into a seed
   (b) contains the microsporophyll
   (c) is produced on the surface of a male cone
   (d) is all of the above

_____ 8. The process by which pollen is transferred to the ovule is called
   (a) transmigration
   (b) fertilization
   (c) pollination
   (d) all of the above

_____ 9. Which statement is true of the female gametophyte of pine?
   (a) It's a product of repeated cell divisions of the functional megaspore
   (b) It's haploid
   (c) It serves as the stored food to be used by the embryo sporophyte upon germination
   (d) All of the above are true

_____ 10. The seed coat of a pine seed
   (a) is derived from the integuments
   (b) is produced by the micropyle
   (c) surrounds the male gametophyte
   (d) is divided into the hypocotyl-root axis and epicotyl

EXERCISE 16

Seed Plants I: Gymnosperms

POST-LAB QUESTIONS

Introduction

1. What survival advantage does a seed have that has enabled the seed plants to be the most successful of all plants?

2. In the diagram below of a seed, give the ploidy level (n or 2n) of each part listed.

3. Distinguish between a homosporous and a heterosporous type of life cycle.

16.1 Phylum Coniferophyta: Conifers

4. List four uses for conifers.

   a.

   b.

   c.

   d.

5. While snowshoeing through the winter woods, you stop to look at a tree branch pictured at the right. Specifically, what are the brown structures hanging from the branch?

(Photo by J. W. Perry.)

(0.5×).

6. Distinguish between *pollination* and fertilization.

7. Are antheridia present in conifers? _____
   Are archegonia present? _____

8. Suppose you saw the seedling pictured at the right while walking in the woods.

   a. To which gymnosperm phylum does the plant belong?

   b. Identify structures A and B.

A _____

B _____

(Photo by J. W. Perry.)

(0.5×).

16.2 Phylum Cycadophyta: Cycads

9. On spring break, you are strolling through a tropical garden in Florida and encounter the plant pictured at the right. Would the xylem of this plant contain tracheids, vessels, or both?

(Photo by A. B. Russell.)

(0.01×).

16.3 Phylum Ginkgophyta: Ginkgo

10. A friend of yours picks up a branch like the one pictured at the right. Knowing that you have taken a biology course and studied plants, she asks you what the plant is. Identify this branch, giving your friend the full scientific name for the plant.

(Photo by J. W. Perry.)

(0.75×).

Seed Plants II: Angiosperms

OBJECTIVES

After completing this exercise, you will be able to

1. define *angiosperm, fruit, pollination, double fertilization, endosperm, seed, germination, annual, biennial, perennial*;

2. describe the significance of the flower, fruit, and seed for the success of the angiosperms;

3. identify the structures of the flower;

4. recognize the structures and events (those in **boldface**) that take place in angiosperm reproduction;

5. describe the origin and function of fruit and seed;

6. identify the characteristics that distinguish angiosperms from gymnosperms.

INTRODUCTION

The **angiosperms,** Phylum Anthophyta, are seed plants that produce flowers. *"Antho"* means flower, and *"phyta"* plant. The word *angiosperm* literally means "vessel seed" and refers to the seeds borne within a fruit.

There are more flowering plants in the world today than any other group of plants. Assuming that numbers indicate success, flowering plants are the most successful plants to have evolved thus far.

The most important characteristic that distinguishes the Anthophyta from other seed plants is the presence of flower parts that mature into a **fruit,** a container that protects the seeds and allows them to be dispersed without coming into contact with the rigors of the external environment. In many instances, the fruit also contributes to the dispersal of the seed. For example, some fruits stick to fur (or clothing) of animals and are brushed off some distance from the plant that produced them. Animals eat others. The undigested seeds pass out of the digestive tract and fall into environments often far removed from the seeds' source.

Our lives and diets revolve around flowering plants. Fruits enrich our diet and include such things as apples, oranges, tomatoes, beans, peas, corn, wheat, walnuts, pecans . . . the list goes on and on. Moreover, even when we are not eating fruits, we're eating flowering plant parts. Cauliflower, broccoli, potatoes, celery, and carrots all are parts of flowering plants.

Biologists believe that flower parts originated as leaves modified during the course of evolution to increase the probability for fertilization. For instance, some flower parts are colorful and attract animals that transfer the sperm-producing pollen to the receptive female parts.

Figure 17-15 depicts the life cycle of a typical flowering plant. Refer to it as you study the specimens in this exercise.

Note: **This exercise provides two alternative paths to accomplish the objectives described above, a traditional approach (17.1–17.2) and an investigative one (17.3). Your instructor will indicate which alternative you will follow.**

17.1 External Structure of the Flower *(About 20 min.)*

The number of different kinds of flowers is so large that it's difficult to pick a single example as representative of the entire division. Nonetheless, there is enough similarity among flowers that, once you've learned the structure of one representative, you'll be able to recognize the parts of most.

MATERIALS

Per student:

- flower for dissection (gladiolus or hybrid lily, for example)
- single-edged razor blade
- dissecting microscope

PROCEDURE

1. Obtain a flower provided for dissection.
2. At the base of the flower, locate the swollen stem tip, the **receptacle,** upon which the whorls of floral parts are arranged.
3. Identify the **calyx,** comprising the outermost whorl. Individual components of the calyx are called **sepals.** The sepals are frequently green (although not always). The calyx surrounds the rest of the flower in the bud stage (see Figure 17-15a).
4. Moving inward, locate the next whorl of the flower, the usually colorful **corolla** made up of **petals.**

It is usually the petals that we appreciate for their color. Remember, however, that the evolution of colorful flower parts was associated with the presence of color-visioned *pollinators,* animals that carry pollen from one flower to another. The colorful flowers attract those animals, enhancing the plants' chance of being pollinated, producing seeds, and perpetuating their species.

Both the calyx and corolla are sterile, meaning they do not produce gametes.

5. The next whorl of flower parts consists of the male, pollen-producing parts, the **stamens** (also called *microsporophylls,* "microspore-bearing leaves"; Figure 17-15b). Examine a single stamen in greater detail. Each stamen consists of a stalklike **filament** and an **anther.** The anther consists of four **microsporangia** (also called *pollen sacs*).
6. Next locate the female portion of the flower, the **pistil** (Figures 17-15a and c). A pistil consists of one or more **carpels,** also called *megasporophylls,* "megaspore-bearing leaves."

If the pistil consists of more than one carpel, they are usually fused, making it difficult to distinguish the individual components. However, you can usually determine the number of carpels by counting the number of lobes of the stigma.

7. How many carpels does your flower contain? _____
8. Identify the different parts of the pistil (Figure 17-15c): at the top, the **stigma,** which serves as a receptive region on which pollen is deposited; a necklike **style;** and a swollen **ovary.** The only members of the plant kingdom to have ovaries are angiosperms!
9. With a sharp razor blade, make a section of the ovary. (Some students should cut the pistil longitudinally; others should cut the ovary crosswise. Then compare the different sections.)
10. Examine the sections with a dissecting microscope, finding the numerous small **ovules** within the ovary. The diagram in Figure 17-15c is oversimplified; many flowers have more than one ovule per ovary.
11. In Figure 17-1, make and label two sketches: one of the cross section and the other of a longitudinal section of the ovary. Notice that the ovules are completely enclosed within the ovary. After fertilization, the ovules will develop into *seeds,* and the ovary will enlarge and mature into the *fruit.*

There are two groups of flowering plants, monocotyledons and dicotyledons. The number of flower parts indicates which group a plant belongs to. Generally, monocots have the flower parts in threes or multiples of three. Dicots have their parts in fours or fives or multiples thereof.

12. Count the number of petals or sepals in the flower you have been examining. Are you studying a monocot or dicot?

_____

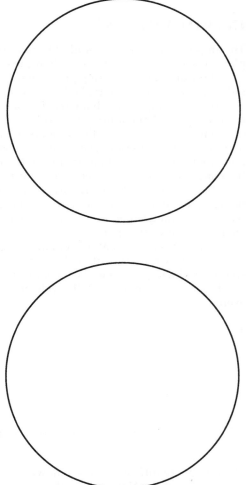

Figure 17-1 Drawings of cross section and longitudinal section of an ovary.
Label: ovules

A. Male Gametophyte (Pollen Grain) Formation in the Microsporangia *(About 20 min.)*

The male gametophyte in flowering plants is the pollen grain; a microscopic sperm-producing structure.

MATERIALS

Per student:

- prepared slide of young lily anther, c.s.
- prepared slide of mature lily anther (pollen grains), c.s.
- *Impatiens* flowers, with mature pollen
- glass microscope slide

- coverslip
- compound microscope

Per student pair:

- 0.5% sucrose, in dropping bottle

PROCEDURE

1. With the low-power objective of your compound microscope, examine a prepared slide of a cross section of an immature anther (Figures 17-2, 17-15d). Find sections of the four **microsporangia** (also called *pollen sacs*), which appear as four clusters of densely stained cells within the anther.

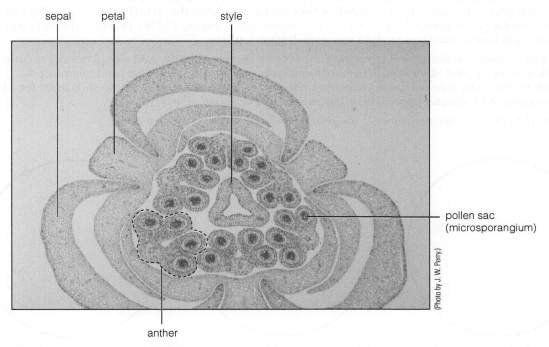

Figure 17-2 Immature anthers within flower bud, c.s. (4×).

2. Study the contents of a single microsporangium. Depending on the stage of development, you will find either diploid *microspore mother cells* (Figure 17-15e) or haploid *microspores* (Figures 17-15f and g).
3. Obtain a prepared slide of a cross section of a mature anther (Figure 17-3). Observe it first with the low-power objective, noting that the walls have split open to allow the pollen grains to be released, as shown in Figure 17-15i.
4. Pollen grains are immature *male gametophytes*, and very small ones at that. Switch to the high-dry objective to study an individual pollen grain more closely (Figure 17-4).
5. The pollen grain consists of only two cells. Identify the large **tube cell** and a smaller, crescent-shaped **generative cell** that floats freely in the cytoplasm of the tube cell (Figure 17-15h).
6. Note the ridged appearance of the outer wall layer of a pollen grain. Within the ridges and valleys of the wall, glycoproteins are present that appear to play a role in recognition between the pollen grain and the stigma.

pollen grains within
a microsporangium

(Photo courtesy Biodisc, Inc.)

Figure 17-3   Mature anther, c.s. (21×).

generative cell nucleus   tube cell nucleus

generative cell   tube cell

(Photo by J. W. Perry.)

Figure 17-4   Pollen grain, c.s. (145×).

Transfer of pollen from the microsporangia to the stigma, called **pollination,** occurs by various means—wind, insects, and birds being the most common carriers of pollen. When a pollen grain lands on the stigma of a compatible flower, it germinates and produces a **pollen tube** that grows down the style (Figure 17-15j). The generative cell flows into the pollen tube, where it divides to form two *sperm* (Figure 17-15k). Because it bears two gametes, the pollen grain is now considered to be a *mature* male gametophyte.

7. Obtain an *Impatiens* flower and tap some pollen onto a clean microslide. Add a drop of 0.5% sucrose, cover with a coverslip, and observe with the medium-power objective of your compound microscope.

8. Look for the *pollen tube* as it grows from the pollen grain. (You may wish to set the slide aside for a bit and re-examine it 15 minutes later to check the progress of the pollen tubes.)

In Figure 17-5, draw a sequence showing the germination of an *Impatiens* pollen grain.

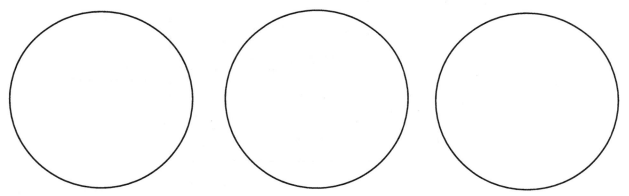

Figure 17-5   Germination of *Impatiens* pollen grain.

B. Female Gametophyte Formation in the Megasporangia *(About 20 min.)*

The female gametophyte is formed inside each ovule within the ovary of the flower. Like the male gametophyte, the female gametophyte in flowering plants consists of only a few cells.

MATERIALS

Per student:

- prepared slide of lily ovary, c.s., megaspore mother cell
- compound microscope

Per lab room:

- demonstration slide of lily ovary, c.s., 7-celled, 8-nucleate gametophyte
- demonstration slide of lily ovary, c.s., double fertilization

PROCEDURE

1. With the medium-power objective of your compound microscope, examine a prepared slide of a cross section of an ovary (Figures 17-6, 17-15l).

2. Find the several **ovules** that have been sectioned. One ovule will probably be sectioned in a plane so that the very large, diploid **megaspore mother cell** is obvious (Figures 17-7, 17-15m).

3. The megaspore mother cell is contained within the **megasporangium,** the outer cell layers of which form two flaps of tissue called **integuments.** Identify the structures in boldface print. After fertilization, the integuments develop into the *seed coat.*

4. Identify the **placenta,** the region of attachment of the ovule the ovary wall.

As the megasporangium develops, the integuments grow, enveloping the megasporangium. However, a tiny circular opening remains. This opening is the **micropyle.** (The micropyle is obvious in Figure 17-15n.) Remember, the micropyle is an opening in the ovule. After pollination, the pollen grain germinates on the surface of the stigma, and the pollen tube grows down the style, through the space surrounding the ovule, through the micropyle, and penetrates the megasporangium (Figure 17-15p).

5. Identify the micropyle present in the ovule you are examining.

Considerable variation exists in the next sequence of events; we describe the pattern found in the lily.

The diploid megaspore mother cell undergoes meiosis, producing four haploid *nuclei* (Figure 17-15n). (Note that cytokinesis does *not* follow meiosis, and thus only nuclei—not cells—are formed.) The cell containing the four nuclei (the old megaspore mother cell) is now called the **female gametophyte** (also called the *embryo sac*).

Three of these four nuclei fuse. Thus, the female gametophyte contains one triploid (3n) nucleus and one haploid (n) nucleus (Figure 17-15o). Subsequently, the nuclei undergo two *mitotic* divisions, forming eight nuclei in the female gametophyte. Cell walls form around six of the eight nuclei; the large cell remaining—the **central cell**—contains two nuclei, one of which is triploid, the other haploid. These two nuclei are called the **polar nuclei.** At the micropylar end of the ovule there are three cells, all haploid. One of these is the **egg cell.** Opposite the micropylar end are three 3n cells. This stage of development is often called the *seven-celled, eight-nucleate female gametophyte* (Figures 17-8, 17-15p). Fertilization takes place at this stage.

6. Study the demonstration slide of the seven-celled, eight-nucleate female gametophyte. Identify the **placenta, integuments, micropyle, egg cell, central cell,** and **polar nuclei** (Figures 17-8, 17-15p).

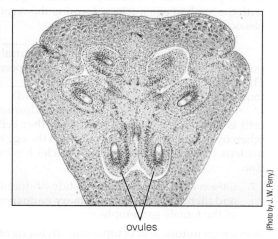

ovules

Figure 17-6   Lily ovary, c.s. (19×).

(Photo by J. W. Perry.)

integument

megasporangium

megaspore mother cell

(Photo by J. W. Perry.)

Figure 17-7   Megaspore mother cell within megasporangium (94×).

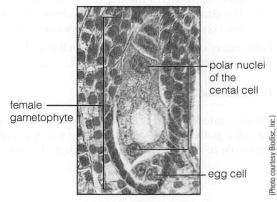

female gametophyte

polar nuclei of the cental cell

egg cell

(Photo courtesy Biodisc, Inc.)

Figure 17-8   Seven-celled, eight-nucleate female gametophyte (170×).

As the pollen tube penetrates the female gametophyte, it discharges the sperm; one of the sperm nuclei fuses with the haploid egg nucleus, forming the *zygote*. Figure 17-15q shows the female gametophyte after fertilization has occurred.

The zygote is a _____ (haploid, diploid) cell.

The other sperm nucleus enters the central cell and fuses with the two polar nuclei, forming the primary endosperm nucleus (Figure 17-15q). Thus, the primary endosperm nucleus is _____ (haploid, diploid, triploid, tetraploid, pentaploid).

The cell containing the primary endosperm nucleus (the old central cell) is now called the **endosperm mother cell.** Traditionally, the process whereby one sperm nucleus fuses with the egg nucleus and the other sperm nucleus fuses with the two polar nuclei has been called **double fertilization.**

7. Observe the demonstration slide of double fertilization (Figure 17-9), and identify the **zygote, primary endosperm nucleus,** and **central cell** of the female gametophyte.

Numerous mitotic and cytoplasmic divisions of the endosperm mother cell form the **endosperm,** a tissue used to nourish the embryo sporophyte as it develops within the seed.

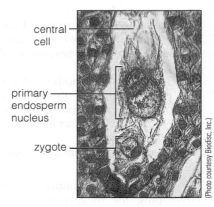

Figure 17-9 Double fertilization (170×).

C. Embryogeny *(About 10 min.)*

The zygote undergoes mitosis and cytokinesis to produce a two-celled **embryo** (also called the *embryo sporophyte*). Numerous subsequent divisions produce an increasingly large and complex embryo.

MATERIALS

Per lab room:

- demonstration slides of *Capsella* embryogeny: globular embryo, emerging cotyledons, torpedo-shaped embryo, mature embryo

PROCEDURE

1. Observe the series of four demonstration slides, which show the stages of embryo development in the female gametophyte of *Capsella* (Figure 17-10).
2. The first slide shows the so-called globular stage (Figure 17-10a), in which a chain of cells (the suspensor) attaches the embryo, a spherical mass of cells, to the wall of the female gametophyte (embryo sac). The very enlarged cell at the base of the suspensor is the *basal cell* and is active in uptake of nutrients that the developing embryo will use. Note the endosperm within the female gametophyte.
3. The second slide shows the heart-shaped stage (Figure 17-10b). Now you can distinguish the emerging **cotyledons** (seed leaves). In many plants, the cotyledons absorb nutrients from the endosperm and thus serve as a food reserve to be used during seed germination.
4. Further development of the embryo has occurred in the third slide, the torpedo stage (Figure 17-10c). Notice that the entire embryo has elongated. Find the *cotyledons*. Between the cotyledons, locate the **epicotyl,** which is the *apical meristem of the shoot.* Beneath the epicotyl and cotyledons find the **hypocotyl-root axis.** At the tip of the hypocotyl-root axis, locate the *apical meristem of the root* and the **root cap** covering it.
5. The final slide (Figure 17-10d) shows a mature embryo, neatly packaged inside the **seed coat.** Identify the seed coat and other regions previously identified in the torpedo stage.

How many cotyledons were there in the slides you examined? _____

Thus, is *Capsella* a monocot or dicot? _____

D. Fruit and Seed *(About 20 min.)*

Simply stated, a **fruit** is a matured ovary, while a **seed** is a matured ovule. Bear in mind that for each seed produced, a pollen grain had to fertilize the egg cells in the ovules. Fertilization not only causes the integuments of the ovule to develop into a seed coat, it also causes the ovary wall to expand into the fruit.

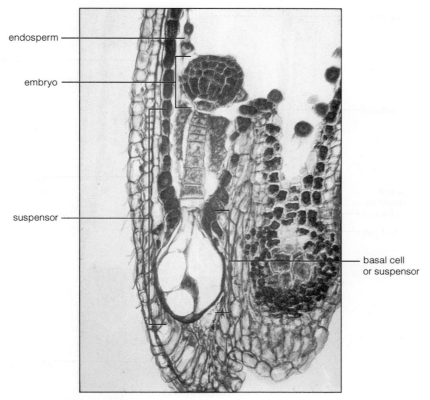

endosperm

embryo

suspensor

basal cell
or suspensor

a Globular embryo stage (232×).

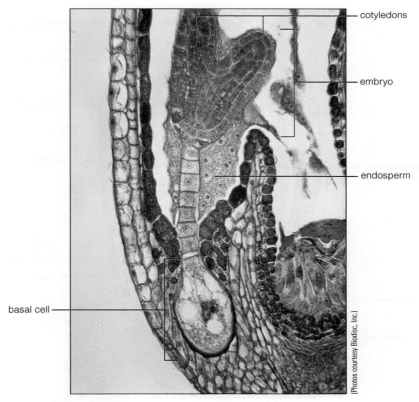

cotyledons

embryo

endosperm

basal cell

(Photos courtesy Biodisc, Inc.)

b Heart-shaped stage (240×).

Figure 17-10 Embryogeny in *Capsella* (shepherd's purse). *Continues on page 314.*

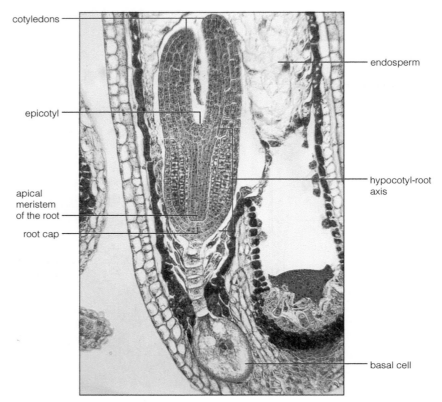

cotyledons

epicotyl

apical
meristem
of the root

root cap

endosperm

hypocotyl-root
axis

basal cell

c Torpedo stage (170×).

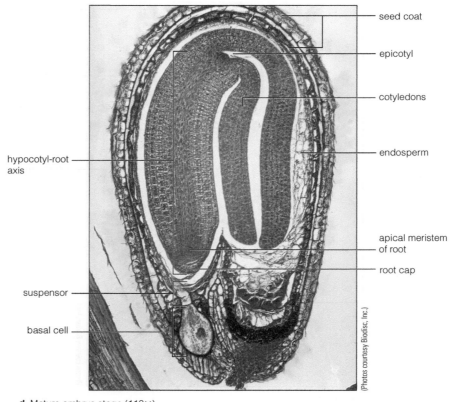

seed coat

epicotyl

cotyledons

endosperm

hypocotyl-root
axis

apical meristem
of root

root cap

suspensor

basal cell

(Photos courtesy Biodisc, Inc.)

d Mature embryo stage (113×).

Figure 17-10   Embryogeny in *Capsella* (shepherd's purse). *Continued.*

MATERIALS

Per student:

- bean fruits
- soaked bean seeds
- iodine solution (I₂KI), in dropping bottle

Per lab room:

- herbarium specimen of *Capsella*, with fruits
- demonstration slide of *Capsella* fruit, c.s.

PROCEDURE

1. Examine the herbarium specimen and demonstration slide of the fruits of *Capsella*. On the herbarium specimen, identify the **fruits,** which are shaped like the bag that shepherds carried at one time (Figure 17-11; the common name of this plant is "shepherd's purse").

2. Now study the demonstration slide of a cross section through a single fruit (Figure 17-12). Note the numerous **seeds** in various stages of embryo development.

3. Obtain a bean pod and carefully split it open along one seam.

   The pod is a matured ovary and thus is a _____.

   Find the *sepals* at one end of the pod and the shriveled *style* at the opposite end. The "beans" inside are

   _____.

4. Note the point of attachment of the bean to the pod. This is the placenta, a term shared by the plant and animal kingdom that describes the nutrient bridge between the "unborn" offspring and parent.

5. In Figure 17-13, draw the split-open bean pod, labeling it with the correct scientific terms. Figure 17-15r shows a section of a typical fruit.

Figure 17-11 Herbarium specimen of *Capsella*, shepherd's purse (0.25×).

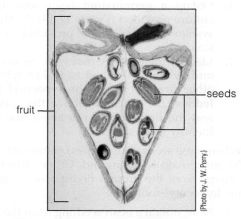

Figure 17-12 Cross section of *Capsella* fruit (8×).

Figure 17-13 Drawing of an open bean pod.
Labels: fruit, seeds, placenta

6. Closely study one of the beans from within the pod or a bean that has been soaked overnight to soften it. Find the scar left where the seed was attached to the fruit wall.
7. Near the scar, look for the tiny opening left in the seed coat.

What is this tiny opening? _____ (*Hint:* The pollen tube grew through it.)

8. Remove the seed coat to expose the two large **cotyledons.** Split the cotyledons apart to find the **epicotyl** and **hypocotyl-root axis.** During maturation of the bean embryo, the cotyledons absorb the endosperm. Thus, bean cotyledons are very fleshy because they store carbohydrates that will be used during seed germination. Add a drop of iodine I_2KI to the cotyledon.

What substance is located in the cotyledon? _____
(*Hint:* Return to Exercise 4 if you've forgotten what is stained by I_2KI.)

E. Seedling *(About 20 min.)*

When environmental conditions are favorable for growth (adequate moisture, oxygen, and proper temperatures), the seed germinates; that is, the seedling (young sporophyte) begins to grow.

MATERIALS

Per student:

- germinating bean seeds
- bean seedlings

Per table:

- dishpan of water

PROCEDURE

1. Obtain a germinating bean seed from the culture provided (Figure 17-14). Wash the root system in the dishpan provided, *not* in the sink.
2. Identify the **primary root** with the smaller **secondary roots** attached to it. Emerging in the other direction will be the **hypocotyl,** the **cotyledons,** the **epicotyl** (above the cotyledons), and the first **true leaves** above the epicotyl. Identify these structures.

When some seeds (like the pea) germinate, the cotyledons remain *below* ground. Others, like the bean, emerge from the ground because of elongation of the hypocotyl-root axis.

3. Now, obtain a bean seedling from the growing medium. Be careful as you pull it up so as not to damage the root system. Wash the root system in the dishpan provided.

Your seedling should be in a stage of development similar to that shown in Figure 17-15s. Much of the growth that has taken place is the result of cellular elongation of the parts present in the seed.

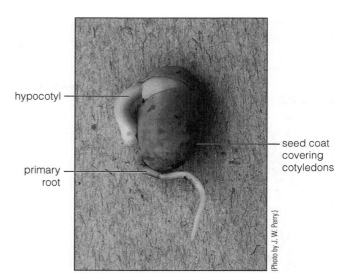

Figure 17-14 Germinating bean seed (2×).

4. On the root system, identify the **primary** and **secondary roots.** As the root system merges into the shoot (aboveground) system, find the **hypocotyl.** (The prefix *hypo-* is derived from Greek, meaning "below" or "underneath.")
5. Next, identify the cotyledons. Notice their shriveled appearance. Now that you know the function of the cotyledons from your previous study, why do you suppose the cotyledons are shriveled?

_____

6. Above the cotyledons, find that portion of the stem called the **epicotyl.**

Knowing what you do about the prefix *hypo-*, speculate on what the prefix *epi-* means.

_____

As noted earlier, the seedling has *true leaves.* Contrast the function of the cotyledons ("seed leaves") with the true leaves. _____

_____

Depending on the stage of development, your seedling may have even more leaves that have been produced by the shoot apex.

The amount of time between seed germination and flowering largely depends on the particular plant. Some plants produce flowers and seeds during their first growing season, completing their life cycle in that growing season. These plants are called **annuals.** Marigolds are an example of an annual. Others, known as **biennials,** grow vegetatively during the first growing season and do not produce flowers and seeds until the second growing season (carrots, for example). Both annuals and biennials die after seeds are produced.

Perennials are plants that live several to many years. The time between seed germination and flowering (seed production) varies, some requiring many years. Moreover, perennials do not usually die after producing seed, but flower and produce seeds many times during their lifetime.

17.3 Experiment: An Investigative Study of the Life Cycle of Flowering Plants

Recent developments with a fast-growing and fast-reproducing plant in the mustard family allow you to study the life cycle of a flowering plant over the course of only 35 days. The plants were bred by a plant scientist at the University of Wisconsin–Madison and are sometimes called Wisconsin Fast Plants™. You will grow these rapid-cycling *Brassica rapa* (abbreviated RCBr for *Rapid Cycling Brassica rapa*) plants from seeds, following the growth cycle and learning about plant structure, the life cycle of a flowering plant, and adaptive mechanisms for pollination.

Because this investigation occurs over several weeks, all Materials and Procedures are listed by the day the activity begins, starting from day 0. Record your measurements and observations in tables at the end of this exercise.

A. Germination

Day 0 (About 30 min.)

MATERIALS

Per student:

- one RCBr seed pod
- metric ruler
- 3 × 5 in. index card
- transparent adhesive tape
- petri dish
- paper toweling or filter paper disk to fit petri dish
- growing quad *or* two 35-mm film canisters
- 12 N-P-K fertilizer pellets (24 if using canister method)
- 4 paper wicks (growing quad) *or* 2 cotton string wicks (canister method)
- disposable pipet with bulb
- pot label (2 if using canister method)

- marker
- forceps
- model seed
- 500-mL beaker
- 2 wide-mouth bottles (film canister method)

Per student group (4):

- 2-L soda bottle bottom or tray
- moistened soil mix
- watertight tray
- water mat

Per lab room:

- light bank

PROCEDURE

The life cycle of a seed plant has no beginning or end; it's a true cycle. For convenience, we'll start our examination of this cycle with germination of nature's perfect time capsule, the seed. **Germination** is the process of switching from dormancy to growth.

1. Obtain an RCBr seed pod that has been sandwiched between two strips of transparent adhesive tape. This pod is the **fruit** of the plant. A fruit is a matured ovary. Measure and record the length of the pod in Table 17-1.
2. Harvest the seeds by scrunching up the pod until the seeds come out. Then carefully separate the halves of the pod to expose the seeds.
3. Roll a piece of adhesive tape into a circle with the sticky side out. Attach the tape to an index card and then place the seeds on the tape. (This keeps the small seeds from disappearing.) You may wish to handle the seeds with forceps. Count the number of seeds and record the number in Table 17-1.

Figure 17-15 Life cycle of an angiosperm. [Color scheme: Haploid (n) structures are yellow, diploid (2n) are green, gold, or red; triploid (3n) are purple.]

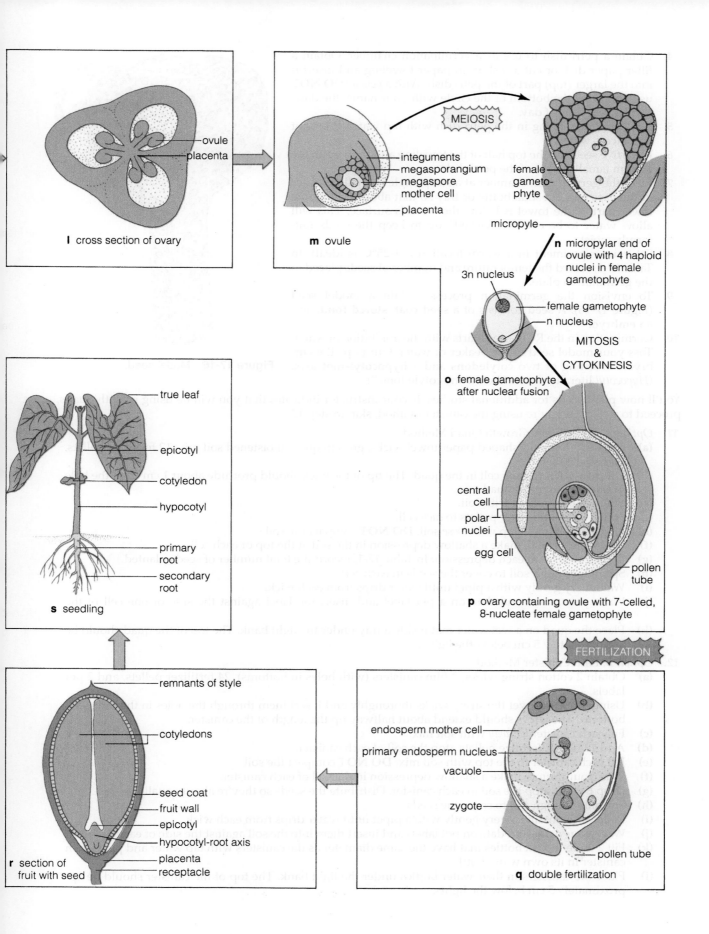

l cross section of ovary

ovule
placenta

m ovule

integuments
megasporangium
megaspore
mother cell
placenta

MEIOSIS

female
gameto-
phyte
micropyle

n micropylar end of
ovule with 4 haploid
nuclei in female
gametophyte

3n nucleus

female gametophyte
n nucleus

MITOSIS
&
CYTOKINESIS

o female gametophyte
after nuclear fusion

central
cell
polar
nuclei
egg cell
pollen
tube

p ovary containing ovule with 7-celled,
8-nucleate female gametophyte

FERTILIZATION

s seedling

true leaf
epicotyl
cotyledon
hypocotyl
primary
root
secondary
root

r section of
fruit with seed

remnants of style
cotyledons
seed coat
fruit wall
epicotyl
hypocotyl-root axis
placenta
receptacle

endosperm mother cell
primary endosperm nucleus
vacuole
zygote
pollen tube

q double fertilization

Seed Plants II: Angiosperms **319**

4. Obtain a petri dish to use as a germination chamber. Obtain a filter paper disk or cut a disk from paper toweling and insert it into the larger (top) part of the petri dish. With a *pencil* (**DO NOT** use ink), label the bottom of the circle with your name, the date, and current time of day.

5. Moisten the toweling in the petri dish with tap water. Pour out any excess water.

6. Place five seeds on the top half of the toweling and cover with the bottom (smaller half) of the petri dish.

7. Place the germination chamber at a steep angle in shallow water in the base of a 2-L soda bottle or tray so that about 1 cm of the lower part of the towel is below the water's surface. This will allow water to be evenly "wicked" up to keep the seeds uniformly moist.

8. Set your experiment in a warm location (20–25°C is ideal). In Table 17-1, record the temperature and number of seeds placed in the germination plate.

9. To envision the germination process, obtain a model seed (Figure 17-16). A **seed** consists of a **seed coat, stored food,** and an **embryo.**

10. Germination in the RCBr seed starts with the imbibition of water. Toss your model seed into a beaker of water. Out pops the embryo, consisting of two **cotyledons** and a **hypocotyl-root axis.** (*Hypocotyl* literally means "below the cotyledons.")

Figure 17-16 Model seed.

You'll now plant seeds for additional studies. If your instructor indicates that you will be using growth quads, proceed to step 11. If you're using the canister method, skip to step 12.

11. *Option A:* Polystyrene Growth Quad Method
    (a) Obtain 4 diamond-shaped paper towel wicks, growth quad, moistened soil mix, 12 fertilizer pellets, and a pot label.
    (b) Drop 1 wick into each cell in the quad. The tip of the wick should protrude about 1 cm from the hole in the bottom of the quad.
    (c) Fill each cell *halfway* with soil.
    (d) Add 3 N-P-K fertilizer pellets to *each* cell.
    (e) Fill each cell to the top with *loose* soil. **DO NOT** compact the soil.
    (f) With your thumb, make a shallow depression in the soil at the top of each cell.
    (g) Drop 3 seeds into each depression. In Table 17-1, record the total number of seeds planted.
    (h) Sprinkle enough soil to cover the seeds in each cell.
    (i) Water very gently with a pipet until water drips from each wick.
    (j) Write your name and date on a pot label and insert the label against the side of one cell of the quad.
    (k) Place the quad on a wet water mat inside a tray under the light bank. The top of the quad should be approximately 5 cm below the lights.

12. *Option B*: Film Canister Method
    (a) Obtain 2 cotton string wicks, 2 film canisters (with holes in bottoms), 24 fertilizer pellets, and 2 pot labels.
    (b) Using tap water, wet the string wicks thoroughly and insert them through the holes in the canisters' bottoms. The wicks should extend about halfway up the length of the canister.
    (c) Fill each canister *halfway* with soil mix.
    (d) Add 12 N-P-K fertilize pellets atop the soil of each canister.
    (e) Fill each canister to the top with soil mix. **DO NOT** compact the soil.
    (f) With your thumb, make a shallow depression in the soil of each canister.
    (g) Drop 6 seeds atop the soil in each canister. Distribute the seeds so they're about equally spaced.
    (h) Sprinkle enough soil to cover the seeds.
    (i) Water the containers very gently with a pipet until water drips from each wick.
    (j) Write your name and date on pot labels and insert them into the soil against the side of each canister.
    (k) Fill 2 wide-mouth bottles that have the same diameter as the canisters with tap water and place each canister in its own water bottle.
    (l) Place the canisters in their water bottles under the light bank. The top of the canister should be approximately 5 cm below the lights.

Day 1 (About 10 min.)

MATERIALS

Per student:

- dissecting microscope
- disposable pipet with bulb
- tap water
- metric ruler

PROCEDURE

1. Water each quad cell or canister from the top using a pipet.
2. Observe your germination experiment in the petri dish chamber with a dissecting microscope. Note the **radicle** (primary root) and **hypocotyl** extending from a split in the brown **seed coat.** What colors are the radicle and the hypocotyl? _____
3. What does the color indicate about the source of carbohydrates for the germinating seeds?
_____

4. Count the number of seeds that have germinated, and record it in Table 17-1. Measure the length of each hypocotyl and attached radicle. Record this in Table 17-1. Replace the cover and return your experiment to its place.

Day 2 (About 15 min.)

MATERIALS

Per student:

- germination experiment started on day 0
- disposable pipet with bulb
- tap water
- metric ruler
- forceps
- dissecting microscope
- 2 additional germination chambers (for gravitropism experiment)
- 2 RCBr seed pods

PROCEDURE

1. Water each quad cell or canister from the top using a pipet.
2. Observe your germination experiment. Count the number of germinated seeds and calculate the percentage of seeds that germinated. Record both numbers in Table 17-1. With a forceps, remove one of the germinating seeds from the toweling, place it on the stage of a dissecting microscope, and observe the numerous **root hairs** attached to the radicle. Root hairs greatly increase the surface area for absorption of water and minerals. Measure the lengths of the hypocotyls and attached radicles and record their average length in Table 17-1.

In what direction (up, down, or horizontal) are the hypocotyl and radicle growing?
hypocotyl: _____
radicle: _____
This directional growth is called **gravitropism,** a plant growth response to gravity.

Day 3 (About 10 min.)

MATERIALS

Per student:

- germination experiment started on day 0
- metric ruler
- disposable pipet with bulb
- tap water

PROCEDURE

1. Water your plants in the quads or canisters from the top using a pipet. Is any part of the plant visible yet? _____ (yes or no) If yes, which part? _____
2. Observe your germination experiment. By this time, the seed coat should be shed, and the **cotyledons,** the so-called seed leaves that were packed inside the seed coat, should be visible. The cotyledons absorb food stored within the seed, making the food available for initial stages of growth before photosynthesis starts to provide carbohydrates necessary for growth.

What color are the cotyledons? _____

What function does this color indicate for the cotyledons? _____

3. Measure the length of the hypocotyls and attached radicles and record their average length in Table 17-1.

B. Growth

Day 4 or 5 (About 10 min.)

MATERIALS

Per student:

- forceps
- metric ruler

- dissecting microscope
- germination experiment started on day 0

PROCEDURE

1. Count the number of seedlings present, and record it in Table 17-1. Use a forceps to thin the plants to one per cell if you are using the quad growing method. If a cell has no plants, transplant one of the extra plants from another cell by inserting the tip of a pencil into the soil to form a hole and then inserting the transplant's root. Gently firm the soil around the transplant. Measure the height of each plant's shoot system—that is, from soil to the apex. Compute the average height and record it in Table 17-1.

2. Observe your germination experiment. Note that the radicle has produced additional roots. These are **lateral roots** (secondary roots). Remove one plant and observe it with the dissecting microscope.

Do lateral roots have root hairs? _____ (yes or no)

At this time, you may discard your germination experiment. Your instructor will indicate what you should do with the materials.

Day 7 (About 10 min.)

MATERIALS

Per student:

- metric ruler

PROCEDURE

1. By now your plant should have its first **true leaves.** Describe how the true leaves differ from the cotyledons.

_____

_____

_____

2. Measure the length of the true leaves, and record their average length in Table 17-1.
3. Measure the height of your plants from soil line to shoot apex, and record the average height in Table 17-1.

C. The Pollinator and Pollination

Pollen grains are actually sperm conveyors that deliver these male gametes to the egg-containing ovules within the ovary. Transfer of pollen from the anther to the stigma, called **pollination,** occurs by various means in different species of flowers, with wind, birds, and insects being the most common carriers of pollen. In the case of *Brassica,* the main pollinator is the common honeybee.

Pollinators and flowers are probably one of the best-known examples of **coevolution.** Coevolution is the process of two organisms evolving together, their structures and behaviors changing to benefit both organisms. Flowering plants and pollinators work together in nearly perfect harmony: The bee receives the food it needs for its respiratory activities from the flower, and the plant receives the male gametes directly to the female structure—it doesn't have to rely on the presence of water, which is necessary in lower plants, algae, and fungi, to get the gametes together.

Flowering plants have considerable advantage over gymnosperms. While gymnosperms also produce pollen grains, the pollinator in these plants is the wind. No organism carries pollen directly to the female structure. Rather, chance and the production of enormous quantities of pollen (which takes energy that might be used otherwise for growth) are integral in assuring reproduction.

In preparation for pollinating your plants' flowers, let's first study the pollinator, the common honeybee.

Day 10 (About 20 min.)

MATERIALS

Per student:

- metric ruler
- 3 toothpicks
- 3 dried honeybees
- dissecting microscope

Per student group (4):

- tube of glue
- scissors

PROCEDURE

1. Measure the lengths of the second set of true leaves and plant height, and record their averages in Table 17-1.
2. Obtain a dried honeybee and observe it with your dissecting microscope. Use Figure 17-17 to aid you in this study. Note the featherlike hairs that cover its body. As a bee probes for nectar, it brushes against the anthers and stigma. Pollen is entrapped on these hairs.
3. Closely study the foreleg of the bee, noticing the notch. This is the *antenna cleaner*. Quick movements over the antennae remove pollen from these sensory organs.
4. Examine the mid- and hind legs, identifying their *pollen brushes,* which are used to remove the pollen from the forelegs, thorax, and head.
5. On the hind leg, note the *pollen comb* and *pollen press.* The comb rakes the pollen from the midleg, and the press is a storage area for pollen collected.

Pollen is rich in the vitamins, minerals, fats, and proteins needed for insect growth. When the baskets are filled, the bee returns to the hive to feed the colony. Partially digested pollen is fed to larvae and to young, emerging bees.

As you can imagine, during pollen- and nectar-gathering at numerous flowers, cross-pollination occurs as pollen grains are rubbed off onto stigmas.

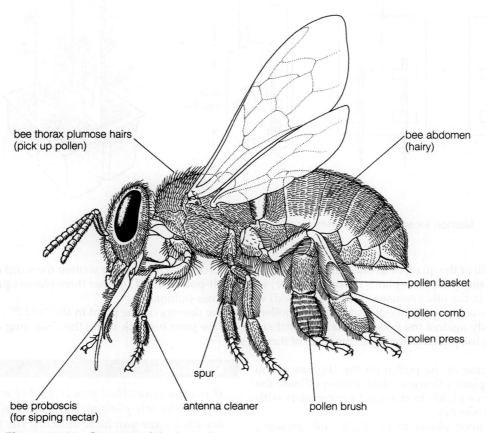

Figure 17-17 Structure of the honeybee.

On day 12, you will start pollinating your flowers. What better means to do it than to use a bee? (In this case, a dead bee that is attached to a stick.) Let's make some beesticks.

6. Add a drop of glue to one end of three round toothpicks. Insert the glue-bearing end of one stick into the top (dorsal) side of the thorax of a bee. Repeat with two more dried bees. Set your beesticks aside to dry.

D. Pollination

It's time to do a pollination study. Some species of flowers are able to **self-pollinate,** meaning that the pollen from one flower of a plant will grow on stigmas of other flowers of that same plant. Hence, the sperm produced by a single plant will fertilize its own flowers. Other species are **self-incompatible.** For fertilization to occur in the latter, pollen must travel from one plant to another plant of the same species. This is **cross-pollination.** In this portion of the exercise, you will determine whether RCBr is self-incompatible or is able to self-pollinate.

Day 12 (About 30 min.)

MATERIALS

Per student:

- beestick prepared on day 10
- metric ruler
- forceps

- index card divider
- pot label
- marker

PROCEDURE

1. Measure the height of each plant, and record the average height in Table 17-1.
2. Separate the cells of your quad or canister with a divider constructed with index cards as shown in Figure 17-18. This keeps the plants from brushing against each other.

Figure 17-18 Method for separating flowers for pollination study.

3. In one cell of the quad, or in one canister, insert a pot label on which you have written the word ("SELF"), to indicate that this plant (plants if using canister) will be self-pollinated. The other three plants (quad method) or those in the other canister (canister method) will be cross-pollinated.
4. Now use one of your beesticks to pick up pollen from the flowers on the plant in the "SELF" cell. Rub the bee's body against the pollen-containing anthers. Examine your beestick using the dissecting microscope, and note the pollen adhering to the hairs of the bee's body.
5. Brush some of the pollen on the stigmas of the "SELF" plant's flowers. Next, cross-pollinate the other three plants in the quad (or canister) with the *same* beestick.
6. Return your plants to the light-bank growing area and discard the beestick.

> ### Caution
>
> *It is important that you DO NOT retouch any of the self-pollinated flowers with the beestick once you have touched the flowers of any of the other plants.*

Day 14 (About 15 min.)

MATERIALS

Per student:

- metric ruler
- beestick

PROCEDURE

1. Measure the height of each plant, and record their average height in Table 17-1.
2. Pollinate the newly opened flowers using the same techniques as described for day 12.
3. Return your plants to the light-bank growing area.

> **Caution**
>
> *Use a new beestick and be sure not to transfer pollen from any of the cross-pollinated plants to the self-pollinated plant.*

Day 17 (About 15 min.)

MATERIALS

Per student:

- metric ruler
- beestick

PROCEDURE

1. Measure the height of each plant, and record their average height in Table 17-1.
2. Count the number of flowers on each plant (opened and unopened), calculate the average number per plant, and record it in Table 17-1. Pinch off the shoot apex of each plant to remove all unopened buds and pinch off any side shoots the plant has produced.
3. Do a final pollination of your flowers, using a fresh beestick and taking the same precautions as on days 12 and 14.
4. Return your plants to the light-bank growing area.

E. Fertilization and Seed Development

Within 24 hours of pollination, a pollen grain that has landed on a compatible stigma will produce a pollen tube that grows down the style and through the micropyle of the ovule.

Within the pollen tube are two **sperm,** the male gametes. As the pollen tube enters the ovule, the two sperm are discharged. One fertilizes the haploid egg nucleus, forming a diploid **zygote.** The second sperm unites with two other nuclei within the ovule, forming a triploid nucleus known as the **primary endosperm nucleus.**

The fusion of one sperm nucleus to form the zygote and the other to form the primary endosperm nucleus is called **double fertilization.**

1. Re-examine Figure 17-9, which illustrates double fertilization.

What is the fate of cells formed by double fertilization? The zygote undergoes numerous cell divisions during a process called **embryogeny** (the suffix *-geny* is derived from Greek, meaning "production") to form the diploid embryo. The triploid primary endosperm nucleus divides numerous times without cytokinesis. The result is the formation of a multinucleate milky **endosperm** (each nucleus is 3n), which serves as the food source for the embryo as it grows. At the same time, changes are taking place in the cell layers of the ovule—they are becoming hardened and will eventually form the seed coat. Also, the ovary is elongating as it matures into the **fruit**—in this case, a pod.

2. Examine your plants, looking for small, elongated pods.
3. At this time, you should be able to tell whether RCBr can self-pollinate or is self-incompatible, because the fruit—a pod—will develop only if fertilization has taken place. Do the cross-pollinated plants have pods? (yes or no) _____
4. Does the self-pollinated plant have pods? (yes or no) _____
5. Make a conclusion regarding the need for cross-pollination in RCBr. _____

_____

The young embryo goes through a continuous growth process, starting as a ball of cells (the globular stage) and culminating in the formation of a mature embryo. The early stages are somewhat difficult to observe, but the later stages can be seen quite easily with a microscope. By day 24, many of the ovules will be at the globular stage, similar to that seen in Figure 17-10a.

Day 26 (About 30 min.)

MATERIALS

Per student:

- dissecting microscope
- 2 dissecting needles
- dH$_2$O in dropping bottle

- glass microscope slide
- iodine solution (I$_2$KI) in dropping bottle

PROCEDURE

1. Remove a pod from one of the plants, place it on the stage of your dissecting microscope, and tease it open using dissecting needles. RCBr flowers have pistils consisting of two carpels; each carpel makes up one longitudinal half of the pod, and the "seam" represents where the carpels fuse.
2. Carefully remove the ovules (immature seeds) inside the pod, placing them in a drop of water on a clean microscope slide.
3. Rupture the ovule by mashing it with dissecting needles and place the slide on the stage of a dissecting microscope.
4. Attempt to locate the embryo, which should be at the heart-shaped stage, similar to Figure 17-10b, and which may be turning green. A portion of the endosperm has become cellular and may be green, too, so be careful with your observation. The "lobes" of the heart-shaped embryo are the young cotyledons. Identify these. Find the trailing **suspensor,** a strand of eight cells that serves as a sort of "umbilical cord" to transport nutrients from the endosperm to the embryo.
5. Add a drop of I$_2$KI to stain the endosperm. What color does the endosperm stain? _____
6. What can you conclude about the composition of the endosperm? (*Hint:* If you've forgotten, consult Exercise 4.)

Day 29 (About 20 min.)

MATERIALS

Per student:

- dissecting microscope
- 2 dissecting needles

- dH$_2$O in dropping bottle
- glass microscope slide

PROCEDURE

1. Remove another pod from a plant and examine it as you did on day 26.
2. Attempt to find the torpedo stage of embryo development, similar to that illustrated in Figure 17-10c.
3. Describe the changes that have taken place in the transition from the heart-shaped to the torpedo stage.

Day 31 (About 20 min.)

MATERIALS

Per student:

- dissecting microscope
- 2 dissecting needles

- dH$_2$O in dropping bottle
- glass microscope slide

PROCEDURE

1. Again, remove and dissect a pod and ovules, and look for the embryo whose cotyledons have now curved, forming the so-called walking-stick stage.
2. Identify the **cotyledons** and the **hypocotyl-root axis** that has curved within the ovules' integuments.

Days 35–37 (About 20 min.)

MATERIALS

Per student:

- dissecting microscope
- 2 dissecting needles

PROCEDURE

The pods of your plants should be drying and have much the same appearance as the pod you started with about a month ago.

1. Remove seeds from mature pods and examine the seeds with your dissecting microscope. Note the bumpy **seed coat,** derived from the integument of the ovule. Look for a tiny hole in the seed coat. This is the **micropyle!**
2. Crack the seed coat and remove the embryo, identifying the cotyledons and hypocotyl-root axis. Separate the cotyledons and look between them, identifying the tiny **epicotyl,** which is the *apical meristem of the shoot.*
3. Harvest the remaining pods and count the number of seeds in each pod. Calculate the average number of seeds per pod and number of seeds per plant. Record this information in Table 17-1.

Congratulations! You have completed the life cycle study of a rapid cycling *Brassica rapa.* Virtually all of the 200,000 species of flowering plants have stages identical to that which you have examined over the course of the past 35–40 days. Most just take longer—from a few days to nearly a century longer!

Conclude your study by preparing the required graphs and answering the questions following Table 17-1.

4. In Figure 17-19, graph the increase in average length of the hypocotyl-root axis produced in the germination chamber.

Does length increase in a constant fashion (linearly), or does extension occur more quickly during a particular time period (logarithmically)? _____

Using the data from Table 17-1, graph in Figure 17-20 the rate of growth of your plants' shoot system as a function of time.

How does the number of seeds produced per pod compare with the number in the original pod from which you harvested your seed at the beginning of the study? _____

What is the *reproductive potential* (the number of possible plants coming from one parent plant) of your RCBr?_____

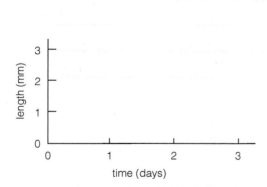

Figure 17-19 Growth of hypocotyl-root axis.

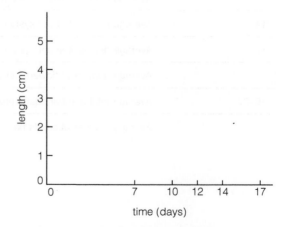

Figure 17-20 Growth of shoot system.

TABLE 17-1 Data for RCBr Life Cycle

Day	Parameter	Measurement
0	Pod length	mm
	Seed number (single pod)	
	Number of seeds sown in germination chamber	
	Temperature, °C	
	Number of seeds sown in quad (total)	
1	Germinated seeds (germination chamber)	
	Average length of hypocotyl-root axis	mm
2	Germinated seeds (germination chamber)	
	Percentage seeds germinated	
	Average length of hypocotyl-root axis	mm
3	Average length of hypocotyl-root axis	mm
4 or 5	Number of seedlings (quad)	
	Average height of shoot system	mm
7	Average length of first set of true leaves	mm
	Average height of shoot system	mm
10	Average length of second set of true leaves	mm
	Average height of shoot system	mm
12	Average number of leaves per plant	
	Average height of shoot system	mm
14	Average height of shoot system	mm
17	Average height of shoot system	mm
	Average number of flowers per plant	
35–37	Average total number seeds produced per plant	
	Average number of seeds per pod	

_____ 1. Plants that produce flowers are
(a) members of the Anthophyta
(b) angiosperms
(c) seed producers
(d) all of the above

_____ 2. All of the petals of a flower are collectively called the
(a) corolla
(b) stamens
(c) receptacles
(d) calyx

_____ 3. Which group of terms refers to the microsporophyll, the male portion of a flower?
(a) ovary, stamens, pistil
(b) stigma, style, ovary
(c) anther, stamen, filament
(d) megasporangium, microsporangium, ovule

_____ 4. A carpel is the
(a) same as a megasporophyll
(b) structure producing pollen grains
(c) component making up the anther
(d) synonym for microsporophyll

_____ 5. The portion of the flower containing pollen grains is
(a) the pollen sac
(b) the microsporangium
(c) the anther
(d) all of the above

_____ 6. Which group of terms is in the correct developmental sequence?
(a) microspore mother cell, meiosis, megaspore, female gametophyte
(b) microspore mother cell, meiosis, microspore, pollen grain
(c) megaspore, mitosis, female gametophyte, meiosis, endosperm mother cell
(d) all of the above

_____ 7. Where does germination of a pollen grain occur in a flowering plant?
(a) in the anther
(b) in the micropyle
(c) on the surface of the corolla
(d) on the stigma

_____ 8. Double fertilization refers to
(a) fusion of two sperm nuclei and two egg cells
(b) fusion of one sperm nucleus with two polar nuclei and fusion of another with the egg cell nucleus
(c) maturation of the ovary into a fruit
(d) none of the above

_____ 9. Ovules mature into _____, while ovaries mature into _____.
(a) seeds/fruits
(b) stamens/seeds
(c) seeds/carpels
(d) fruits/seeds

_____ 10. A bean pod is
(a) a seed container
(b) a fruit
(c) a part of the stamen
(d) both a and b

EXERCISE 17

Seed Plants II: Angiosperms

POST-LAB QUESTIONS

Introduction

1. There are two major groups of seed plants, gymnosperms (Exercise 16) and angiosperms. Compare these two groups of seed plants with respect to the following features:

Feature	Gymnosperms	Angiosperms
a. type of reproductive structure	_____	_____
b. source of nutrition for developing embryo	_____	_____
c. enclosure of mature seed	_____	_____

17.1 External Structure of the Flower

2. What *event*, critical to the production of seeds, is shown at the right?

3. Distinguish between *pollination* and *fertilization*.

(0.84×).

4. Identify the parts of the trumpet creeper flower shown at the right.

    a.

    b.

    c.

    d.

    e.

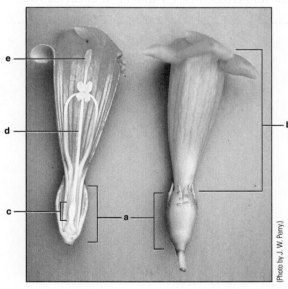

(1×).

5. Examine the photo of the *Trillium* flower pictured at the right.

   a. Is *Trillium* a monocotyledon or dicotyledon?

   b. Justify your answer.

(0.75×).

6. Based on your observation of the stigma of the day-lily flower in the photo at the right, how many carpels would you expect to comprise the ovary?

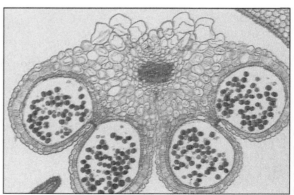

(1×).

17.2 The Life Cycle of a Flowering Plant

7. The photo is a cross section of a (an) _____

   _____.

   The numerous circles within the four cavities are

   _____.

(74×).

8. The photo shows a flower of the pomegranate some time after fertilization. Identify the parts shown.

a. _____

b _____

c. _____

d. _____

a

b

c

d —

(Photo by J. W. Perry.)

(2×).

9. Some biologists contend that the term *double fertilization* is a misnomer and that the process should be called *fertilization* and *triple fusion.* Why do they argue that the fusion of the one sperm nucleus and the two polar nuclei is *not* fertilization?

Food for Thought

10. Your roommate says that you need vegetables and asks you to pick up tomatoes at the store. To your roommate's surprise, you say a tomato is not a vegetable, but a fruit. Explain.

9. Some biologists contend that the term double fertilization is a misnomer and that the process should be called fertilization and triple fusion. Why do they argue that the fusion of the one sperm nucleus and the two polar nuclei is not fertilization?

Food for Thought

10. Your roommate says that you need vegetables and asks you to pick up tomatoes at the store. To your roommate's surprise, you say a tomato is not a vegetable but a fruit. Explain.

Sponges, Cnidarians, Flatworms, and Rotifers

OBJECTIVES

After completing this exercise, you will be able to

1. define *larva, asymmetry, radial symmetry, bilateral symmetry, cephalization, coelom, pseudocoelom, monoecious, dioecious, invertebrates, spongocoel, osculum, spicules, choanocyte (collar cell), budding, sponging, polyp, tentacles, medusa, nematocyst, gastrovascular cavity epidermis, gastrodermis, mesoglea, acoelomate, regeneration, host, intermediate host, cuticle, scolex, proglottid, pseudocoelomate, cloaca,* and *bladder worm;*

2. describe the tissue and organ-system levels of organization;

3. list the characteristics of animals;

4. describe how the phyla Porifera and Cnidaria respectively show the cell-specialization and tissue levels of organization;

5. explain the basic body plan of members of the phyla Porifera and Cnidaria;

6. identify representatives of the classes Calcarea and Demospongiae of the phylum Porifera and classes Hydrozoa, Scyphozoa, and Anthozoa of the phylum Cnidaria;

7. identify structures (and indicate associate functions) of representatives of these classes;

8. explain the basic body plan of members of the phyla Platyhelminthes and Rotifera;

9. describe the natural history of members of the phyla Platyhelminthes and Rotifera;

10. identify representatives of the classes Turbellaria, Trematoda, and Cestoda of the phylum Platyhelminthes and representatives of phylum Rotifera;

11. identify structures (and indicate associated functions) or representatives of these groups;

12. outline the life cycles of human liver fluke;

13. outline the live cycle of *Ascaris*;

14. compare and contrast the anatomy and live cycles of free-living and parasitic flatworms.

INTRODUCTION

Animals are multicellular, oxygen-consuming, heterotrophic (heterotrophs feed on other organisms or on organic waste) *organisms that exhibit considerable motility.* Most animals are *diploid* and *reproduce sexually,* although asexual reproduction is also common. The animal life cycle includes a *period of embryonic development, often with a larva*—sexually immature, free-living form that grows and transforms into an adult—or equivalent stage. During the embryonic development of most animals, *three primary germ layers—ectoderm, mesoderm,* and *endoderm*—form and give rise to the adult tissues. Evidence accumulated from centuries of study supports the notion that animals evolved from a group of protistanlike ancestors distinct from those that gave rise to the plants and fungi.

Animal diversity is usually studied in the approximate order of a group's first appearance on the earth. Table 18-1 summarizes the trends evident in this sequence for the phyla considered in this and subsequent diversity exercises:

- In terms of habitat, marine animals precede freshwater and terrestrial forms.
- The organization of animal bodies is initially **asymmetrical**—cannot cut the body into two like halves—but rapidly becomes symmetrical, exhibiting first **radial symmetry**—any cut from the oral (mouth) to the other end through the center of the animal yields two like halves and then bilateral symmetry (Figure 18-1). In **bilateral symmetry,** a cut in only one plane, parallel to the main axis and dividing the body into right and

TABLE 18-1 Trends in the Evolution of Animals

Phylum	Common Name	Habitat	Body Organization	Level of Organization
Porifera	Sponges	Aquatic, mostly marine	None or crude radial symmetry	Cell specialization
Cnidaria	Cnidarians	Aquatic, mostly marine	Radial symmetry, incomplete gut	Tissue (ectoderm and endoderm only)
Platyhelminthes	Flatworms	Aquatic, moist terrestrial, or parasitic	Bilateral symmetry, head, incomplete gut	Organ system (all three primary germ layers)
Rotifera	Rotifers	Aquatic (mostly freshwater) or moist terrestrial	Bilateral symmetry, head, complete gut, pseudocoelom	Organ system
Annelida	Annelids some parasitic	Aquatic or moist terrestrial, bilateral symmetry, some parasitic	Bilateral symmetry, head, segmented, complete gut, coelom	Organ system
Mollusca	Molluscans	Aquatic or terrestrial, mostly marine	Unique body plan, complete gut, coelom	Organ system
Nematoda	Roundworms	Aquatic, moist terrestrial, or parasitic	Bilateral symmetry, head, complete gut, pseudocoelom	Organ system
Arthropod	Arthropods	Aquatic, terrestrial (land and air), some parasitic	Bilateral symmetry, head, complete gut, segmented, coelom	Organ system
Echinodermata	Echinoderms	Aquatic, marine	Radial symmetry (larvae are bilaterally symmetrical), no well-defined head, no segmentation, usually complete gut, coelom	Organ system
Chordata	Chordates	Aquatic, terrestrial (land and air)	Bilateral symmetry, head and postanal tail, segmentation, complete gut, coelom	Organ system

left pieces, yields like halves. Bilateral symmetry accompanies the movement of sensory structures and the mouth to the front end of the body to form a head, a process called **cephalization.** Spaces within the body are first "baskets" used to filter seawater, then incomplete guts (no anus) appear, and finally complete guts (with an anus) are suspended in an entirely enclosed ventral body space. This ventral cavity is called a **coelom** if it is lined by tissue derived from mesoderm, and a **pseudocoelom** if the mesodermal lining is incomplete (Figure 18-2).

- The level of organization of the animal body proceeds through aggregates of specialized cells, tissues formed by associations of similarly specialized cells, organs comprised of different tissues, and systems of functionally related organs.
- Body support moves from self-associating scaffolds in sponges to hydrostatic bodies to shells and exoskeletons or endoskeletons comprised of internal support structures.
- Sexual reproduction predominates in animals, but earlier forms are asexual as well. Earlier forms are often **monoecious** or *hermaphroditic*—individuals have both male and female reproductive structures. Latter

Body Support	Life Cycle	Special Characteristics
Spicules, spongin	Sexual reproduction (mostly monoecious), larva (amphiblastula), asexual reproduction (budding)	Spongocoel, osculum, gemmules, choanocytes (collar cells)
Hydrostatic gut	Sexual reproduction (monoecious or dioecious), larva (planula), asexual reproduction (budding and fragmentation)	Nerve net, nematocysts, two adult body forms—polyp (sessile) and medusa (free swimming)
Muscular	Sexual reproduction (mostly monoecious with internal fertilization); parasites have very complicated life cycles; some asexual reproduction (mostly transverse fission)	Brain, flame cells
Hydrostatic pseudocoelom	Sexual (dioecious with internal fertilization), some parthenogenesis, males much smaller than females or absent	Brain, flame cells, wheel organ, mastax, microscopic animals
Hydrostatic coelom	Sexual reproduction (monoecious or dioecious with mostly internal fertilization), larvae in some, asexual reproduction (mostly transverse fission)	Brain, nephridia, gills in some
Shells, floats (aquatic)	Sexual (monoecious or dioecious with external or internal fertilization), larvae in some	Brain, nephridium or nephridia, most have gills or lungs, external body divided into head, mantle, and foot
Hydrostatic pseudocoelom	Sexual reproduction (mostly dioecious with internal fertilization)	Brain, molt to grow
Exoskeleton of chitin	Sexual reproduction (mostly dioecious with internal fertilization), larvae, metamorphosis, some parthenogenesis	Brain, green glands or Malphigian tubules, gills, tracheae or book lungs, body regions (head, thorax, and abdomen), specialized segments form mouthparts and jointed appendages, molt to grow
Dermal endoskeleton of calcium carbonate (mesoderm)	Sexual reproduction (mostly dioecious with external fertilization), larvae, metamorphosis, high regenerative potential	Radial symmetry, water-vascular system
Most have an endoskeleton of cartilage or bone	Sexual reproduction (mostly dioecious with internal or external fertilization), some larvae, some metamorphosis	Brain, ventral heart, notochord, gill slits, and dorsal hollow nerve cord at some stage of life cycle

forms are **dioecious** with male and female reproductive structures in separate sexes. Fertilization of the egg by sperm is usually external in *sessile* (immobile and attached to a surface such as the sea bottom) animals and internal in most mobile forms, and *pathenogenesis* (the egg develops without fertilization) occurs sporadically.

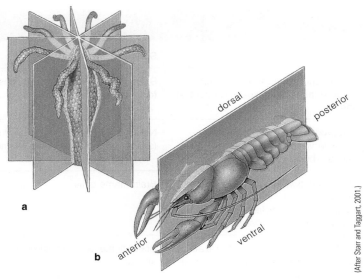

Figure 18-1 Examples of body symmetry. (**a**) Radial symmetry in a cnidarian polyp. (**b**) Bilateral symmetry in a crayfish, an arthropod.

epidermis — gut cavity

no body cavity; region between gut and body wall packed with organs

a No coelom (*acoelomate* animals)

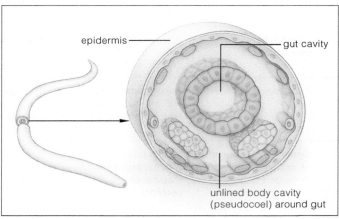

epidermis — gut cavity

unlined body cavity (pseudocoel) around gut

b Pseudocoel (*pseudocoelomate* animals)

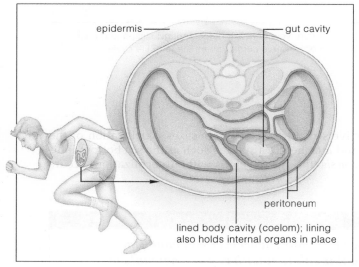

epidermis — gut cavity

peritoneum

lined body cavity (coelom); lining also holds internal organs in place

c Coelom (*coelomate* animals)

Figure 18-2 Development of ventral body cavity in animals. (After Starr and Taggart, 2001.)

Habitat:	aquatic, mostly marine
Body Arrangement:	asymmetrical or crude radial symmetry
Level of Organization:	cell specialization
Body Support:	spicules and/or spongin
Life Cycle:	sexual reproduction (mostly monoecious),
	larva (amphiblastula), asexual reproduction (budding and fragmentation)
Special Characteristics:	spongocoel, osculum, gemmules, choanocytes (collar cells)

Aristotle in his *Scala Naturae* said of sponges, "In the sea there are things which it is hard to label as either animal or vegetable." This was a reference to their sensitivity to stimulation and their relative lack of motility.

Sponges evolved directly from protistanlike ancestors and diverged early from the main line of animal evolution (Figure 18-3). Most sponges are marine, and all forms are *aquatic*. As adults, sponges are *sessile*, but many disperse as free-swimming larvae. Although sponges possess a variety of different types of cells, they are atypical animals in their lack of definite tissues. They exhibit the *cell-specialization level of organization*, as there is a division of labor among the different cell types. Cells are organized into layers, but these associations of cells do not show all the characteristics of tissues. Sponges have a *crude radial symmetry or are asymmetrical.* Sponges along with the animals of most phyla are **invertebrates**—animals that do not posses a backbone or vertebral column.

Three body plans exist in sponges (Figure 18-4). They are referred to as *asconoid, syconoid,* and *leuconoid* and increase in the complexity of their structure in this order.

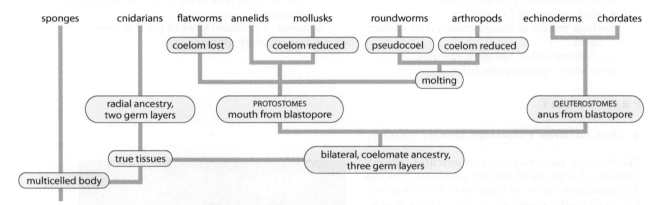

Figure 18-3   Presumed family tree for animals. (After Starr and Taggart, 2006.)

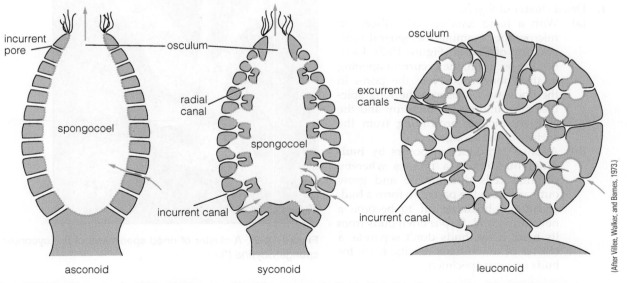

Figure 18-4   Three body plans of sponges. The blue arrows indicate the direction of water flow. Pink areas are lined by collar cells.

Water enters a vase-shaped asconoid sponge through *incurrent pores*; flows directly to a large central internal cavity, the **spongocoel;** and exits through a larger opening, the **osculum.** A syconoid sponge is similar, except that the inner side of the body wall pockets in to form *radial canals* into which *incurrent canals* drain water through channels in their walls. In a leuconoid sponge, the radial canals are internalized as chambers within the sponge. These chambers empty into *excurrent canals* that in turn lead to the osculum. Concurrent with the development of increasingly complex patterns of water flow, the area lined with *collar cells*, which in asconoid sponges is the inner wall of the spongocoel, also becomes internalized, first lining the radial canals of syconoid sponges and then the chambers of leuconoid sponges.

MATERIALS

Per student:

- dissection microscope
- hand lens
- compound microscope, lens paper, a bottle of lens-cleaning solution (optional), a lint-free cloth (optional)
- clean microscope slide and coverslip (optional)

Per student pair:

- preserved specimen of *Scypha (Grantia)*
- prepared slides of
    Scypha spicules (optional)
    a longitudinal section of *Scypha*
    a whole mount of *Leucosolenia*
    a whole mount of teased commercial sponge
      fibers
    a whole mount of *Spongilla* spicules
    freshwater sponge gemmules

Per student group (4):

- 100-mL beaker of heatproof glass (optional)
- bottle of 5% sodium hydroxide (NaOH) or potassium hydroxide (KOH) (optional)
- waste container for 5% hydroxide solution (optional)
- hot plate (optional)
- squeeze bottle of dH_2O (optional)

Per lab room:

- demonstration collection of commercial sponges
- squeeze bottle of 50% vinegar and water
- demonstration of living or dried freshwater sponges
- boxes of different sizes of latex gloves
- box of safety glasses

PROCEDURE

A. Class Calcarea: Calcareous Sponges *(15 min.)*

Members of this class contain **spicules** (skeletal elements) composed of calcium carbonate ($CaCO_3$). All three body plans are represented in this group. You will study members of the genera *Scypha*, which all have the syconoid body plan, and *Leukosolenia*, which all have asconoid body plans.

1. Dried cluster of *Scypha*.
    (a) With a hand lens or your dissection microscope, examine the general morphology of *Scypha* (Figure 18-5). Identify the osculum, the excurrent opening of the spongocoel. Note the pores in the body wall. Observe the long spicules surrounding the osculum and the shorter spicules protruding from the surface of the sponge.
    (b) Asexual reproduction occurs by **budding.** Budding is a process whereby parental cells differentiate and grow outward from the parent to form a bud, sometimes breaking off to become a new individual. *Scypha* often buds from its base. If the buds don't separate, a cluster of individuals results. Look for buds on your specimen.

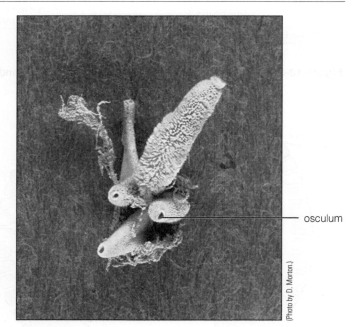

(Photo by D. Morton.)

Figure 18-5 A cluster of dried specimens of the syconoid sponge *Scypha* (3×).

osculum

2. Examine a wet mount (w.m.) or a prepared slide of *Scypha* spicules with your compound microscope, using the medium-power objective. Draw what you observe in Figure 18-6. Follow these instructions to prepare the wet mount:

   (a) Put on a pair of safety goggles and place a small piece of a specimen of *Scypha* in a 100-mL heatproof beaker.

   (b) Carefully add enough 5% sodium hydroxide or potassium hydroxide solution to the beaker to cover the piece and bring this to a boil on the hot plate. Allow the beaker to cool.

   (c) Allow the remains of the sponge to settle to the bottom of the beaker and pour off the liquid into the waste container while retaining the residue.

   (d) Wash the residue by adding distilled water. After the remains of the sponge settle, pour off the water into the waste container.

   (e) Make a wet mount of the residue.

3. Longitudinal section of *Scypha*.

   (a) Examine a longitudinal section of *Scypha* (Figure 18-7) with a compound microscope. In your section, trace the path of water as it flowed into and through the sponge in nature (Figure 18-8). Identify the following structures and place them in the correct order for the water's circulation through the sponge by writing 1st, 2nd, and 3rd, and so on in the second column of Table 18-2.

   (b) Examine the **collar cells,** which appear as numerous small, dark bodies lining the radial canals. Each bears a flagellum that projects into the radial canal, but it's unlikely that you will be able to see the flagella, even with the high-dry objective. Examine the structure of a collar

Figure 18-6 Calcium carbonate spicules of *Scypha*, w.m. (_____ ×).

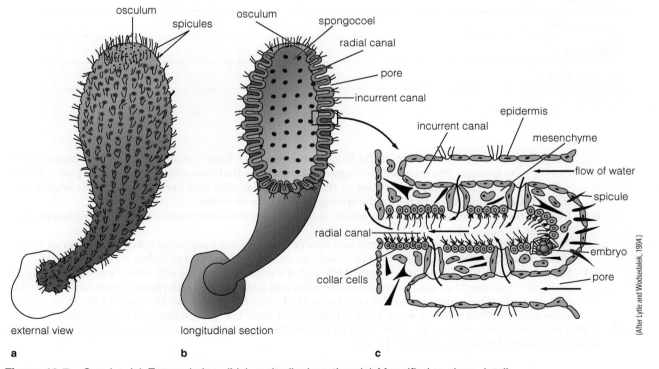

Figure 18-7 *Scypha.* (a) External view. (b) Longitudinal section. (c) Magnified to show detail.

Figure 18-8 Longitudinal sections of *Scypha*. (a) The arrow indicates the path of water flow (96×). (b) 384×.

(Photos by D. Morton.)

TABLE 18-2	Circulation of Water Through the Syconoid Sponge *Scypha*
Structure	**Order for Water Circulation**
Spongocoel	
Incurrent canals	
Radial canals	
Incurrent pores	
Osculum	

cell in Figure 18-9. The beating of the flagella of collar cells likely creates currents that move water through the sponge. The microvilli—fingerlike projections that comprise their collars—play a major role in filtering fine food particles out of the water. Collar cells and perhaps other cells engulf and digest food fragments carried into the sponge by the flow of water.

(c) Identify the *epidermis* with its flat protective cells. It covers the outer surface and incurrent canals, and lines the spongocoel.

(d) Note that between the outer epidermis and inner epidermis lies a region of gelatinous material sometimes called the *mesohyle*, embedded in which are amoeboid cells and spicules.

(e) Sexual reproduction occurs in sponges. Although it's unlikely that you will observe gametes, look for early developmental stages (embryos) of *amphiblastula larvae* in the wall, perhaps protruding into the radial canals. These appear as relatively large, dark structures (Figures 18-7 and 18-8). They would have soon finished development, broken loose, and exited the sponge through the osculum.

4. With your compound microscope, look for spicules and buds on the prepared slide of a whole mount of the asconoid sponge *Leucosolenia* (Figure 18-10).

(After Starr and Taggart, 2001.)

flagellum microvilli nucleus

Figure 18-9 Choanocyte (collar cell).

osculum

bud

(Photo by D. Morton.)

Figure 18-10 Whole mount of *Leucosolenia* (34×).

B. Class Demospongiae: Commercial and Freshwater Sponges *(15 min.)*

This class contains the majority of sponge species. Most sponges in this class are supported by **spongin** (Figure 18-11b, a flexible substance chemically similar to human hair), by spicules of silica, or both. Silica is silicon dioxide, a major component of sand and of many rocks, such as flint and quartz. All sponges in this class are leuconoid and are able to hold and pass large volumes of water in and through their bodies because of their complex canal systems. Some sponges with skeletons composed only of spongin fibers were once commercially valuable as bath sponges, but synthetic sponges have largely replaced them in today's marketplace.

1. Look over the demonstration specimens of commercial sponges available in your lab room (Figure 18-11a).

a
b

Figure 18-11 (**a**) Bath sponge. (**b**) Spongin (74×).

2. With your compound microscope, examine a prepared slide of teased commercial sponge fibers and draw them in Figure 18-12.
3. Examine a prepared slide of silica spicules obtained from a common freshwater sponge of the genus *Spongilla* and draw several of them in Figure 18-13.

Figure 18-12 Teased spongin fibers of a commercial sponge, w.m. (_____ ×).

Figure 18-13 Silica spicules of *Spongilla*, w.m. (_____ ×).

4. Freshwater and some marine sponges in this class reproduce asexually by forming *gemmules,* resistant internal buds. In the freshwater varieties, a shell of silica and spicules surrounds groups of cells. During the unfavorable conditions of winter, disintegration of the sponge releases the gemmules. Under the favorable conditions of spring, cells emerge from the gemmules and develop into new individuals. Find and examine a gemmule on the prepared slide of freshwater sponge gemmules (Figure 18-14).

Figure 18-14 Freshwater sponge gemmule, w.m. (150×).

5. Observe the demonstration of living freshwater sponges available in your lab room (Figure 18-15). They look like yellowish-brown, wrinkled scum with perforations and sometimes have a greenish tint due to the presence of symbiotic algae. They are fairly easy to find in nature; search for them in clear, well-oxygenated water, encrusting submerged plant stems and debris such as a waterlogged twig. Slow streams and the edges of ponds where there is some wave action are good places to find freshwater sponges.

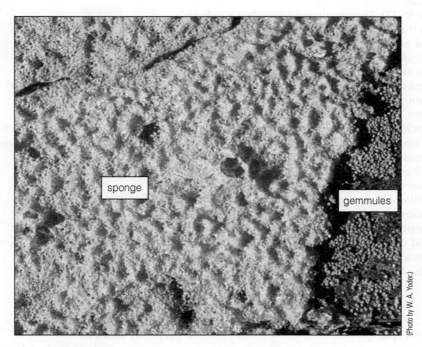

Figure 18-15 Dried freshwater sponges, *Sporilla fragilis* with gemmules (0.5×).

Habitat:	aquatic, mostly marine
Body Arrangement:	radial symmetry, gut (incomplete)
Level of Organization:	tissue (derived from ectoderm and endoderm)
Body Support:	hydrostatic (gastrovascular cavity and epitheliomuscular cells)
Life Cycle:	sexual reproduction (monoecious or dioecious), larva (planula), asexual reproduction (budding)
Special Characteristics:	tissues, two adult body forms—polyp (sessile) and medusa (free swimming)—nematocysts, nerve net

This phylum contains some of the most beautiful organisms in the seas, many of which are brightly colored and superficially plantlike or flowerlike, with tentacles that move in response to water currents (Figure 18-16).

Cnidarians derive from the protistanlike ancestors that gave rise to the main line of evolution from which other animals sprang. Cnidarians diverged early from this evolutionary lineage (Figure 18-3).

These animals are *aquatic* and found mostly in shallow marine environments, with the notable exception of the freshwater hydras. Cnidarians have definite tissues and thus show a *tissue level of organization.* They are mostly *radially symmetrical.* Members of this phylum have a *gut* and a definite *nerve net.*

Two main body forms exist in cnidarians (Figure 18-17). The usually sessile **polyp** is cylindrical in shape, with the oral end and **tentacles** directed upward and the other end attached to a surface. The free-swimming **medusa** (jellyfish) is bell- or umbrella-shaped, with the oral end and tentacles directed downward. Either or both body forms may be present in the Cnidarian life cycle. Also found throughout the group is a larval form called a *planula.*

Cnidarians are efficient predators. All are carnivorous and possess tentacles that capture unwary invertebrate and vertebrate prey. Food is captured with the aid of stinging elements called **nematocysts** (Figure 18-18). The nematocysts are discharged by a combination of mechanical and chemical stimuli. The prey is either pierced by the nematocyst or entangled in its filament and pulled toward the mouth by the tentacles. In some species, nematocysts discharge a toxin that paralyzes the prey. The mouth opens to receive the food, which is deposited in the gut. Digestion is started in the gut cavity by enzymes secreted by its lining. It is completed inside the lining cells after they engulf the partially digested food.

(Photo by W. A. Yoder.)

Figure 18-16   Pink-tipped sea anemone with mutalistic spotted cleaning shrimp (1×).

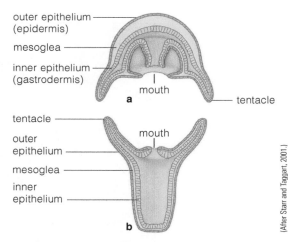

(After Starr and Taggart, 2001.)

Figure 18-17   Two body forms of Cnidarians. **(a)** medusa. **(b)** polyp.

MATERIALS

Per student:

- dissection microscope
- compound microscope
- clean microscope slide and coverslip

Per student pair:

- prepared slides of
  whole mounts of *Hydra* (showing testes, ovaries, buds, and embryos)
  cross section of *Hydra*
- whole mounts of *Obelia* (showing colonial polyps and medusa)

Per student group (4):

- small finger bowl
- scalpel or razor blade
- preserved specimen of *Gonionemus*
- prepared slides of
  a whole mount of the medusa (*ephyra*) of
    Aurelia
  a whole mount of planula larvae of *Aurelia*
  a whole mount of scyphistoma of *Aurelia*
  a whole mount of the strobila of *Aurelia*

Per lab room:

- demonstration specimens of *Physalia* and *Metridium*
- demonstration collection of corals
- boxes of different sizes of latex gloves

Per lab section:

- culture of live *Hydra*
- container of fresh stream water
- dropper bottle of glutathione
- culture of live copepods or cladocerans
- dropper bottle of vinegar

PROCEDURE

A. Class Hydrozoa: Hydrozoans

This is mostly a marine group, except for the hydras, which live in fresh water. A polyp, medusa, or both may be present in the life cycle of a hydrozoan. Marine polyps tend to be colonial.

Figure 18-18 One type of nematocyst, a capsule with an inverted thread inside. This one has a bristlelike trigger (**a**). When prey (or predators) touch the trigger, the capsule becomes more "leaky" to water. As water diffuses inward, pressure inside the capsule increases and the thread is forced to turn inside out (**b**). The thread's tip extends to penetrate the prey, releasing a toxin as it does this (**c**).

1. *Hydra* is a solitary polyp, and it does not have a medusae stage in its life cycle.
   (a) Place a live specimen of *Hydra* in a finger bowl of fresh stream water. Examine the live *Hydra* with a dissection microscope, along with prepared slides of whole mounts with the compound microscope, noting its polyp body form and other structural details (Figure 18-19).
   (b) Observe the tentacles at the oral end (Figure 18-19a). Find the elevation of the body at the base of the tentacles, in the center of which lies a mouth (Figure 18-19b). Note the swellings on the tentacles (Figure 18-19a); each is a stinging cell (*cnidocytes*) that contains a nematocyst. The clear area in the center of the body represents the gut or **gastrovascular cavity** (Figure 18-19d).
   (c) Look for evidence of sexual reproduction: one to several *testes* or an *ovary* on the body, both of which may occur on the same individual. Testes (Figure 18-19a) are conical and located more orally than the broad, flattened ovary (Figure 18-19b). You may be able to see a zygote or embryo marginally attached to or detached from the body of the *Hydra* (Figure 18-19c). Is *Hydra* monoecious or dioecious?

   _____

   (d) *Hydra* also reproduces asexually by budding (Figure 18-19d). Look for buds on your specimens.
   (e) Examine a cross section of *Hydra* (Figure 18-20) and locate the **epidermis.** The epidermis is derived from ectoderm, one of the primary germ layers. The epidermis contains *epitheliomuscular cells, interstitial cells,* and a few stinging cells. Locate the lining of the gastrovascular cavity, or **gastrodermis,** which is derived from the endoderm and composed of epitheliomuscular cells (sometimes called *nutritive muscular cells*), gland cells, and interstitial cells. Between these two layers is a thin gelatinous membrane called the **mesoglea.** In *Hydra,* the mesoglea is without cells.

The two layers of epitheliomuscular cells contract in opposite directions, although in the *Hydra* epidermis the longitudinally arranged contractile filaments are more developed than the circular filaments of the gastrodermis. How might two layers of epitheliomuscular cells function to maintain and change the body shape of a Cnidarian?

_____

_____

_____

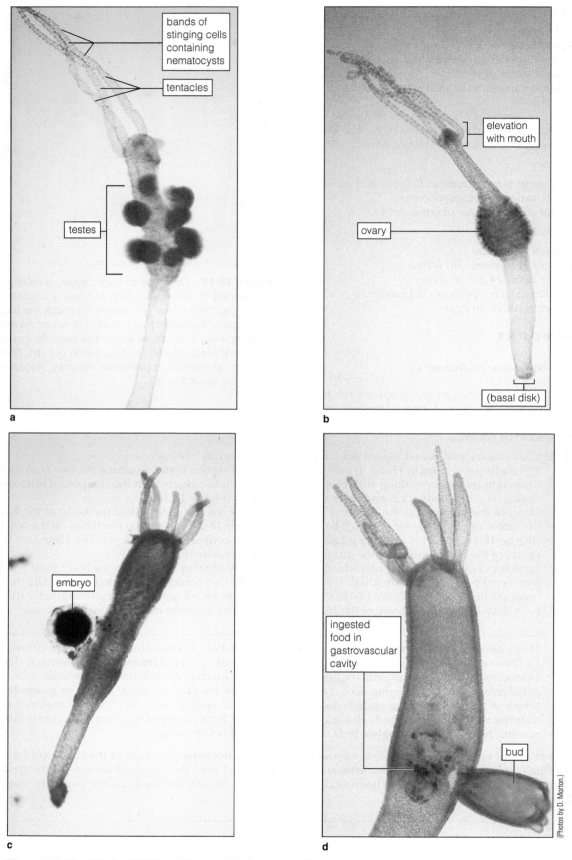

a

bands of stinging cells containing nematocysts

tentacles

testes

b

elevation with mouth

ovary

(basal disk)

c

embryo

d

ingested food in gastrovascular cavity

bud

(Photos by D. Morton.)

Figure 18-19 Whole mounts of *Hydra* with (**a**) testes, (**b**) an ovary, (**c**) an embryo, and (**d**) a bud (30×).

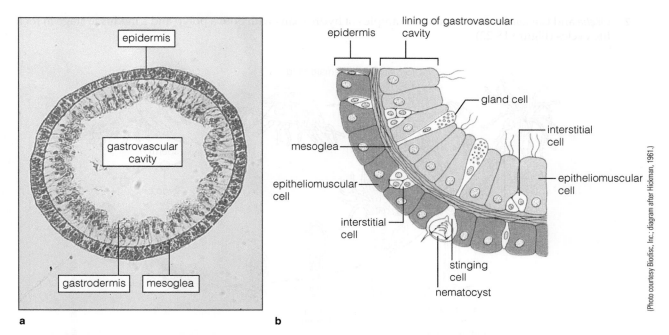

Figure 18-20 *Hydra.* (**a**) Cross section (100×). (**b**) Part of the wall.

(Photo courtesy Biodisc, Inc.; diagram after Hickman, 1961.)

What additional function can you suggest for the epithelio-muscular cells of the gastrodermis? (*Hint:* What happens to partially digested food?)

_____

_____

_____

_____

Interstitial cells can give rise to sperm, eggs, and any other type of cell in the body.

(f) If it is not already there, place the live *Hydra* in a small finger bowl to the dissection microscope. Add a drop of glutathione and a number of live copepodan or cladoceran crustaceans under the water. The glutathione stimulates the feeding response of *Hydra.* Look for feeding behavior by the *Hydra.* Note the action of the tentacles and the nematocysts. If you do not observe the discharge of nematocysts (Figure 18-21), place a drop of vinegar in the finger bowl and observe carefully. Describe what you observe.

_____

_____

_____

_____

_____

Figure 18-21 Portion of a tentacle of *Hydra* with fired and unfired nematocysts, w.m. (800×).

(Photo by D. Morton.)

(g) Are any of your *Hydra* green? If so, use a scalpel or razor blade to remove a tentacle. Make a wet mount of the tentacle, being certain to crush it with the coverslip. What do you observe with your compound microscope? Can you explain the green color of your *Hydra?*

_____

_____

_____

2. *Obelia* and *Gonionemus* are common examples of hydrozoans with both a polyp and a medusae stage in their life cycles (Figure 18-22).

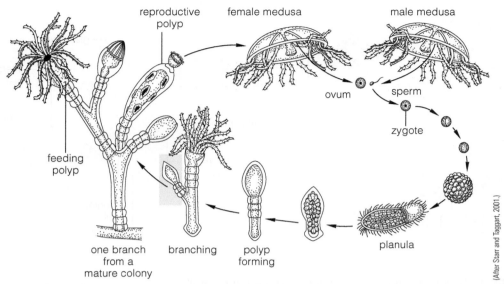

Figure 18-22 Life cycle of the marine hydrozoan *Obelia* that includes medusa and polyp stages. The medusa stage, produced asexually by a reproductive polyp, is free swimming. Fusion of gametes from male and female medusae leads to a zygote, which develops into a planula. The swimming or crawling planula develops into a polyp, which branches to start a new colony. As growth continues, new polyps are formed.

(a) With your compound microscope, examine a prepared slide of a whole mount of a colony of *Obelia* polyps (Figure 18-23a). Identify *feeding* and *reproductive polyps*. The reproductive polyps contain developing medusae.

Figure 18-23 Whole mounts of *Obelia*.
(a) Colonial polyps (15×). (b) Side view of a medusa (92×). (c) Top view of a medusa (86×).

(b) Similarly observe a whole mount of a medusa and identify the *mouth,* the umbrellalike *bell,* and *tentacles* bearing bands of stinging cells (Figures 18-23b and c).

(c) Switch to a slide of a whole mount of a *Gonionemus* medusa. Compare your preserved specimen to the live medusa seen in Figure 18-24. In addition to the structures listed in Figure 18-23c, identify the muscular *velum* and the *adhesive pads* on the tentacles. Between the bases of the tentacles are balancing organs called *statocysts.* Medusa move by "jet propulsion." Contractions of the body bring about a pulsing motion that alternately fills and empties the cavity of the bell.

3. Look at the demonstration specimen of a preserved Portuguese man-of-war (*Physalia*) (Figure 18-25).

Figure 18-24 Live hydrozoan medusa, *Gonionemus* (4×).

Figure 18-25 The Portuguese man-of-war. (**a**) Preserved specimen. (**b**) The tentacles contain several types of modified polyps and medusae.

This organism is really a colonial hydrozoan composed of several types of modified polyps and medusae. Note the conspicuous gas-filled *float*. Its sting is very painful to humans, and a possibly fatal neurotoxin is associated with the nematocysts of the tentacles.

B. Class Scyphozoa: True Jellyfish

This marine class contains the true jellyfish. The medusa is the predominant stage of the life cycle and is generally larger than hydrozoan medusae. The nematocysts in the tentacles and oral arms of jellyfish such as the sea nettle can produce painful stings. A tropical group called the sea wasps is more dangerous to humans than the hydrozoan Portuguese man-of-war. Some forms are bioluminescent, producing flashes of light by chemical reactions. Bioluminescence may lure prey toward the jellyfish or scare potential predators.

1. Look at a prepared slide of a whole mount of the medusa (ephyra) of *Aurelia* with your compound microscope (Figure 18-26). The structure of this medusa is similar to that of the hydrozoan, *Gonionemus*. However, note that the *tentacles* are short and that four *oral arms* surround the square mouth. In this case, prey is captured with the oral arms instead of the tentacles. Also, a velum is absent.

2. Examine prepared slides of planula larvae, a scyphistoma, and a strobila (Figure 18-27). Sexes are separate, and fertilization is internal. The zygote develops into a planula larva, which swims for a while before becoming a sessile polyp called a *scyphistoma*. This is an active, feeding stage, equipped with tentacles and a mouth. At certain times of the year, young medusae are produced asexually by transverse budding. This stage is called a *strobila*, and the process is called strobilization.

Figure 18-26 Scyphozoan jellyfish, *Aurelia*, w.m. (5×).

(radial canals)

(ring canal)

(sense organ)

gastrovascular cavity

(gonad)

four oral arms surrounding mouth

tentacles

(Photo courtesy Biodisc, Inc.)

C. Class Anthozoa: Corals and Sea Anemones

Class Anthozoa is a marine group in which all members are heavy-bodied polyps that feed on small fish and invertebrates. The largest organisms in this class are the anemones. Both corals (Figure 18-28) and sea anemones attach to hard surfaces or burrow in the sand or mud.

1. Examine the demonstration exoskeletons of a variety of corals (Figure 18-29).

The epidermis of each colonial coral polyp secretes an exoskeleton of calcium carbonate. After a polyp dies, another polyp uses the remaining skeleton of the dead polyp as a foundation and secretes its own skeleton. In this fashion, corals have built up various types of reefs, atolls, and islands.

2. Examine the demonstration of a preserved or living specimen of *Metridium*, the common sea anemone (Figure 18-30). Note its stout, stumplike body, with the mouth and surrounding tentacles at the oral end and the *pedal disk* at the other end. What do you think is the function of the pedal disk?

_____

_____

Some species of anemones form symbiotic relationships with certain small fishes and invertebrates that live among their tentacles. These animals receive protection from the tentacles, which for some reason do not discharge their nematocysts into the animals' bodies. In return for the protective cover of the tentacles, the anemones benefit—for example, by ingesting food particles not eaten by the predatory fish.

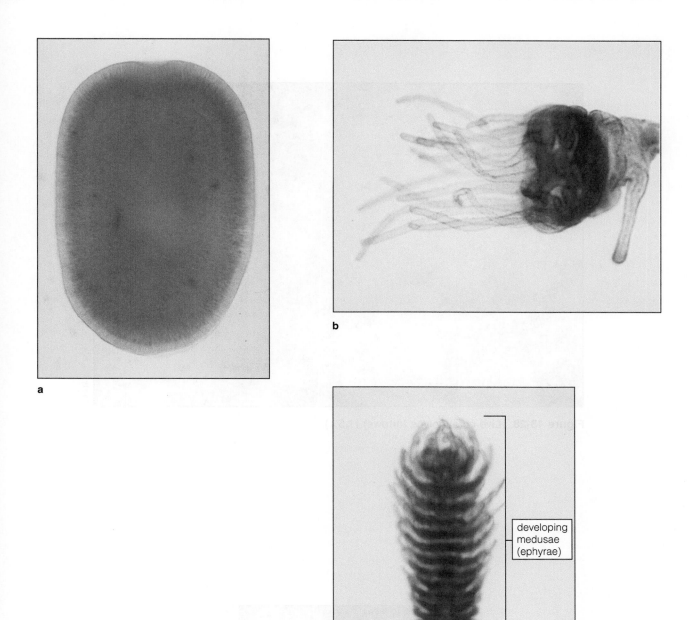

Figure 18-27 Stages in the life cycle of *Aurelia*. (**a**) Planular larvae, w.m. (400×). (**b**) Scyphistoma, w.m. (50×). (**c**) Strobilia, w.m. (30×). (Photos by D. Morton.)

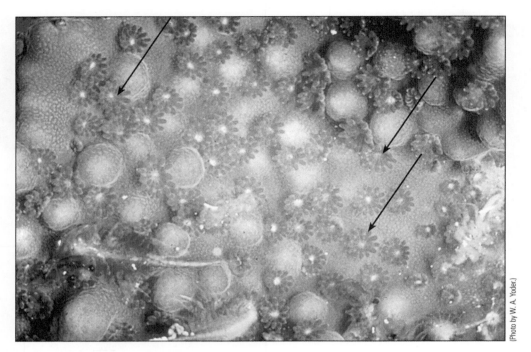

(Photo by W. A. Yoder.)

Figure 18-28   Live coral polyps (arrows) (1.5×).

(Photo by D. Morton.)

Figure 18-29   Hard coral (0.30×).

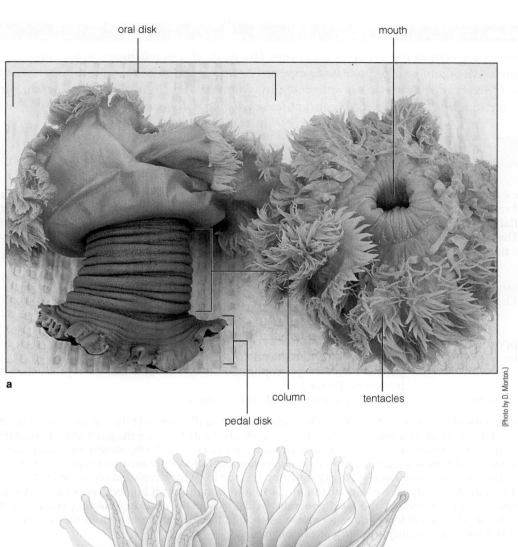

oral disk

mouth

column

pedal disk

tentacles

(Photo by D. Morton.)

a

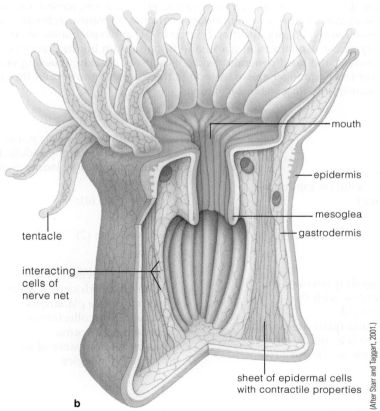

mouth

epidermis

mesoglea

gastrodermis

tentacle

interacting
cells of
nerve net

sheet of epidermal cells
with contractile properties

(After Starr and Taggart, 2001.)

b

Figure 18-30 (a) Top and side views of preserved specimens of the common sea anemone, *Metridium* (1.5×). (b) Organization of a sea anemone.

18.3   Flatworms (Phylum Platyhelminthes) *(About 75 min.)*

If you've ever turned over rocks and leaves in a clear, cool, shallow stream or roadside ditch, you may have observed representatives of phylum Platyhelminthes without realizing it. Do you recall any dark, smooth, soft-bodied, flattened or ovoid masses approximately 1 cm or less in length attached to the bottom of the rocks or leaves? This description fits that of a free-living flatworm or planarian. Parasitic flukes and tapeworms also belong to this phylum.

Habitat:	aquatic, moist terrestrial, or parasitic
Body Arrangement:	bilateral symmetry, acoelomate, head (cephalization), gut (incomplete)
Level of Organization:	organ system (tissues derived from all three primary germ layers); nervous system with brain; excretory system with flame cells; no circulatory respiratory, or skeletal systems
Body Support:	muscles
Life Cycle:	sexual reproduction (mostly monoecious with internal fertilization); parasites have very complicated life cycles; some asexual reproduction (mostly transverse fission)
Special Characteristics:	bilateral symmetry, head, organ systems

Flatworms have soft, flat, wormlike bodies with *bilateral symmetry* (Figure 18-1). This is the same type of symmetry we exhibit. Flatworms are **acoelomates** in that they lack a body cavity between the gut and body wall (Figure 18-2). The *tissues* of flatworms are *derived from all three primary germ layers:* ectoderm, mesoderm, and endoderm.

Organizationally, these animals represent an important evolutionary transition because they are the simplest forms to exhibit an organ-system level of organization (Figure 18-31) and *cephalization* (a definite head with sense organs). In an evolutionary sense, cephalization goes hand in hand with bilateral symmetry. When an animal with bilateral symmetry moves, the head generally leads, its sensors quickly detecting environmental stimuli that indicate the presence of food or danger ahead. Although there are definite organs, the *digestive system* is still of the *gastrovascular type, incomplete with a mouth and no anus.*

MATERIALS

Per student:

- dissection microscope
- compound microscope, lens paper, a bottle of lens-cleaning solution (optional), a lint-free cloth (optional)
- scalpel
- blunt probe

Per student pair:

- prepared slides of
  a whole mount of *Dugesia* (planaria)
  a whole mount of planaria with the digestive system stained
  a cross section of planaria (pharyngeal region)
  a whole mount of *Fasciola hepatica*
  a whole mount of *Clonorchis sinensis*

- whole mount(s) of *Taenia pisiformis,* with scolex and different types of proglottids
- a whole mount of a bladder worm (cysticercus) of *Taenia solium*

Per student group (4):

- penlight
- glass petri dish (2)

Per lab room:

- chunk of beef liver
- container of fresh stream water
- container of live planarians
- demonstration collection of preserved tapeworms
- boxes of different sizes of latex gloves
- box of safety goggles

PROCEDURE

A. Class Turbellaria: Planarians

Most species in this class are free-living flatworms, although a few species are parasitic or symbiotic with other organisms. Free-living flatworms are found in marine and fresh waters on the underside of submerged rocks,

Figure 18-31 Organ systems of one type of flatworm. (**a**) Digestive system, which includes a pharynx that opens to the gut. The pharynx protrudes onto food sources, and then it retracts into its own chamber between feedings. (**b**) Water-regulating system, (**c**) nervous system, and (**d**) reproductive system. (After Starr, 2000.)

leaves, and sticks. They are especially abundant in cool freshwater streams and along the ocean shoreline. Some live in wet or moist terrestrial habitats.

Free-living freshwater planarians of the genus *Dugesia* are the representatives of this class typically studied in biology courses. They are relatively small flatworms, usually 2 cm or less in length. Planarians are monoecious—an individual has both male and female reproductive structures—but apparently do not self-fertilize. Individuals possess testes, ovaries, a penis, and a vagina; and copulation occurs. Planarians exhibit a high degree of **regeneration,** in which lost body parts are gradually replaced.

1. Microscopically examine a whole mount of a planarian. Refer to Figure 18-32 and locate the **head, eyespots,** and **auricles,** lateral projections of the head that are organs sensitive to touch and to molecules dissolved in the water. The **eyespots** are photoreceptors. They are sensitive to light but do not form images.

2. Obtain and similarly examine a whole mount of a planarian with an injected digestive system. Identify the muscular **pharynx** within the **pharyngeal pouch.** The *mouth* is located at the free end of the pharynx. The mouth opens into the pharyngeal cavity, which in turn is continuous with the cavity of the **intestine.** To feed, a free planarian protrudes the pharynx from its ventral (belly) side and sucks up organic morsels (insect larvae, small crustaceans, and other small living and dead animals). The intestine is elaborately branched and occupies much of the animal's body. What function does the extensive branching of the intestine facilitate?

_____

_____

_____

_____

_____

_____

3. To observe feeding behavior, place a small piece of beef liver in a clean glass petri dish containing fresh stream water and add several live planarians. Describe what you see with a dissection microscope.

_____

_____

_____

_____

_____

You may observe the elimination of waste from the gastrovascular cavity. If you do, describe what you see; if not, state the route by which this must occur.

_____

_____

_____

Set the dish aside and examine it later, especially if you did not observe feeding behavior.

4. Examine a cross section through the pharynx of a planarian with your compound microscope (Figure 18-33). Find the following structures: *pharynx, pharyngeal pouch,* **nerve cords, epidermis, portions of the intestine,** and the several layers of muscles in the body wall. Note that the bottom epidermis is lined by **cilia.** What is the function of these cilia?

_____

_____

_____

Much of the rest of the body wall contains three layers of muscle: an outer circular layer, a middle diagonal layer, and an inner longitudinal layer. It is often difficult to distinguish all three layers.

5. Working in groups of four, use a dissection microscope to observe a living planarian in a clean glass petri dish filled with fresh stream water. Note its general size and shape. Touch the animal with a probe. What is its reaction? How does its shape change? Which muscle layers likely contract to produce this shape change?

_____

_____

_____

_____

_____

_____

Figure 18-32 Whole mount of planaria, with injected digestive system (45×).

B. Class Trematoda: Flukes

Flukes are small, leaf-shaped, parasitic flatworms with complex life cycles. They are generally internal parasites of vertebrates, including humans. A protoplasmic but noncellular cuticle covers the surface of their bodies. What is a likely explanation for the presence of this tough, resistant cuticle?

_____

_____

_____

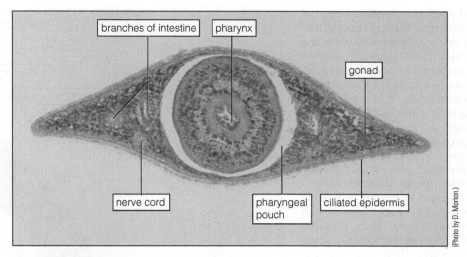

Figure 18-33 Cross section of planaria (150×).

1. Examine a whole mount of a sheep liver fluke, *Fasciola hepatica*, noting its general morphology. Identify the structures indicated in Figure 18-34.
2. Examine a whole mount of an adult *Clonorchis sinensis*, a human liver fluke. This animal is a common parasite in Asia, and humans are the final **host.** Identify the structures indicated in Figure 18-35. *Clonorchis* has two suckers for attachment to its host: an **oral sucker** surrounding the mouth and a **ventral sucker.** The digestive tract begins with the **mouth** and continues with a muscular **pharynx,** a short **esophagus,** and two blind pouches or **intestinal ceca.** Nitrogenous wastes are excreted at the tip of the back end through the **excretory pore.**

Clonorchis is monoecious. Find the following female reproductive structures: **ovary, yolk glands, seminal receptacle,** and **uterus.** Find the following male reproductive structures: **testes** and **seminal vesicle,** which may be visible in your specimen. During copulation, sperm is conveyed from the testes to the *genital pore* by paired vasa efferentia, which fuse to form the vas deferens. These ducts are difficult to see in most specimens. Copulating individuals exchange sperm at the genital pore, and the sperm is stored temporarily in the seminal receptacle. The yolk glands provide yolk for nourishment of the developing eggs. *Eggs* can be seen as black dots in the uterus, where they mature.

The life cycle of *Clonorchis sinensis* (Figure 18-36) involves two **intermediate hosts,** a snail and the golden carp. Intermediate hosts harbor sexually immature stages of a parasite.

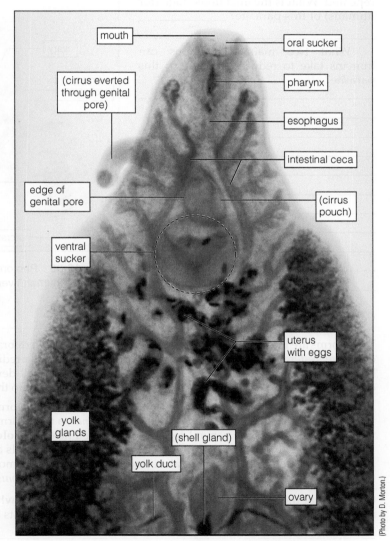

Figure 18-34 Anterior portion of *Fasciola hepatica*, the sheep liver fluke, w.m. (20×).

Fertilized eggs are expelled from the adult fluke into the human host's bile duct and are eventually voided with the feces of the host. If the eggs are shed in the appropriate moist or aquatic environment, they may be ingested by snails (the first intermediate host). A larva emerges from the egg inside the snail. The larva passes through several developmental stages and gives rise to a number of tadpolelike larvae. These free-swimming larvae leave the snail, encounter a golden carp (the second intermediate host), and burrow into this fish to encyst in muscle tissue. If raw or improperly cooked fish is eaten by humans, cats, dogs, or some other mammal, the larvae emerge from the cysts and make their way up the host's bile duct into the liver, where they mature into adult flukes. The cycle is then repeated. What is the infectious stage (for humans) of this parasite? _____

What two main precautions can humans take to reduce exposure to this parasite?

_____
_____
_____
_____
_____
_____
_____
_____
_____
_____
_____
_____

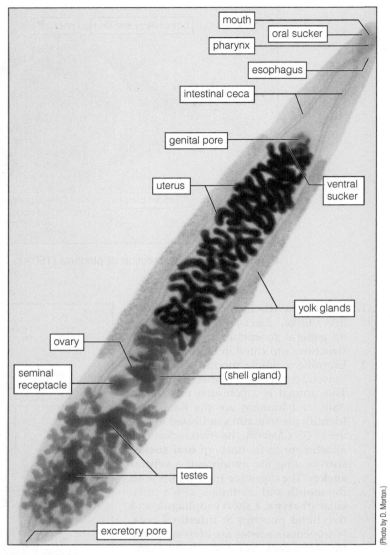

Figure 18-35 Photomicrograph of a whole mount of *Clonorchis sinensis*, a human liver fluke (20×).

C. Class Cestoda: Tapeworms

Tapeworms are internal parasites that inhabit the intestine of vertebrates. Their flattened, multiunit bodies have no digestive system; instead, they absorb across their body walls predigested nutrients provided by the host. Their bodies are essentially reproductive machines, with extensive, well-developed reproductive organs occupying much of each mature body unit. A thick cuticle, similar in construction to that found in trematodes, covers the body.

1. Look over the demonstration collection of preserved tapeworms taken from a variety of vertebrate hosts.
2. Examine a preserved specimen of *Taenia pisiformis*, a tapeworm of dogs and cats (Figure 18-37). Note that it is divided into three general regions: specialized head or **scolex,** *neck,* and **body.** The body is composed of successive units, the **proglottids.** New immature proglottids are added at the neck. As they move farther from the scolex, proglottids mature and, therefore, the hindmost gravid proglottids are the oldest.
3. Look at a prepared slide of a whole mount of a *Taenia pisiformis* scolex (Figure 18-38).

Observe that the scolex is covered with hooks and suckers. For what task does the tapeworm use these **hooks** and **suckers**? Note the **neck** and the new proglottids forming at its base.

_____
_____
_____

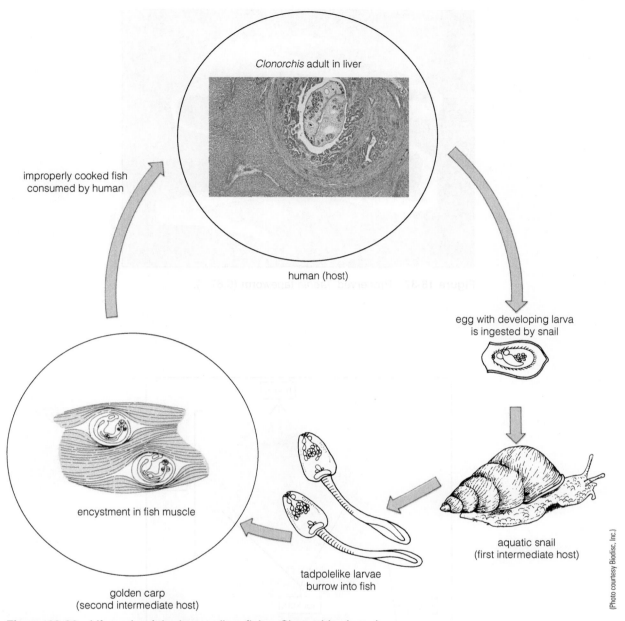

Figure 18-36 Life cycle of the human liver fluke, *Clonorchis sinensis*.

4. Find a whole mount of mature proglottids of *Taenia pisiformis* and examine them with a dissection microscope. Identify the structures indicated in Figure 18-39. The lateral **genital pore** opens into the **vagina** and receives sperm from the **vas deferens.** The *uterus* is usually visible as a line running top to bottom in the middle of the proglottid. The *ovaries* are represented by dark, diffuse masses of tissue lateral to the uterus at the vaginal end of the proglottid. The **testes** are paler, more diffuse masses of tissue lateral to the uterus at the other end. Tapeworms are monoecious. They are one of the few animals that can self-fertilize, perhaps a result of their isolation from each other. Flanking most of the reproductive organs are the **excretory canals.**

5. Locate a gravid proglottid of *Taenia pisiformis* (Figure 18-40). Gravid proglottids are almost completely filled with zygotes in an expanded uterus ready for release as eggs.

6. The life cycle of the pork tapeworm, *Taenia solium,* involves two host organisms, the pig and a human (Figure 18-41).

Figure 18-37 Preserved *Taenia* tapeworm (0.67×).

(Photo by D. Morton.)

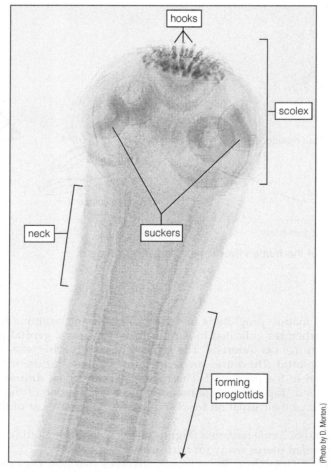

hooks

scolex

neck

suckers

forming proglottids

(Photo by D. Morton.)

Figure 18-38 Tapeworm scolex (*Taenia pisiformis*), w.m. (40×).

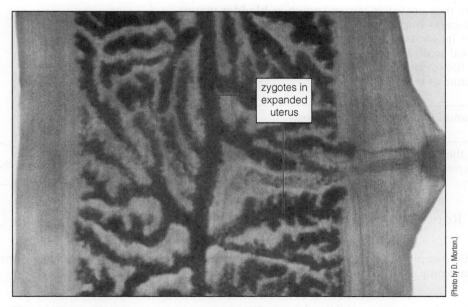

Figure 18-39 Tapeworm mature proglottids (*Taenia pisiformis*). (**a**) Whole mount (30×). (**b**) Diagram.

Figure 18-40 Tapeworm gravid proglottid (*Taenia pisiformis*), w.m. (30×).

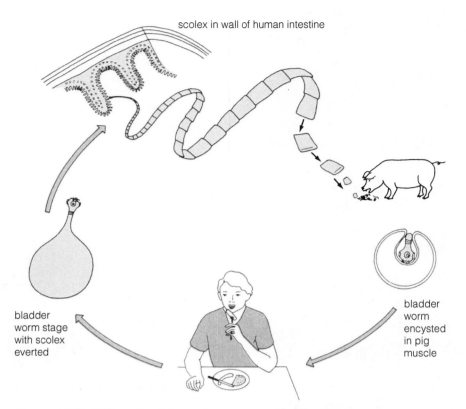

scolex in wall of human intestine

bladder
worm stage
with scolex
everted

bladder
worm
encysted
in pig
muscle

Figure 18-41   Life cycle of the pork tapeworm, *Taenia solium.*

Gravid proglottids containing embryos are voided with the feces of a human. If a pig ingests a proglottid, the embryos escape from the proglottid and bore into the intestinal wall and enter a blood or lymphatic vessel. From there they make their way to muscle, where they encyst as larvae known as **bladder worms.** If a human ingests improperly cooked pork, a bladder worm "pops" out of its encasement (bladder) and attaches its scolex to the intestinal wall. Here it matures and adds proglottids to complete the life cycle.

Which mammal is the host?

_____

Which mammal is the intermediate host?

_____

Examine the bladder worm stage of *Taenia solium* with the dissection microscope. Draw what you see in Figure 18-42.

Figure 18-42   Drawing of the bladder worm of *Taenia solium* (_____×).

| 18.4 | **Rotifers (Phylum Rotifera)** *(About 10 min.)* |

Rotifers are microscopic, the smallest animals. They are mostly bottom-dwelling, freshwater forms, and they are an important prey of larger animals in aquatic food chains.

Habitat: aquatic or moist terrestrial, mostly fresh water
Body Arrangement: bilateral symmetry,
                                                          pseudocoelomate, head,
                                                          gut (complete)

Level of Organization:	organ system (tissues derived from all three primary germ layers); nervous system with brain; excretory system with flame cells; no circulatory, respiratory, or skeletal systems
Body Support:	hydrostatic (pseudocoelom)
Life Cycle:	sexual (dioecious with internal fertilization), some parthenogenesis, males much smaller than females or absent
Special Characteristics:	microscopic animals, wheel organ, mastax

Rotifers are easily found in rain gutters and spouts, and in the slimy material around the bases of buildings. Their thin, usually transparent body wall is covered by a cuticle composed of protein. Also like the nematodes to be studied later, rotifers are pseudocoelomates. Rotifers are dioecious; however, many species have no males, and the eggs develop parthenogenetically.

MATERIALS

Per student:

- clean microscope slide and coverslip
- compound microscope

Per lab room:

- live culture of rotifers
- disposable transfer pipet

PROCEDURE

1. With a disposable transfer pipet, place drop from the rotifer culture on clean slide and make a wet mount.
2. Observe the microscopic rotifers with the compound microscope. The elongate, cylindrical body is divisible into the **trunk** and the **foot** (Figure 18-43).

The foot bears two to several "sticky" *toes* for adhering to objects. The upper end of the trunk bears a **corona** of cilia. These cilia beat in such a fashion as to give the appearance of a wheel (or two) turning, hence the common references to this structure as the wheel organ

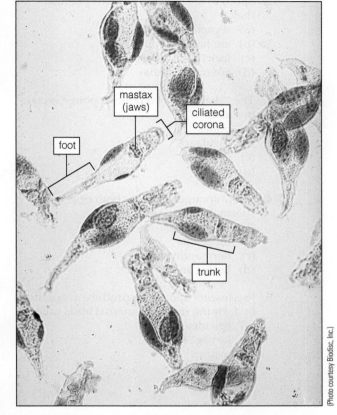

Figure 18-43 Prepared whole mount of rotifers (130×).

(Photo courtesy Biodisc, Inc.)

and to these animals as wheel animals. The cilia create currents that sweep organic food particles into the mouth at the center of the wheel organ. The cilia also enable the organism to move. Inside the trunk, below the wheel organ, look for the movement of a grinding organ, the **mastax.** This structure is equipped with jaws made hard by a substance called chitin. Considering its location, what is the likely function of the mastax?

_____

_____

_____

_____ 1. Which of the following is characteristic of animals?
(a) heterotrophy
(b) autotrophy
(c) photosynthesis
(d) both b and c

_____ 2. Sponges are atypical animals because they
(a) reproduce sexually
(b) are heterotrophic
(c) lack definite tissues
(d) are multicellular

_____ 3. The "skeleton" of a typical sponge is composed of
(a) bones
(b) cartilages
(c) spicules
(d) scales

_____ 4. Many sponges produce both eggs and sperm and thus are
(a) monoecious
(b) dioecious
(c) hermaphroditic
(d) both a and c

_____ 5. Freshwater sponges reproduce asexually by forming resistant internal buds called
(a) spicules
(b) larvae
(c) ovaries
(d) gemmules

_____ 6. Cnidarians evolved from an ancestral group of
(a) sponges
(b) protists
(c) fungi
(d) plants

_____ 7. A free-swimming jellyfish has a body form known as a
(a) polyp
(b) strobila
(c) medusa
(d) hydra

_____ 8. Cnidarians capture their prey with the use of
(a) poison claws
(b) nematocysts
(c) oral teeth
(d) pedal disks

_____ 9. Which statement is true for scyphozoan medusae?
(a) They are the dominant body form
(b) They are generally smaller than hydrozoan medusae
(c) Most live in fresh water
(d) They are scavengers

_____ 10. Coral reefs, atolls, and islands are the result of the buildup of coral
(a) polyps
(b) medusae
(c) exoskeletons
(d) wastes

_____ 11. Cephalization is
   (a) the division of the trunk into a scolex, neck, and body
   (b) the presence of a head with sense organs
   (c) sexual reproduction involving self-fertilization
   (d) the ability to replace lost body parts

_____ 12. Flatworms
   (a) are radially symmetrical
   (b) possess a body cavity
   (c) reproduce by parthenogenesis
   (d) have tissues derived from all three primary germ layers

_____ 13. Free-living flatworms (planaria) move by using
   (a) cilia
   (b) flagella
   (c) pseudopodia
   (d) a muscular foot

_____ 14. The flukes and tapeworms are covered by a protective
   (a) cuticle
   (b) shell
   (c) scales
   (d) slime layer

_____ 15. The life cycle of the human liver fluke has _____ intermediate hosts.
   (a) one
   (b) two
   (c) three
   (d) four

_____ 16. Tapeworms do not have a
   (a) reproductive system
   (b) head
   (c) excretory system
   (d) digestive system

_____ 17. The oldest proglottid of a tapeworm is
   (a) the scolex
   (b) the one nearest its neck
   (c) the one in its middle
   (d) the one at its end

_____ 18. Bladder worms are found in
   (a) proglottids in human feces
   (b) proglottids in the human intestine
   (c) improperly cooked pork
   (d) none of the above

_____ 19. Nematodes and rotifers have a body cavity that is
   (a) called a coelom
   (b) called a pseudocoelom
   (c) completely lined by tissues derived from mesoderm
   (d) both a and c

_____ 20. Rotifers obtain their food by the action of
   (a) tentacles
   (b) cilia on the wheel organ
   (c) a muscular pharynx
   (d) pseudopodia

EXERCISE 18

Sponges, Cnidarians, Flatworms, and Rotifers

POST-LAB QUESTIONS

Introduction

1. List six characteristics of the animal kingdom.

2. Define *asymmetry* and *radial symmetry*.

3. Identify the symmetry (asymmetry, radial symmetry, or bilateral symmetry) of the following objects.
   a. fork
   b. jagged piece of rock
   c. rubber ball

18.1 Sponges (Phylum Porifera)

4. Define *cell specialization* and indicate how sponges exhibit this phenomenon.

5. Describe three ways that sponges reproduce.

6. Identify this photo; it is magnified 186×.

_____

(Photo by D. Morton)

18.2 Cnidarians (Phylum Cnidaria)

7. Define the tissue level of organization and indicate how cnidarians exhibit this phenomenon.

8. Name and draw the two body forms of cnidarians.

9. Describe the means by which the cnidarians seize and eat faster organisms.

Food for Thought

10. What adaptations of sponges and cnidarians have helped them to endure for so long on earth?

18.3 Flatworms (Phylum Platyhelminthes)

11. How is bilateral symmetry different from radial symmetry?

12. List the characteristics of flatworms.

13. Distinguish between a host and an intermediate host.

14. Identify and label this illustration. It is magnified 9×.

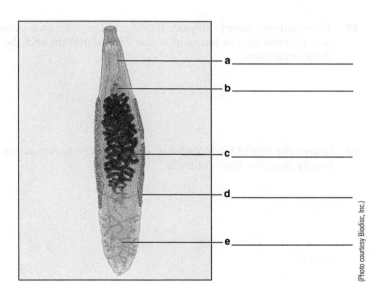

a _____

b _____

c _____

d _____

e _____

(Photo courtesy Biodisc, Inc.)

15. Describe several adaptations of parasitic flatworms to their external environment.

18.4 Rotifers (Phylum Rotifera)

16. *Pseudocoel* means "false body cavity." Why is this term applied to the body cavity of rotifers?

Food for Thought

17. Contrast the digestive systems of free-living and parasitic flatworms.

18. Explain the relationship between the tremendous numbers of eggs produced by flukes and tapeworms and the complexity of their life cycles.

19. The relatively simple animals *Hydra* and *Dugesia* can regenerate lost body parts, but humans generally cannot. Discuss this in terms of tissue differentiation and the comparative levels of structural complexity of these organisms.

20. Search the World Wide Web for sites that include references to flatworms or rotifers. List two addresses and briefly describe their contents.

    http://

    http://

Segmented Worms, Mollusks, Roundworms, and Joint-Legged Animals

OBJECTIVES

After completing this exercise, you will be able to

1. define *coelom, coelomate, protostome, deuterostome, segmentation, peritoneum, setae, clitellum, cocoon, foot, mantle, pseudocoelomate, cloaca, bladder worm exoskeleton, hemolymph, chitin, carapace, sexual dimorphism, gills*, and *tracheae*;

2. differentiate between protostomes and deuterostomes;

3. describe the natural history of members of the phyla Annelida and Mollusca;

4. identify representatives of the classes Oligochaeta, Polychaeta, and Hirudinea of the phylum Annelida;

5. outline the life cycle of an earthworm;

6. identify representatives of the classes Bivalvia, Gastropoda, and Cephalopoda of the phylum Mollusca;

7. outline the life cycle of a freshwater clam;

8. identify structures (and indicate their associate functions) of the representatives of these phyla classes;

9. explain the term *ecdysis*;

10. identify representatives of the phylum Nematoda;

11. identify representatives of the subphyla Crustacea, Hexapoda, Myriapoda, and Chelicerata of the phylum Arthropoda;

12. identify structures (and indicate their associated functions) of the representatives of these phyla and classes.

INTRODUCTION

Some time after the origin of bilateral symmetry, the animals that subsequently evolved developed a true ventral body cavity or **coelom**. A true body cavity is lined by tissue derived entirely from mesoderm. The appearance of the coelom has great evolutionary significance, for it accommodates, cushions, and protects organs; allows an increase in overall body size and flexibility; and contributes to the development of systems primarily derived from mesoderm.

  Coelomates, animals possessing a coelom, took two divergent evolutionary paths based on whether the *blastopore*—the first opening in a developing embryo—became the mouth (**protostomes**) or anus (**deuterostomes**) (Table 19-1). During subsequent evolutionary change, the coelom was reduced (mollusks and joint legged animals), lost (flatworms), or modified to a pseudocoel (rotifers and roundworms).

TABLE 19-1   Evolution of Coelomates

Path	Blastopore Becomes	Phyla
Protostomes	Mouth	Mollusca, Annelida, and Arthropoda
Deuterostomes	Anus	Echinodermata, Hemichordata, and Chordata

19.1   Annelids (Phylum Annelida) *(45 min.)*

Habitat:	aquatic or moist terrestrial, some parasitic
Body Arrangement:	bilateral symmetry, coelomate, head, body segmented, gut (complete)
Level of Organization:	organ system (tissues derived from all three primary germ layers), nervous system with brain, circulatory system (closed), excretory system (nephridia), respiratory system (gills in some), no skeletal system
Body Support:	hydrostatic (coelom)
Life Cycle:	sexual reproduction (monoecious or dioecious with mostly internal fertilization), larvae in some, asexual reproduction (mostly transverse fission)
Special Characteristics:	segmented, closed circulatory system

The most striking annelid characteristic is the division of the cylindrical trunk into a series of similar segments. *Annelids* were the first animals to evolve the condition of **segmentation.** Segmentation is internal as well as external, with segmentally arranged components of various organ systems and the body cavity. The coelom is more or less divided by *septa* into compartments within each segment, each lined by **peritoneum.** Unlike the proglottids of the cestodes, segments cannot function independently of each other. The *circulatory system* is *closed*, with the blood entirely contained in vessels. There is a well-developed *nervous system* with a central nervous system composed of two fused dorsal ganglia (brain) and ventral nerve cords. The circulatory system is not segmented. Segmentation is significant in evolutionary history because each segment or group of segments can become specialized. Although this is an important characteristic of most of the phyla we have yet to study, it is barely evident in the earthworm.

MATERIALS

Per student:

- pins
- blunt probe or dissecting needle

Per student pair:

- preserved earthworm
- dissection microscope
- dissection pan
- fine dissecting scissors
- *Eisenia foetida* cocoons

Per lab room:

- labeled demonstration dissection of the internal anatomy of the earthworm (optional)
- demonstration collection of living and preserved polychaetes living earthworms
- several preserved leeches
- live freshwater leeches in an aquarium
- large plastic bag for disposal of dissected specimens
- boxes of different sizes of latex gloves

A. Oligochaetes (Class Oligochaeta)

PROCEDURE

1. Refer to Figure 19-1 as you examine the living earthworms on demonstration in the lab. You probably already know several characteristics of oligochaetes because of past observations with the earthworm (*Lumbricus terrestris*), especially if you fish. Recalling past experiences with this organism, list as many features of the earthworm as you can.

   _____

   _____

   _____

   _____

2. Let's see how you did! Obtain a preserved earthworm and have a dissection microscope handy. Is its body bilaterally or radially symmetrical? _____

3. Examine the external anatomy (Figure 19-2). Note the segments.
   Count them and record the number: _____

   (a) Very few segments are added after hatching. Note the **prostomium,** a fleshy lobe that hangs over the **mouth;** both structures are part of the first segment.

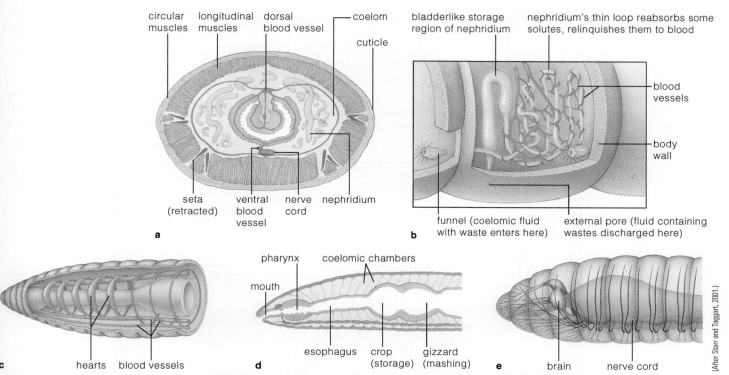

circular muscles · longitudinal muscles · dorsal blood vessel · coelom · cuticle

seta (retracted) · ventral blood vessel · nerve cord · nephridium

a

bladderlike storage region of nephridium · nephridium's thin loop reabsorbs some solutes, relinquishes them to blood

blood vessels · body wall

funnel (coelomic fluid with waste enters here) · external pore (fluid containing wastes discharged here)

b

pharynx · coelomic chambers · mouth · esophagus · crop (storage) · gizzard (mashing)

hearts · blood vessels

brain · nerve cord

(After Starr and Taggart, 2001.)

c · **d** · **e**

Figure 19-1 Earthworm body plan. (**a**) Midbody, transverse section. (**b**) A nephridium, one of many functional units that help maintain the volume and the composition of body fluids. (**c**) Portion of the closed circulatory system. The system is linked in its functioning with nephridia. (**d**) Part of the digestive system, near the worm's head end. (**e**) Part of the nervous system.

(b) Look for **setae,** tiny bristlelike structures on the ventral surface, with the dissection microscope. Take the specimen between your fingers and feel for them. What is their likely function?

_____

_____

_____

_____

(c) Use the dissection microscope to help you find the following. A pair of small **excretory pores** is found on the lateral or ventral surfaces of each segment, except the first few and the last. On the sides of segment 14, the openings (*female pores*) of the oviducts can be seen. The openings (*male pores*) of the sperm ducts, with their swollen lips, can be found on segment 15. The **clitellum** is the enlarged ring beginning at segment 31 or 32 and ending with 37. This glandular structure secretes a slimy band around two copulating individuals. The **anus** is the vertical slit in the terminal segment.

4. *Dissection of earthworm internal anatomy.*
   (a) Place your worm in a dissection pan and stick a pin through each end of the specimen. With fine scissors, make an incision just to the right of the dorsal black line (blood vessel), 10 segments anterior to the anus, and cut superficially to the mouth. (You can use the prostomium as an indicator of the dorsal side of the animal if the black line cannot be seen.) Gently pull the incision apart and note that the coelom is divided into a series of compartments by septa. Carefully cut the septa free of the body wall with a scalpel and pin both sides to the pan at 5- to 10-segment intervals. Cover the specimen with about 0.5–1.0 cm of tap water and examine the internal anatomy (Figure 19-3).
   (b) Use your blunt probe or dissection needle to find the male reproductive organs, the light-colored **seminal vesicles.** These can be found in segments 9–12. They are composed of three sacs, within which are the *testes.* A sperm duct leads from the *seminal* vesicles to the male pore.
   (c) Find two pairs of female reproductive organs—the white, spherical **seminal receptacles** in segments 9 and 10. There are ovaries in segment 13. An oviduct runs from each ovary to the female pore.
   (d) Locate the organs of the digestive tract. The *buccal cavity* occupies the first three segments. The muscular **pharynx** is the swelling in the digestive tract just behind the mouth. This organ is responsible for sucking soil particles containing food into the mouth. The *esophagus* extends from the pharynx through

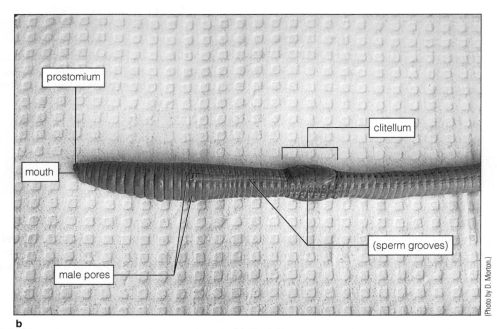

Figure 19-2 (**a**) External anatomy of the earthworm (numbers refer to the segment numbers). (**b**) External view of preserved earthworm.

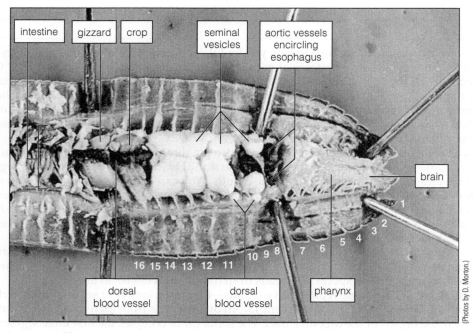

Figure 19-3 Dissection of the anterior end of an earthworm. The first 16 segments are numbered.

segment 14. The *crop* is a large, thin-walled sac in segments 15 and 16 that serves as a temporary storage organ for food. The **gizzard,** a grinding organ, is posterior to the crop. The **intestine,** the site of digestion and absorption, extends from the gizzard to the anus.

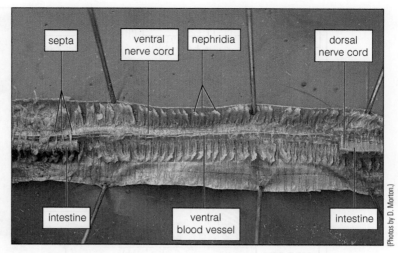

Figure 19-4 Dissection of the posterior end of an earthworm. The intestine has been partially removed to expose the ventral nerve cord.

(e)   Trace the parts of the circulatory system. The **dorsal blood vessel** runs along the dorsal side of the digestive tract and contains blood that flows toward the head. Five pairs of **aortic vessels** ("hearts") encircle the esophagus in segments 7–11, connecting the dorsal blood vessel with the **ventral blood vessel** (Figure 19-4). The ventral vessel runs along the ventral side of the digestive tract, carrying blood backward. The primary pumps of the circulatory system are the dorsal and ventral vessels. The dorsal vessel contains valves to prevent blood from flowing backward.

(f)   Find the two-lobed **brain** (cerebral ganglia) on the anterior, dorsal surface of the pharynx in segment 3. The **ventral nerve cord** arises from the brain and extends along the floor of the body cavity to the last segment. Although they are difficult to locate, paired lateral nerves branch from the segmental ganglia along the nerve cord.

(g)   Locate a pair of **nephridia**—coiled white tubes—at the base of every segment but the first three and last one. These structures constitute the "kidneys" of the earthworm (Figure 19-4).

(h)   Dispose of your dissected specimen in the large plastic bag provided for this purpose.

5.   Use a dissection microscope to examine cocoons from *Eisenia foetida,* another species of earthworm. Identify eggs and embryos.

The earthworm is monoecious—individuals have both male and female reproductive tracts. Copulation in earthworms usually takes 2–3 hours. Individuals face belly to belly in opposite directions and come together at their clitellums. These organs secrete a slimy substance that forms a band around the worms. Sperm are transferred between the participants, and the sperm are stored temporarily in the seminal receptacles. A few days after the individuals separate, each worm secretes a **cocoon.** The cocoon receives eggs and stored sperm from the seminal receptacles. The eggs are fertilized, and the cocoon moves forward as the worm backs out. The cocoon then slips off the front end of the worm and is deposited in the soil. In *Lumbricus terrestris,* a single young earthworm completes development using the other fertilized eggs as food, eventually breaks free of the cocoon, and becomes an adult in several weeks. As long as the stored sperm lasts, the earthworm continues to form cocoons.

6.   Use your dissection microscope to examine a prepared slide of a cross section of the earthworm (Figure 19-5). First look at the body wall. A thin **cuticle** covers the body. The **epidermis,** which lies beneath it, secretes the cuticle, and internal to this are an **outer circular layer** and an **inner longitudinal layer** of muscle. Identify the other labeled structures in Figure 19-5.

B. Polychaetes (Class Polychaeta)

The polychaetes are abundant marine annelids with dorsoventrally flattened bodies. They are most common at shallow depths in the intertidal zone at the seashore and are prey for a variety of marine invertebrates.

Examine the polychaetes on demonstration in the lab. Although they resemble oligochaetes in many ways, notice that the polychaetes have fleshy, segmental outgrowths called **parapodia** (Figure 19-6). These structures are equipped with numerous setae, the characteristic for which they get their class name, *Polychaeta,* meaning "many bristles." Notice also the relatively complex **head.**

C. Leeches (Class Hirudinea)

The leeches are dorsoventrally flattened annelids that are usually found in fresh water.

1.   Examine the preserved specimens of leeches (Figure 19-7). They lack parapodia and setae. They are predaceous or parasitic; parasitic species suck blood with the aid of a muscular pharynx. The segments

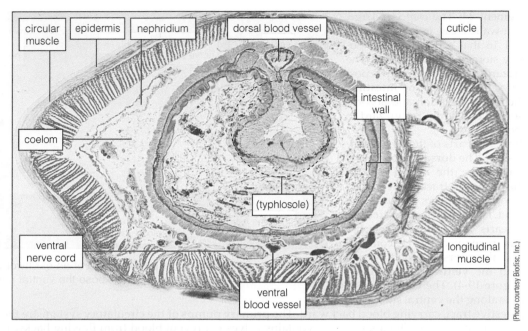

Figure 19-5 Cross section of an earthworm (20×).

(Photo courtesy Biodisc, Inc.)

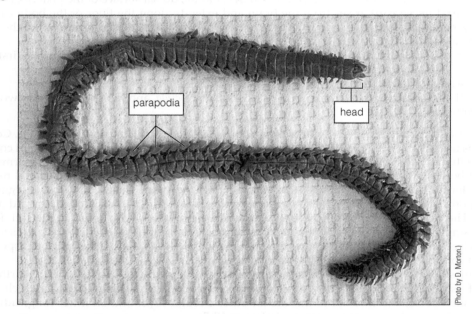

Figure 19-6 External anatomy of the clamworm, *Neanthes.*

(Photo by D. Morton.)

Figure 19-7 A leech (class Hirudinea).

(Photo by D. Morton.)

surrounding the mouth are modified into a small **anterior sucker.** The mouth is supplied with jaws, made hard with the substance chitin, used to wound the host and supply the leech with blood. Parasitic leeches secrete an anticoagulant into the wound to prevent the blood from clotting. A **posterior sucker** helps the leech attach to the host or prey.

2. Observe the movement of living freshwater leeches as they swim through the water in an aquarium. Explain their movements in terms of the contraction and relaxation of circular and longitudinal layers of muscle that comprise part of their body wall.

_____

_____

_____

_____

19.2   Mollusks (Phylum Mollusca) *(45 min.)*

Habitat:	aquatic or terrestrial, mostly marine
Body Arrangement:	head and unique body plan, gut (complete)
Level of Organization:	organ system (tissues derived from all three primary germ layers), nervous system with brain, excretory system (nephridium or nephridia), circulatory system (open), respiratory system (most have gills or lungs), no skeletal system
Body Support:	shells, floats (aquatic)
Life Cycle:	sexual (monoecious or dioecious with external or internal fertilization), larvae in some
Special Characteristics:	coelomate; open circulatory system; respiratory system; external body divided into head, mantle, and foot

This is the second largest animal phylum and includes snails and nudibranchs, slugs, bivalves—clams, mussels, and oysters, octopuses, cuttlefish, and squids. Bodies are typically soft (*molluscus* in Latin means "soft") and often covered by protective shells. Apart from the squids and some octopuses (and the land snails and slugs, which have adopted a terrestrial existence), *mollusks inhabit shallow marine and fresh waters,* where they crawl along or burrow into the soft substrate. Many species are valued foods for humans.

Two characteristics distinguish the mollusks from other animals. They possess a ventral, muscular **foot** for movement and a dorsal integument, the **mantle,** which in different groups of mollusks secretes shells, functions in gaseous exchange, and facilitates movement. Even forms without shells usually have mantles.

MATERIALS

Per student:

- scalpel
- blunt probe or dissecting needle
- compound microscope, lens paper, a bottle of lens-cleaning solution (optional), a lint-free cloth (optional)

Per student pair:

- preserved freshwater clam
- dissection pan
- prepared slide of a cross section of clam gill
- dissection microscope
- glass petri dish
- prepared slide of glochidia

Per lab room:

- labeled demonstration dissection of a freshwater clam (optional) the internal anatomy of a squid
- demonstration collection of bivalve shells, and living and preserved specimens
- freshwater aquarium with snails (for example, *Physa*)
- demonstration collection of gastropod shells, and living and preserved specimens
- several preserved squids, octopuses, and chambered nautiluses
- large plastic bag for disposal of dissected specimens
- boxes of different sizes of latex gloves
- box of safety goggles

A. Bivalves (Class Bivalvia)

Bivalves are so named because they have shells composed of *two* halves or *valves*. Included in this class are the clams, mussels, oysters, and scallops. They have a hatchet-shaped (laterally flattened) body and a foot used for burrowing in soft substrates.

1. *External features of the freshwater clam.*
   (a) Obtain and examine a freshwater clam in a dissection pan (Figure 19-8). Each **valve** has a hump on the dorsal surface (back), the **umbo,** which points toward the front of the organism. The umbo is the oldest part of the valve.
   (b) Encircling the umbo are concentric rings of annual growth; the raised portions (*growth ridges*) represent periods of restricted winter growth. Determine the age of your clam by counting the number of ridges formed by the growth rings. Age of clam: _____

2. *Dissection of the freshwater clam.*
   (a) Remove the left valve by cutting the *anterior* and *posterior adductor muscles* that hold the valves together. To do this, first identify the anterior adductor muscle in Figure 19-9 and then

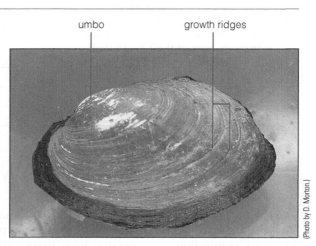

Figure 19-8 External view of a freshwater clam.

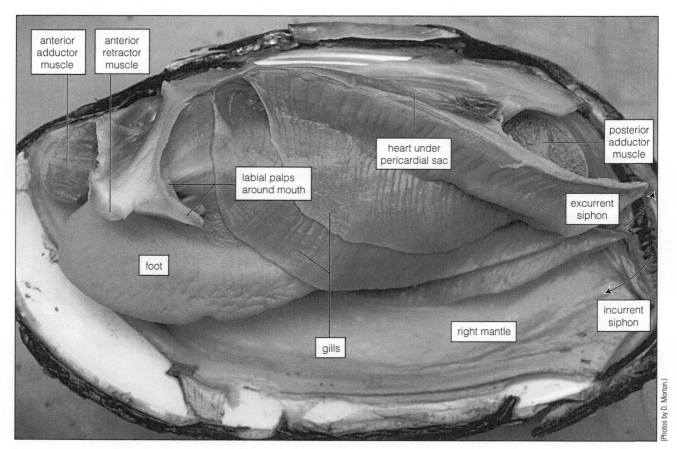

Figure 19-9 Dissection of a freshwater clam. The left valve and mantle have been removed. Arrows indicate the path of water flow into the incurrent siphon and out the excurrent siphon.

slip a scalpel between the valves at its approximate location feeling for a firm structure with the scalpel edge. Once you find it, cut back and forth. Repeat this process for the posterior adductor muscle. Once these muscles are severed, slide the scalpel between the valve to be removed and the tissues that line its inner surface. With the flat side of the scalpel, hold the tissues down while you remove the valve.

(b) The membrane that lines the inner surface of each valve is the **mantle,** which secretes the calcium carbonate shell. Pearls form as a result of irritations (usually grains of sand or small pebbles) in the mantle and sometimes are found embedded in the *pearly layer,* the inner of three layers that comprise the shell. Note that the mantle forms **incurrent** and **excurrent siphons** at the rear end.

(c) Remove the mantle on the left side by cutting it free with a scalpel. The relatively simple body plan includes a ventral foot and a dorsal visceral mass. Identify the **foot** and two sets of **gills,** one on each side of the *visceral mass.* The gills function in gaseous exchange. Water enters the incurrent siphon and flows over the gills, ultimately leaving through the excurrent siphon. Gills also trap food particles contained in incoming water; these are transported to the mouth by the cilia on the gills. Find the **labial palps,** which are situated around the mouth.

(d) The circulatory system is *open,* so the blood passes from arteries leading from the heart through body spaces called sinuses. Blood is returned to the heart by veins draining the mantle and gills. Find the **heart** in the pericardial sac between the visceral mass and the hinge between the valves.

(e) Dispose of your dissected specimen in the large plastic bag provided for this purpose.

(f) Examine the labeled dissection prepared by your instructor. Identify the **mouth, esophagus, stomach, intestine, digestive gland** (liver), **anus, nephridium** (kidney), and **gonad** (Figure 19-10).

3. Examine the demonstration slide of a transverse section of the gill with your compound microscope. Identify the structures labeled in Figure 19-11.

4. Fertilization is internal in bivalves. Sperm taken in through the female's incurrent siphon fertilize eggs in the gills. In many bivalves, *glochidia* larvae develop from the fertilized eggs and after several months leave the gill area via the excurrent siphons to parasitize fish by clamping onto the gills or fins with their jawlike valves. The fish grows tissue over the parasite, which remains attached for 2–3 months. The glochidium then breaks out of the fish to develop into an adult on the lake or river bottom. Microscopically look at glochidia in a prepared slide (Figure 19-12).

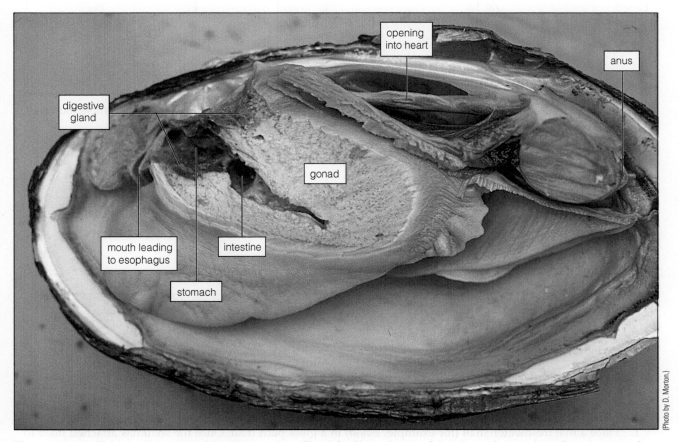

Figure 19-10 Further dissection of freshwater clam. The left gills and part of the visceral mass have been removed.

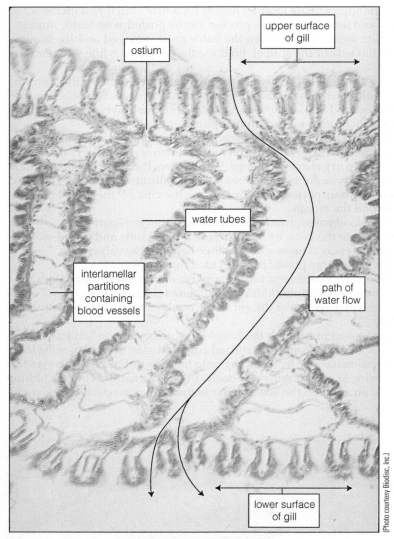

Figure 19-11 Cross section of clam gill (150×).

upper surface
of gill

ostium

water tubes

interlamellar
partitions
containing
blood vessels

path of
water flow

lower surface
of gill

(Photo courtesy Biodisc, Inc.)

Figure 19-12 Whole mount of glochidia (250×).

(Photo by D. Morton.)

5. *Assorted bivalves.* Examine the assortment of bivalve shells and preserved specimens on demonstration.
List the features they have in common.

_____

_____

_____

List some of the differences.

_____

_____

_____

How can you tell which live on sandy bottoms?

_____

B. Snails, Slugs, and Nudibranchs (Class Gastropoda)

Slugs and nudribranchs (Figure 19-13) have no shell; the former are terrestrial, the latter marine. Nudibranchs are very ornate gastropods, often brightly colored, and frequently adorned with numerous fleshy projections.
1. Place a live freshwater snail (for example, *Physa*) in a glass petri dish. Once the snail has attached itself to the glass, invert the petri dish and use the dissection microscope to observe it moving along a slimy path.

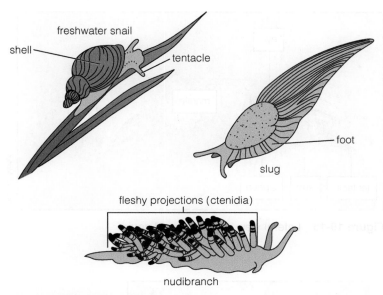

Figure 19-13 Gastropods.

A *slime gland* in the front of the foot secretes mucus. Briefly describe the muscular contractions of the foot that allow the animal to glide over this mucus. _____

_____

Looking at the foot through the glass, you can see the **mouth**. Describe its location. _____

_____

2. In snails with spirally coiled shells, the shell either spirals to the snail's right or left as it grows. Which way does your snail's shell spiral? _____

C. Squids, Octopuses, and Nautiluses (Class Cephalopoda)

Several significant modifications of the basic molluskan body plan occur in cephalopods (Figure 19-14), which are adapted for rapid swimming and catching prey. The foot of the squid has become divided into four pairs of arms and two tentacles, each with suckers, and a siphon. The tentacles, with their terminal suckers, shoot out to grasp prey. The muscular mantle draws water into its chamber when it relaxes.

Subsequent contraction of the mantle wall seals the cavity and forces water out of the siphon, resulting in jet propulsion propelling the animal through the water. Two lateral fins provide guidance. In addition, there are two large eyes that superficially resemble those of vertebrates. A relatively large brain coordinates all of these activities.

Nautiluses have shells, but shells are reduced in squids and absent in octopuses. The shell of the squid lies dorsally beneath the mantle and is called the pen.

1. Examine the external morphology of a squid. Identify the structures labeled in Figure 19-15.
2. Identify those structures indicated in Figure 19-16 on the demonstration dissection of the internal anatomy of the squid.
3. Look at the variety of cephalopod shells and preserved specimens on display in your lab room.

Figure 19-14 Cephalopods.

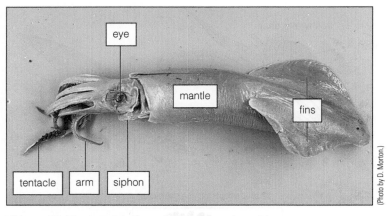

Figure 19-15 Lateral view of a preserved squid.

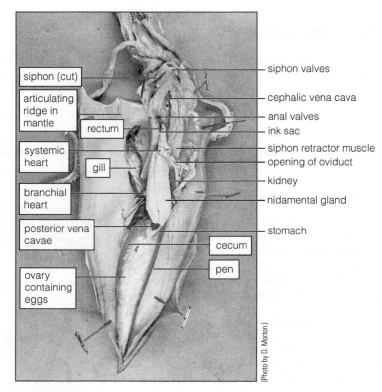

Figure 19-16 Internal anatomy of female squid. Nidamental glands and the ovary are absent in male specimens, and a penis occupies the same location as the oviduct.

Habitat:	aquatic, moist terrestrial, or parasitic
Body Arrangement:	bilateral symmetry, pseudocoelomate, head, gut (complete)
Level of Organization:	organ system (tissues derived from all three primary germ layers); nervous system with brain; no circulatory, respiratory, or skeletal systems
Body Support:	hydrostatic (pseudocoelom)
Life Cycle:	sexual reproduction (mostly dioecious with internal fertilization)
Special Characteristics:	pseudocoelomate, complete gut

Nematodes or *roundworms*, like rotifers, are **pseudocoelomates,** which means they have a false body cavity or *pseudocoel*. This term is somewhat unfortunate, because there *is* a body cavity. It is not considered a true body cavity because tissues derived from mesoderm incompletely line it. Also, in an evolutionary sense it is likely dervived from the body cavity of ancestral coelomates, Unlike flatworms, roundworms have a complete gut with both a mouth and an anus. Together, the pseudocoel and the complete digestive system comprise a tube-within-a-tube arrangement, a body plan that is seen in most of the phyla yet to be discussed. Roundworms have slender, cylindrical bodies that taper at both ends. A tough, nonliving cuticle of protein covers them. This cuticle is shed all at once when roundworms molt, a characteristic they share with joint-legged animals. Molting, or ecdysis, is the periodic loss of the outer covering of the integument during growth. Unlike our epidermis, which in two to three weeks renews itself one cell at a time, the exoskeleton of joint-legged animals and the cuticle of roundworms are shed all at once. Actually, our hairs, which are grown in follicles derived from the epidermis, are likewise shed as a whole.

Parasitic roundworms include *Ascaris* (species), the hookworms, *Trichinella* worms of mammals (Figure 19-17), pinworms of humans, and the filarial worms of humans that cause elephantiasis by obstructing lymphatic vessels.

MATERIALS

Per student:

- dissection microscope
- dissecting needle

Per student pair:

- finger bowl

Per lab room:

- collection of free-living roundworms
- tray of moist soil
- container of fresh stream water
- demonstration dissections of
    a male *Ascaris*
    a female *Ascaris*
- demonstration microscope of a cross section of
    a male *Ascaris*
    a female *Ascaris*
- boxes of different sizes of latex gloves

(Photo courtesy Biodisc, Inc.)

encysted larvae

Figure 19-17 *Trichinella spiralis* larvae encysted in muscle (46×). This organism causes the disease trichinosis, which is usually contracted by eating undercooked pork or wild game.

A. Free-Living Roundworms

PROCEDURE

1. Examine the demonstration collection of free-living roundworms.
2. Place some moist soil in a finger bowl with some fresh stream water. Using a dissection microscope, look for translucent roundworms in the soil sample (Figure 19-18).

    Describe the behavior of any roundworms you find and make a note of any visible anatomical features they possess.

_____

_____

_____

_____

_____

_____

_____

_____

_____

_____

B. Ascaris

Ascaris is a common parasite of humans, pigs, horses, and other mammals. Adults range from 15 to 40 cm in length, with males being smaller and having a hook shape to the posterior part of the body.

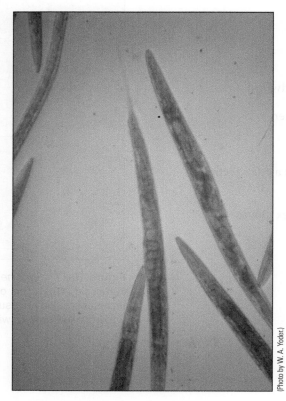

(Photo by W. A. Yoder.)

Figure 19-18 Free-living nematodes, *Rhabditella* females, w.m. (350×).

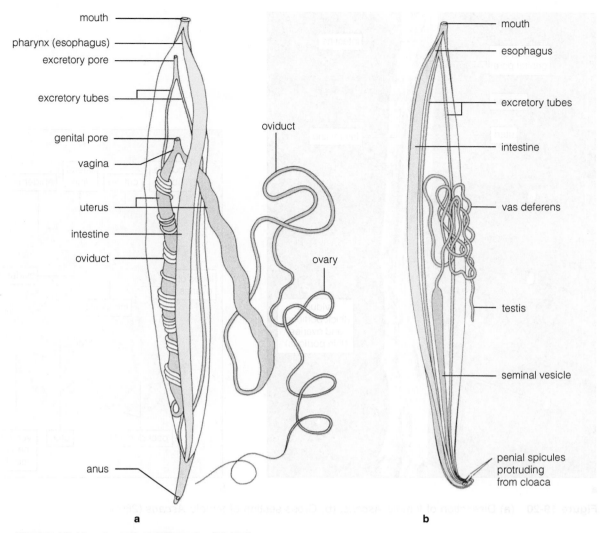

Figure 19-19 *Ascaris.* (**a**) Female. (**b**) Male.

1. Examine a female *Ascaris* (Figure 19-19a). At the front end, the triangular *mouth* is surrounded by three lips. The opening on the ventral surface near the other end of the body is the *anus*. A *genital pore* is located about one-third the distance from the mouth.
2. Look at the demonstration dissection and demonstration cross section of a female *Ascaris* and identify the structures labeled in Figures 19-20a and b. The paired **lateral lines** each contain an *excretory tube*. These tubes open to the outside through a single **excretory pore** located near the mouth on the ventral surface. The **ovaries** are the threadlike ends of a Y-shaped reproductive tract. The ovary leads to a larger **oviduct** and a still larger **uterus.** The two uteri converge to form a short, muscular **vagina** that opens to the outside through the **genital pore.**
3. Examine a male *Ascaris* (Figure 19-19b). The lips and mouth are the same as the female's. However, the male has a *cloaca*—an exit for both the reproductive and digestive systems—instead of an anus. A pair of *penial spicules* protrudes from this opening.

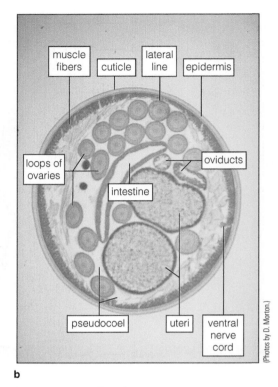

(Photos by D. Morton.)

Figure 19-20 (a) Dissection of female *Ascaris.* (b) Cross section of female *Ascaris* (26×).

4. Look at the demonstration dissection and demonstration cross section of a male *Ascaris* and identify the structures labeled in Figures 19-21a and b. The reproductive system superficially resembles that of the female. It consists of a single tubular structure that includes a threadlike **testis** joined to a larger **vas deferens,** an even larger **seminal vesicle,** and terminally a short, muscular ejaculatory duct that empties into the cloaca.
5. After copulation, the eggs are fertilized in the female oviduct. The eggs, surrounded by a thick shell, are expelled through the genital pore to the outside; as many as 200,000 may be shed into the host's intestinal tract per day. Examine a prepared slide with whole *Ascaris* eggs and draw what you see in Figure 19-22.

The eggs are eliminated in the host's feces. They are very resistant and can live for years under adverse conditions. Infection with *Ascaris* results from ingesting eggs in food or water contaminated by feces or soil. The eggs pass through the stomach and hatch in the small intestine. The small larvae migrate through the bloodstream, exit the circulatory system into the respiratory system, and crawl up the respiratory tubes and out the trachea into the throat. There they are swallowed to reinfect the intestinal tract and mature. Sometimes larvae exit the nasal passages rather than being swallowed. The entire journey of the larva from intestine back to intestine takes about 10 days.

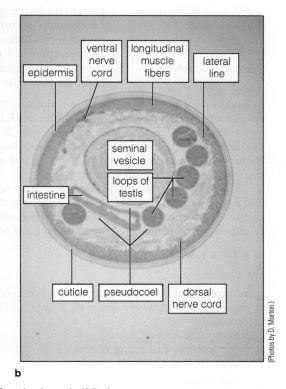

a

b

Figure 19-21 (a) Dissection of male *Ascaris*. (b) Cross section of male *Ascaris* (35×).

(Photos by D. Morton.)

Labels in image a: lateral lines, testis, vas deferens, intestine, seminal vesicle, cloacal opening

Labels in image b: epidermis, ventral nerve cord, longitudinal muscle fibers, lateral line, seminal vesicle, loops of testis, intestine, cuticle, pseudocoel, dorsal nerve cord

Figure 19-22 Drawing of the *Ascaris* eggs
(_____×).

Habitat:	aquatic, terrestrial (land and air), some parasitic
Body Arrangement:	bilateral symmetry, coelomate, body regions (head, thorax, and abdomen), segmented (specialized segments form mouthparts and jointed appendages), gut (complete)
Level of Organization:	organ system (tissues derived from all three primary germ layers), nervous system with brain, excretory system (green glands or Malphigian tubules), circulatory system (open), respiratory system (gills, trachae, or book lungs)
Body Support:	exoskeleton of chitin
Life Cycle:	sexual reproduction (mostly dioecious with internal fertilization), larvae, metamorphosis, some parthenogenesis
Special Characteristics:	specialized segments, exoskeleton of chitin, metamorphosis, flight in some, complex behavior

In numbers of both species and individuals, this is the largest animal phylum. There are more than 1 million species of arthropods, more in fact than in all of the other animal phyla combined. Arthropods are believed to be evolved from annelid ancestors, the cuticle becoming thicker and harder to form an **exoskeleton** (external skeleton) of **chitin**—a structural polysaccharide. Like the annelids, the bodies of arthropods are segmented. Arthropod ancestors had one pair of legs per segment. In modern arthropods, some of these appendages have evolved into other useful structures.

The body is typically divided into three regions: the *head, thorax,* and *abdomen.* The mouthparts are modified appendages (legs). The coelom is filled with the blood, or **hemolymph,** and connected to an *open circulatory system.* In addition to the exoskeleton, the evolutionary success of arthropods is due in large part to their *highly developed central nervous system, well-developed sense organs,* and *complex behavior.*

MATERIALS

Per student:

- compound microscope, lens paper, a bottle of lens-cleaning solution (optional), a lint-free cloth (optional)
- dissecting scissors
- blunt probe or dissecting needle
- scalpel

Per student pair:

- dissection microscope
- preserved crayfish
- dissection pan
- grasshopper (*Romalea*)

- prepared slide of a whole mount of grasshopper mouthparts

Per lab room:

- demonstration collections of living and preserved and mounted crustaceans living and preserved and mounted insects living and preserved centipedes living and preserved millipedes living and preserved and mounted spiders, horseshoe crabs, scorpions, ticks, and mites
- large plastic bag for disposal of dissected specimens
- boxes of different sizes of latex gloves

PROCEDURE

A. Crustaceans (Subphylum Crustacea)

Some of our most prized seafoods are crustaceans. This group contains shrimps, lobsters, crabs, and crayfish—and animals of considerably less culinary interest, including water fleas, sand fleas, isopods (sow or pill bugs), ostracods, copepods, and barnacles. Most species are marine, but some live in fresh water. Most isopods occupy moist areas on land. For the most part, crustaceans are carnivorous, scavenging, or parasitic.

Crustaceans have two pairs of antennae on the head, and their exoskeleton is hardened on top and sometimes on the sides to form a protective **carapace.**

1. Examine the demonstration specimens of crustaceans on display in the lab.
2. *External features of a crayfish.*
   (a) Obtain a crayfish, a fairly typical crustacean, and rinse it in water at the sink. Place the rinsed crayfish in a dissection pan.
   (b) Recognize the two major body regions (Figure 19-23): an anterior **cephalothorax,** composed of a fused head and thorax, and a posterior *abdomen.* Note the **carapace.** The portion of the carapace that extends between the eyes is the **rostrum.**
   (c) Identify the pair of large **compound eyes** (comprised of many closely packed photosensory units) each one atop a movable stalk, a pair of **antenna,** and two pairs of smaller and shorter **antennules.**
   (d) Find the **mouth,** which is comprised of three pairs of mouthparts—one pair of **mandibles** and two pairs of **maxillae.** Three pairs of **maxillapeds** (Figure 19-24) surround the mouthparts.

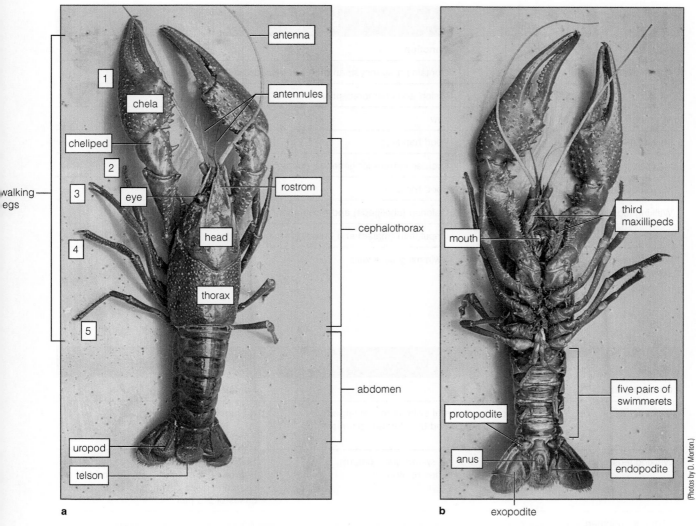

Figure 19-23 (a) Dorsal and (b) ventral views of the external anatomy of the crayfish. The five walking legs are numbered in (a).

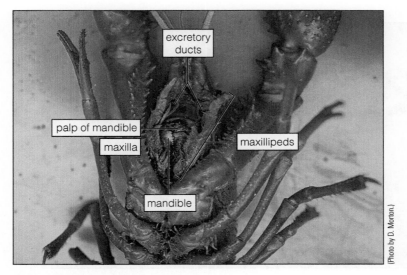

Figure 19-24 Crayfish mouthparts.

TABLE 19-2 Function of Crayfish Legs and Modified Appendages

Structure	Function
Antennule	Contains a statocyst, an organ of balance, in the basal segment
Antenna	Vision and chemoreception
Mandible	Jaw
Maxilla (first)	Food handling
Maxilla (second)	Creates current for gaseous exchange in the gills
Maxillipeds (first, second, and third)	Food handling
Walking legs (1–5)	Defense (chelipeds) and movement
Swimmerets (1–5)	Copulation (males) and brooding young (female)
Uropod (combines with telson and other uropod to form tail fan)	Swimming backward

TABLE 19-3 Sexual Dimorphisms in Crayfish (Figure 19-25)

Characteristic	Male	Female
Swimmerets	Front two pairs of swimmerets enlarged for copulation and transferring sperm to the female	No modifications
Walking legs	Openings of the *sperm ducts* (sperm ducts) at the bases of 5th pair	*Seminal receptacle* in the middle between the bases of the 4th and 5th pairs and discs covering the oviducts at bases of 3rd pair
Width of abdomen (broad or narrow)		

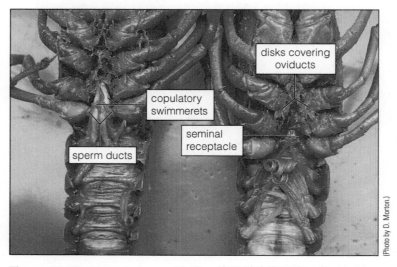

Figure 19-25 Ventral views of (left) a male, (right) a female

(Photo by D. Morton.)

(e) Locate the five pairs of large **walking legs;** the first, called the **chelipeds,** bear large pincers called **chelae.** Continuing toward the tail, count the five pairs of abdominal **swimmerets.** Near the end of the abdomen, locate the **uropods,** a pair of large, flattened lateral appendages located on both sides of the *telson,* which is an extension of the last abdominal segment. The **anus** opens onto the ventral surface of the telson.

(f) Table 19-2 summarizes in order from front to back down one side of the body those structures that are legs or modified appendages. Review them in order and familiarize yourself with their functions.

(g) Crayfish exhibit **sexual dimorphism** (morphological differences between male and female). Look at a number of specimens of both sexes, observe any differences in the characteristics listed in Table 19-3 (and shown in Figure 19-25), and fill in any blanks.

3. *Crayfish dissection.*

(a) Locate the **gills** within the branchial chambers by carefully cutting away the lateral flaps of the carapace with your scissors (Figure 19-26). The gills are feathery structures containing blood channels that function in gaseous exchange.

(b) With scissors, superficially cut forward from the rear of the carapace to just behind the eyes. With your scalpel, carefully separate the hard carapace from the thin, soft, underlying tissue. Next, remove the gills to reveal the internal organs (Figure 19-27).

Figure 19-26 Internal anatomy of the crayfish with side of carapace removed.

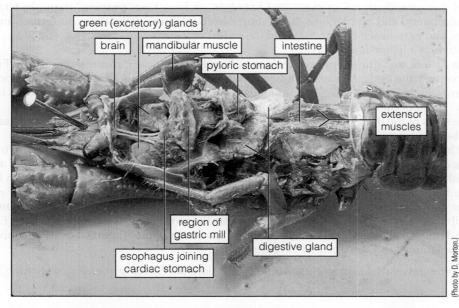

Figure 19-27 Internal anatomy of the crayfish with carapace, gills, and heart removed.

(c) Note the two longitudinal bands of *extensor muscles* that run dorsally through the thorax and abdomen. In the abdomen, find the large *flexor muscles* lying ventrally below the extensor muscles and intestine. What is the function of these two sets of muscles?

_____

_____

_____

(d) Locate the small, membranous heart or its location just posterior to the stomach. Remember, the circulatory system is open; from the arteries, blood flows into open spaces, or *sinuses*, before returning to the heart through openings in the wall of this organ.

(e) Identify the organs of the upper digestive tract. The mouth leads to the tubular **esophagus,** which empties into the **cardiac stomach.** At the border between the cardiac stomach and the **pyloric stomach** is the **gastric mill,** a grinding apparatus composed of three chitinous teeth. What role in digestion do you think this structure plays?

_____

_____

_____

(f) Note the large **digestive gland.** This organ secretes digestive enzymes into the cardiac stomach and takes up nutrients from the pyloric stomach. Absorption of nutrients from the tract continues in the intestine, which runs from the abdomen to the *anus.*

(g) Locate the **green glands,** the excretory organs situated ventrally in the head region near the base of the antennae. A duct leads to the outside from each green gland.

(h) The gonads lie beneath the heart. They will be obvious if your specimen was obtained during the reproductive season. If not, they will be small and difficult to locate. In a female, try to find the *ovaries* just beneath the heart. In the male, two white *testes* will occupy a similar location.

(i) Remove the organs in the cephalothorax to expose the *ventral nerve cord.* Observe the segmental ganglia and their paired lateral nerves. Trace the nerve cord forward to locate the **brain.** Note the nerves leading from the brain to the eyes, antennules, antennae, and mouthparts. Dispose of your dissected specimen in the large plastic bag provided for this purpose.

B. Insects (Subphylum Hexapoda)

Of the more than 1 million species of arthropods, more than 850,000 of them are insects. These animals occupy virtually every kind of terrestrial and freshwater habitat. This extraordinary proliferation of species is almost certainly due to the evolution of wings. Insects were the first organisms to fly and thus were able to exploit a variety of opportunities not available to other animals.

1. Examine insects on demonstration in the lab. Groups of insects you are probably familiar with—dragon flies and damsel flies; grasshoppers, crickets, and katydids; cockroaches; "praying" mantids; termites; cicadas, aphids, leafhoppers, and spittlebugs; "true" bugs; beetles; "true" flies; fleas; butterflies and moths; and wasps, bees, and ants—each belong to one of the orders of insects.

2. *External features of a typical insect.*

    (a) Obtain a preserved grasshopper of the genus *Romalea* and place it in a dissection pan (Figure 19-28).

    (b) Observe that the body consists of a **head, thorax,** and **abdomen.** The thorax is composed of three segments, each of which bears a pair of legs. The middle and back segments also each bear a pair of wings. The abdomen, unlike the situation in crustaceans, has no appendages.

    (c) On the sides of the thorax and abdomen find the **spiracles,** tiny openings into the **tracheae,** or breathing tubes, which course through the body and function in gaseous exchange.

    (d) Note that the **head** of the grasshopper contains a pair of **compound eyes** between which are three simple eyes, the **ocelli,** light-sensitive organs that do not form images. A single pair of antennae distinguishes the insects from the crustaceans (which have two) and the arachnids (which have none).

    (e) Locate the feeding appendages (Figure 19-29)—a pair of **mandibles** and two pairs of **maxillae,** the second pair fused together to form the lower lip, the **labium.** The upper lip, the **labrum,** covers the mandibles. Near the base of the labium is a tonguelike process called the **hypopharynx** (Figure 19-30).

3. Look at the demonstration slide of a whole mount of grasshopper mouthparts. Locate and label a mandible, a maxilla, the labium, and the labrum in Figure 19-30.

Mouthparts are extremely variable in insects, with modifications for chewing, piercing, siphoning, and sponging (Figure 19-31).

a

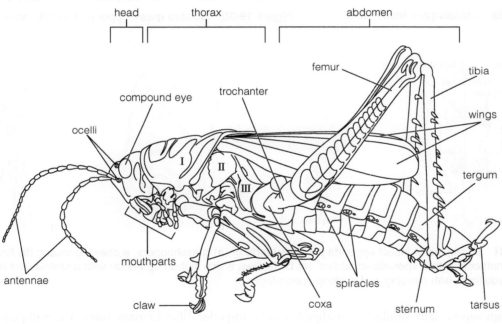

b

Figure 19-28 Photograph (**a**) and diagram (**b**) of the external anatomy and body form of a grasshopper, a typical insect.

C. Centipedes and Millipedes (Subphylum Myriapoda)

Centipedes are swift, predaceous arthropods adapted for running. The body is flattened with one pair of legs per segment, except for the head and the rear two segments (Figure 19-32a). The first segment of the body bears a pair of legs modified as *poison claws* for seizing and killing prey. In some tropical species (which can get as long as 20 cm), the poison can be dangerous to humans. Centipedes live under stones or the bark of logs. Their prey consists of other arthropods, worms, and mollusks. The common house centipede eats roaches, bedbugs, and other insects.

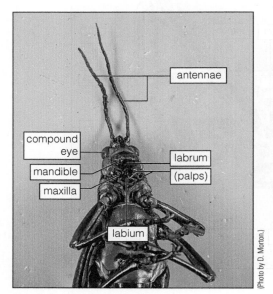

Figure 19-29 Grasshopper mouthparts.

(Photo by D. Morton.)

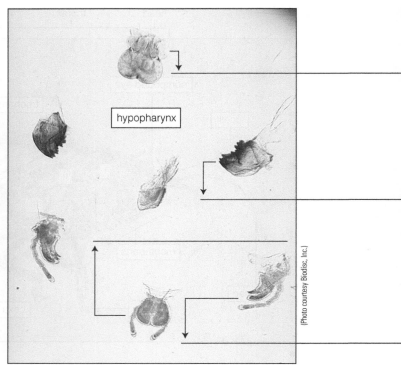

hypopharynx

(Photo courtesy Biodisc, Inc.)

Figure 19-30 Isolated grasshopper mouthparts, w.m. (7×).

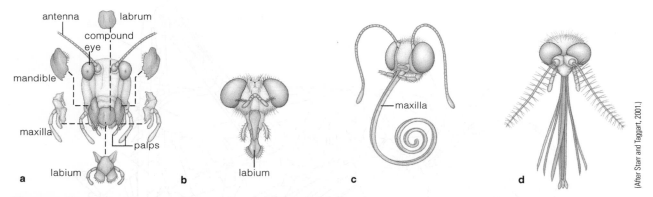

Figure 19-31 Examples of insect appendages. Headparts of (**a**) grasshoppers, a chewing insect; (**b**) flies, which sponge up nutrients with a specialized labium; (**c**) butterflies, which siphon up nectar with a specialized maxilla; and (**d**) mosquitoes, with piercing and sucking appendages.

(After Starr and Taggart, 2001.)

Although superficially similar, the millipedes and centipedes differ in many ways. The millipedes typically have cylindrical bodies. All segments, except those of the short thorax, bear two pairs of legs. There are no poison claws (Figure 19-32b). Millipedes are very slow arthropods that live in dark, moist places. They scavenge on decaying organic matter. When handled or disturbed, they often curl up into a ball and secrete a noxious fluid from their scent glands as a means of defense.

1. Examine the centipedes on demonstration in the lab.
2. Similarly observe the millipedes on display in the lab.

D. Subphylum Chelicerata: Spiders, Horseshoe Crabs, Scorpions, Ticks, and Mites

Today most species are terrestrial, but the first chelicerates were marine. Horseshoe crabs represent these ancient marine forms. Their bodies and five pairs of walking legs are concealed under a tough carapace (Figure 19-33a).

The body of spiders and scorpions consists of a *cephalothorax* and *abdomen*. In ticks and mites, these parts are fused. The cephalothorax bears six pairs of appendages, the rear four of which are walking legs (Figure 19-33b).

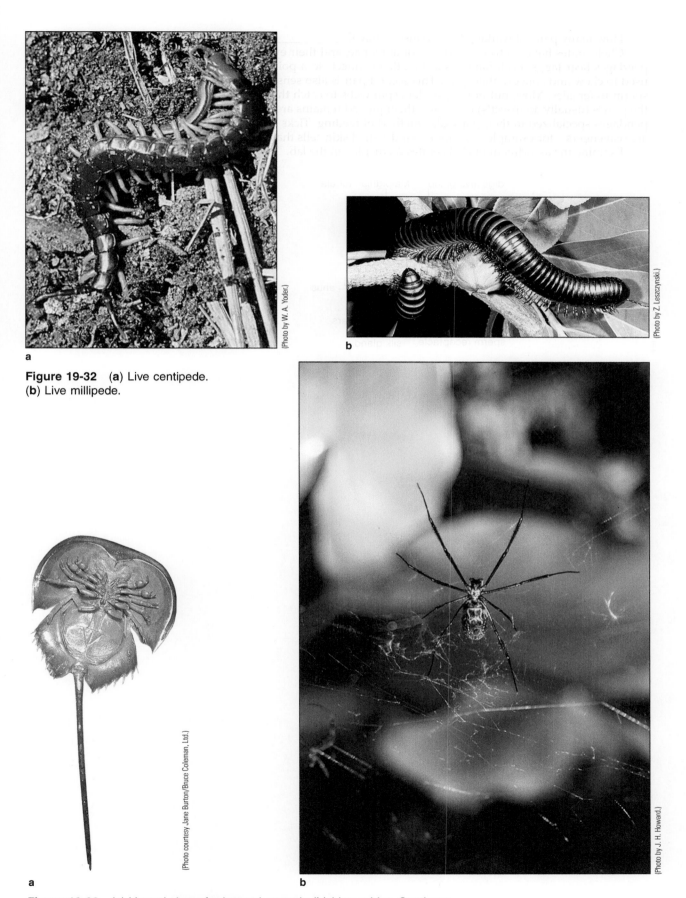

Figure 19-32 (a) Live centipede. (b) Live millipede.

(Photo by W. A. Yoder.)

(Photo by Z. Leszczynski.)

(Photo courtesy Jane Burton/Bruce Coleman, Ltd.)

(Photo by J. H. Howard.)

a

b

Figure 19-33 (a) Ventral view of a horseshoe crab. (b) Live spider. *Continues*

How many pairs of walking legs do insects have? _____

Chelicerates have no true mandibles or antennae, and their eyes are simple. In spiders, the first pair of appendages bear fangs. Each fang has a duct that connects to a poison gland. The second pair of appendages is used to chew and squeeze their prey. This second pair is also sensory, and males use them to store and transfer sperm to females. Most, but not all, spiders spin webs to catch their prey. They secrete digestive enzymes into the prey's (usually an insect's) body, and the liquefied remains are sucked up. Other chelicerates have front appendages specialized to their particular method of feeding. Ticks suck the blood of vertebrates and most mites are scavengers—for example, dust mites eat the shed skin cells that are a major component of house dust.

Examine the assortment of chelicerates on display in the lab.

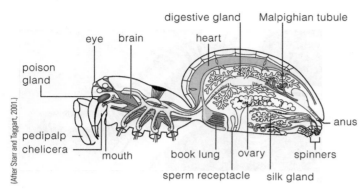

(After Starr and Taggart, 2001.)

c

Figure 19-33 (c) Internal anatomy of a spider. *Continued*

PRE-LAB QUESTIONS

_____ 1. The protostomes are animals whose
   (a) stomach is in front of the crop
   (b) mouth is covered by a fleshy lip
   (c) blastopore becomes a mouth
   (d) digestive tract is lined by mesoderm

_____ 2. The deuterostomes are animals whose
   (a) stomach is in front of the crop
   (b) mouth is covered by a fleshy lip
   (c) blastopore becomes the anus
   (d) digestive tract is lined by mesoderm

_____ 3. Further evolution of the protostomes changed the coelom by
   (a) losing it
   (b) reducing it
   (c) it becoming a pseudocoel
   (d) all of the above

_____ 4. Earthworms exhibit segmentation, defined as the
   (a) division of the body into a series of similar segments
   (b) presence of a true coelom
   (c) difference in size of the male and female
   (d) presence of a "head" equipped with sensory organs

_____ 5. The copulatory organ of the earthworm is the
   (a) penis
   (b) clitellum
   (c) gonopodium
   (d) vestibule

_____ 6. Leeches belong to the phylum
   (a) Arthropoda
   (b) Mollusca
   (c) Annelida
   (d) Cnidaria

_____ 7. One of the two major distinguishing characteristics of mollusks is
   (a) the presence of three body regions
   (b) the mantle
   (c) segmentation of the body
   (d) jointed appendages

_____ 8. Functions of the mantle include
   (a) secreting the shell
   (b) forming peals around irritating grains of sand
   (c) forming the incurrent and excurrent siphons
   (d) all of the above

_____ 9. Which of the following is a gastropod?
   (a) clam
   (b) snail
   (c) squid
   (d) octopus

_____ 10. Which of the following is a cephalopod?
   (a) clam
   (b) snail
   (c) slug
   (d) octopus

_____ 11. Structures that are shed in one piece include
(a) the cuticle of roundworms
(b) the exoskeleton of arthropods
(c) human hair
(d) all of the above

_____ 12. Nematodes and rotifers have a body cavity that is
(a) called a coelom
(b) called a pseudocoelom
(c) completely lined by tissues derived from mesoderm
(d) both a and c

_____ 13. Filarial roundworms cause elephantiasis by
(a) encysting in muscle tissue
(b) promoting the growth of fatty tumors
(c) obstructing lymphatic vessels
(d) laying numerous eggs in the joints of their hosts

_____ 14. Digestive wastes of the male _Ascaris_ roundworm exit the body through the
(a) anus
(b) cloaca
(c) mouth
(d) excretory pore

_____ 15. The animal phylum with the most species is
(a) Mollusca
(b) Annelida
(c) Arthropoda
(d) Platyhelminthes

_____ 16. The body of arthropods includes
(a) a head
(b) a thorax
(c) an abdomen
(d) all of the above

_____ 17. Sexual dimorphism, as seen in the crayfish, is
(a) the presence of male and female individuals
(b) the production of eggs and sperm by the same individual
(c) another term for copulation
(d) the presence of observable differences between males and females

_____ 18. The grinding apparatus of the digestive system of the crayfish is/are the
(a) oral teeth
(b) gizzard
(c) pharyngeal jaw
(d) gastric mill

_____ 19. The insects were the first organisms to
(a) show bilateral symmetry
(b) exhibit segmentation
(c) fly
(d) develop lungs

_____ 20. Like the insects, the arachnids (spiders and so on) have
(a) three pairs of walking legs
(b) one pair of antennae
(c) true mandibles
(d) an abdomen

EXERCISE 19

Segmented Worms, Mollusks, Roundworms, and Joint-Legged Animals

POST-LAB QUESTIONS

Introduction

1. Indicate the differences between protostomes and deuterostomes.

2. List the animal phyla that are protostomes and those that are deuterostomes.

3. What happens to the coelom as each phyla of protostomes evolve?

4. Indicate the differences between protosomes and deuterosomes, and list the phyla of animals in each group.

5. Describe ecdysis in roundworms and joint-legged animals.

19.1 Annelids (Phylum Annelida)

6. Briefly describe the life cycle of an earthworm.

7. Label this diagram of an annelid and identify its class (Oligochaeta, Polychaeta, or Hirudinea).

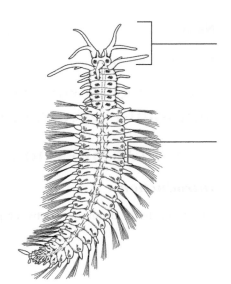

19.2 Mollusks (Phylum Mollusca)

8. Explain what causes the growth ridges found on the shells of bivalves.

9. List some structures that distinguish bivalves from the other molluscan classes.

10. What characteristics distinguish slugs from nudibranchs?

19.3 Roundworms (Phylum Nematoda)

11. *Pseudocoel* means "false body cavity." Why is this term applied to the body cavity of roundworms?

19.4 Joint-Legged Animals (Phylum Arthropoda)

12. Define *sexual dimorphism*, describe it in the crayfish, and list two other animals that exhibit this phenomenon.

13. Identify and label the structures noted in this diagram.

a. _____   e. _____   h. _____

b. _____   f. _____   i. _____

c. _____   g. _____   j. _____

d. _____

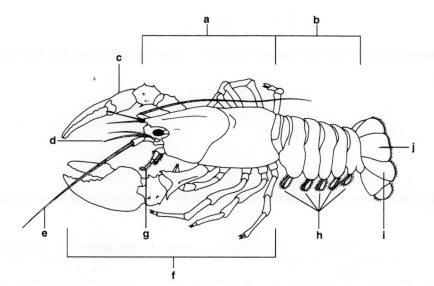

14. How has flight been at least partly responsible for the success of the insects?

15. List several differences between insects and spiders.

Food for Thought

16. Is it possible that some of the monsters reported by ancient mariners were giant squid or octopi? Search the Internet before giving and explaining your answer.

17. Define *segmentation* and indicate how the annelids and your body exhibit this phenomenon.

18. List the roundworm parasites and use the Internet to learn how they gain entry into the body. Describe that process here.

19. Write the phylum and choose the appropriate description for each animal (or group of animals) listed in the following table.

Animal	Phylum	Symmetry	Level of Organization	Body Cavity	Gut
Sponge	None				
Hydra and jellyfish	None				
Flatworm					
Rotifer					
Segmented worm					
Clam, snail, and octopus					
Roundworm					
Crayfish, insect, and spider					

20. Define *segmentation* and indicate how the annelids, arthropods, and your body exhibit this phenomenon.

Echinoderms, Invertebrate Chordates, and Vertebrates

OBJECTIVES

After completing this exercise, you will be able to

1. define *dermal endoskeleton, water vascular system, notochord, pharyngeal gill slits, dorsal hollow nerve cord, postanal tail, invertebrate, vertebrate, vertebral column, cranium, vertebrae, cloaca, lateral line, placoid scale, operculum, atrium, ventricle, artery, vein, ectothermic, endothermic,* and *viviparous;*

2. describe the natural history of members of phylum Echinodermata and the invertebrate members of phylum Chordata;

3. identify some representatives of the echinoderm classes (sea stars, brittle stars, sea urchins, and sea cucumbers);

4. compare and contrast the invertebrate chordates (subphyla Urochordata and Cephalochordata);

5. identify structures (and indicate associated functions) of the representatives of these phyla and subphyla;

6. describe the basic characteristics of members of the subphylum Vertebrata;

7. identify representatives of the vertebrate classes, Cephalaspidomorphi, Chondrichthyes, Osteichthyes, Amphibia, Reptilia, Aves, and Mammalia;

8. identify structures (and indicate associated functions) of representatives of the vertebrate classes.

INTRODUCTION

The deuterostome (animals whose blastopore—first opening of developing embryo—becomes an anus) branch of coelomates leads to echinoderms and chordates, the phylum to which we belong. Although the adult forms of these two phyla look quite different, chordates are thought to have evolved from the bilaterally symmetrical larvae of ancestral echinoderms some 600 million years ago.

There is an additional small phylum, the Hemichordata, whose members (acorn worms) have both echinoderm and chordate characteristics. Acorn worms are *long, slender, wormlike* animals (Figure 20-1). Most *live in shallow seawater.* They *obtain food by burrowing in mud and sand or filter feeding.* Evidence of their former activity can be seen on exposed tidal flats where mud or sand that has passed through their bodies is left in numerous coiled, ropelike piles.

In terms of the numbers of individuals and species, chordates do not constitute a large phylum; however, chordates known as vertebrates have had a disproportionately large ecological impact. The **vertebrates** have the *four basic characteristics of chordates* listed in the previous exercise, plus a cranium and a **vertebral column.** The dorsal hollow nerve cord has differentiated into a *brain* and a *spinal cord.* Bones protect both of these structures, the brain by the bones of the **cranium** (braincase) and the spinal cord by the **vertebrae,** the bones that make up the vertebral column.

Like echinoderm larvae and sea squirt larvae and lancelets, vertebrates are *cephalized, bilaterally symmetrical,* and *segmented.* In adults, segmentation is most easily seen in the musculature, vertebrae, and ribs. The body is typically divided into a *head, neck, trunk,* and *tail.* If appendages are present, they are paired, lateral *thoracic appendages* (pectoral fins, forelimbs, wings, and arms) and *pelvic appendages* (pelvic fins, hindlimbs, and legs), which are linked to the vertebral column and function to support and to help move the body. Seven classes of vertebrates have representatives alive today (lampreys, cartilaginous fishes, bony fishes, amphibians, reptiles, birds, and mammals), and one class is completely extinct (armored fishes).

(Photos by D. Morton.)

Figure 20-1 (a) Preserved acorn worm. (b) Ropelike piles of sand formed by burrowing acorn worms.

20.1 Echinoderms (Phylum Echinodermata) *(45 min.)*

Habitat: aquatic, marine

Body Arrangement: radial symmetry (larvae are bilaterally symmetrical), coelomate, no well-defined head, no segmentation, gut (usually complete)

Level of Organization: organ system (tissues derived from all three primary germ layers), circular nervous system with radial nerves, reduced circulatory system, no respiratory and excretory system, dermal endoskeleton (mesoderm)

Body Support: endoskeleton of calcium carbonate

Life Cycle: sexual reproduction (mostly dioecious with external fertilization), larvae, metamorphosis, high regenerative potential

Special Characteristics: radial symmetry, no segmentation, water-vascular system, dermal endoskeleton

Caution

Specimens are kept in preservative solutions. Use latex gloves whenever you handle a specimen. Wash any part of your body exposed to this solution with copious amounts of water. If preservative solution is splashed into your eyes, wash them with the safety eyewash bottle for 15 minutes. If you wear contact lenses during a dissection, wear safety goggles.

Echinoderm means "spiny skin." These are marine animals; they live on the bottom of both shallow and deep seas. Their feeding methods range from trapping organic particles and plankton (for example, sea lilies and feather stars) to scavenging (sea urchins) and predatory behavior (sea stars).

The echinoderms exhibit five-part *radial symmetry* and a calcareous (contains calcium carbonate) **dermal endoskeleton** (internal skeleton) composed of many small plates. Much of the *coelom* is taken up by a unique *water-vascular system,* which functions in movement, attachment, respiration, excretion, food handling, and sensory perception.

MATERIALS

Per student:

- dissecting scissors
- blunt probe or dissecting needle

Per student pair:

- dissection microscope
- preserved sea star
- dissection pan

- dissection pins
- prepared slide of
    a cross section of a sea star arm (ray)
    a whole mount of bipinnaria larvae
- compound microscope, lens paper,
    a bottle of lens-cleaning solution (optional),
    and a lint-free cloth (optional)

Per lab room:

- collections of
    preserved or mounted brittle stars
    sea urchins, sea biscuits, and sand dollars
    (preserved specimens and skeletons)
    preserved sea cucumbers
- live specimens (optional)

- collection of preserved or mounted feather stars and sea lilies
- large plastic bag for disposal of dissected specimens
- boxes of different sizes of latex or vinyl gloves
- box of safety goggles

A. Sea Stars (Class Asteroidea)

The sea stars are familiar occupants of the sea along shores and coral reefs. They are slow-moving animals that sometimes gather in large numbers on bare areas of rock. Many are brightly colored. Some sea stars are more than 1 m in diameter.

PROCEDURE

1. Obtain a preserved specimen of a sea star and keep your specimen moist with water in a dissection pan. Note the **central disk** on the *aboral* side—the side without the mouth; the **five arms;** and the **sieve plate** (madreporite), a light-colored calcareous sieve near the edge of the disk between two arms (Figure 20-2a). The pores in the sieve plate open into the water-vascular system.

2. With a dissection microscope, note the many protective **spines** scattered over the surface of the body. Near the base of the spines are many small pincerlike structures, the **pedicellariae** (Figure 20-2b). The *valves* of these structures grasp objects that land on the surface of the body, such as potential parasites. Also among the spines are many soft, hollow **skin gills** (dermal branchiae) that communicate directly with the coelom and function in the exchange of gases and excretion of ammonia (a nitrogen-containing metabolic waste).

3. Locate the **mouth** on the oral side (Figure 20-3a). Note that an **ambulacral groove** extends from the mouth down the middle of the oral side of each arm. Numerous **tube feet** extend from the water-vascular system and occupy this groove. Each tube foot consists of a bulblike structure attached to a **sucker** (Figure 20-3b). The animal moves by alternating the suction and release mechanisms of the tube feet. Tube feet are also used to adhere to the shells of bivalves and to pry them open to get at their soft insides. The tube feet, along with the skin gills, also function in the exchange of gases and excretion of ammonia.

4. With your dissecting scissors, cut across the top of an arm about 1 cm from the tip. Next, cut out a rectangle of spiny skin by carefully cutting along each side of the arm to the central disk and then across the top of the arm at the edge of the disk. Observe the hard, calcareous plates of the dermal endoskeleton as you cut. Remove the rectangle of skin to uncover the large *coelom,* which contains the internal organs (Figure 20-4).

5. Cut around the *sieve plate* to remove the upper portion of the body wall of the *central disk.* The *mouth* connects via an extremely short esophagus to the clearly visible pouchlike **cardiac stomach.** The cardiac stomach opens into the upper *pyloric stomach.* A slender, short *intestine* leads from the upper side of the stomach to the *anus.* Find the two green, fingerlike **digestive glands** in each arm, which produce digestive enzymes and deliver them to the pyloric stomach.

a

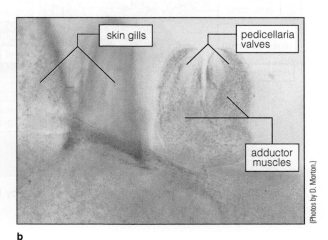

(Photos by D. Morton.)

b

Figure 20-2 (a) Aboral view of sea star. (b) Pedicellaria and skin gills, w.m. (205×).

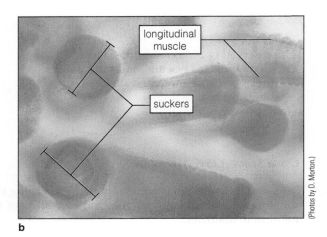

Figure 20-3 (**a**) Oral view of sea star. (**b**) Close-up of tube feet, w.m. (78×).

6. Identify the **dark gonads** that are located near the base of each arm. The sexes are separate but difficult to distinguish, except by microscopic examination. In nature, sperm and eggs are released into the seawater, and the fertilized eggs develop into bipinnaria larvae.

7. The water-vascular system is unique to echinoderms (Figure 20-5). Note that the *sieve plate* leads to a short **stone canal,** which in turn leads to the *circular canal* surrounding the mouth. Five *radial canals* lead from the circular canal into the ambulacral grooves. Each radial canal connects by short side branches with many pairs of tube feet.

8. The nervous system (not shown in Figure 20-3) is simple. A circular *nerve ring* surrounds the mouth, and a *radial nerve* extends from this into each arm, ending at a light-sensitive eyespot. There are no specific excretory organs. Dispose of your dissected specimen in the large plastic bag provided for this purpose.

9. Examine a prepared slide of a cross section of an arm with the compound microscope. Identify the structures labeled in Figure 20-6.

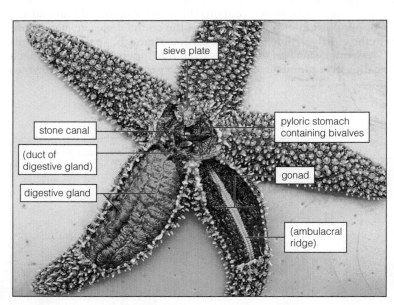

Figure 20-4 Internal anatomy of a sea star. (Photo by D. Morton.)

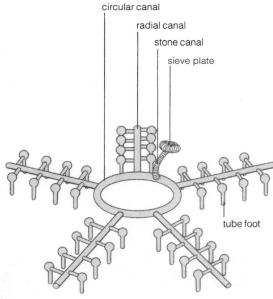

Figure 20-5 The water-vascular system of a five-armed sea star. The ring canal is located in the central disk, and each radial canal extends into one of the arms.

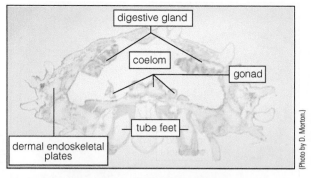

Figure 20-6   Cross section of a sea star arm (23×).

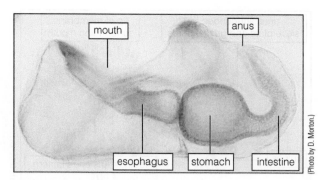

Figure 20-7   Bipinnaria larva (196×).

10. Examine a prepared slide of a whole mount of bipinnaria larvae. The digestive tract, including the *mouth, esophagus, stomach, intestine,* and *anus,* is clearly visible (Figure 20-7).
11. Observe preserved, plastic-mounted, or living specimens of sea stars.

B. Other Echinoderms

PROCEDURE

1. *Class Ophiuroidea* includes the brittle stars (Figure 20-8). These echinoderms have slender arms and move relatively rapidly, for echinoderms! In life, the rays are much more flexible than those of the sea stars. Examine preserved, plastic-mounted, or living specimens of brittle stars.
2. *Class Echinoidea* contains the sea urchins, animals that lack arms. They have long, movable spines, which surround the top and sides of a compact skeleton called the **test** (Figure 20-9). Sea urchins ingest food by means of a complex structure, *Aristotle's lantern,* which contains teeth. The sea biscuits and sand dollars are also members of this class. They have flat, disk-shaped bodies. Sea urchins, sea biscuits, and sand dollars, despite their lack of arms, all exhibit five-part radial symmetry and move by means of tube feet. Study preserved or living specimens and the tests (Figure 20-10) of members of this class.
3. *Class Holothuroidea* are the sea cucumbers (Figure 20-11). No spines are present. A collection of tentacles at one end surrounds the mouth. In some forms, the tube feet occur over the entire surface of the body. Sea cucumbers move in wormlike fashion as a result of the contractions of two layers of circular and longitudinal muscles. Examine preserved or living sea cucumbers.

a

b

Figure 20-8   (a) Dried and (b) live brittle star.

Figure 20-9 (a) Aboral and (b) oral views of a sea urchin.

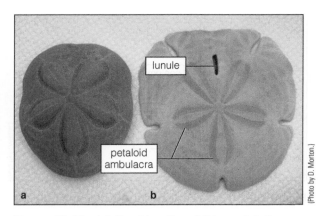

Figure 20-10 (a) Sea biscuit and (b) sand dollar tests.

Figure 20-11 (a) Preserved and (b) live sea cucumber.

4. *Class Crinoidea* contains the graceful, flowerlike feather stars and sea lilies (Figure 20-12). These stationary animals attach to the sea floor by a long stalk. The arms are featherlike; each contains a ciliated groove and tentacles (derived from tube feet) to direct food to the mouth. There can be from 5 to over 200 arms, some of which reach 35 cm. *Class Concentricycloidea* contains the sea daisies. Examine any available specimens and illustrations of these classes.

Figure 20-12 Feather star.

Habitat:	aquatic, terrestrial (land and air)
Body Arrangement:	bilateral symmetry, coelomate, head and postanal tail, segmentation, gut (complete)
Level of Organization:	organ system (tissues derived from all three primary germ layers), nervous system with brain, circulatory system (closed with a ventral heart), organ systems highly developed, many have an endoskeleton (mesoderm)
Body Support:	most have an endoskeleton of cartilage or bone
Life Cycle:	sexual reproduction (mostly dioecious with internal or external fertilization), some larvae, some metamorphosis
Special Characteristics:	notochord, pharyngeal gill slits, dorsal hollow nerve cord, and a postanal tail at some stage of life cycle

The word *chordate* refers to one of the four major diagnostic characteristics shared by all members of this phylum at least some time in their life span, a **notochord, pharyngeal gill slits,** a **dorsal hollow nerve cord,** and a **postanal tail** (Table 20-1). Most chordates are also vertebrates—animals that possess a backbone or vertebral column—but a few are not. The latter animals belong to the subphyla Urochordata and Cephalochordata. They are **invertebrates** because they lack a vertebral column. All of the animal phyla you have studied so far are also invertebrates.

TABLE 20-1 Chordate Characteristics

Characteristic	Definition	Developmental Fate in Humans
Notochord	A dorsal, flexible rod that provides support for most of the length of the body	Center of intervertebral disks
Pharyngeal gill slits	Paired, lateral outpockets of pharynx that perforate through its wall	Auditory tubes and endocrine glands of neck
Dorsal hollow nerve cord	A tube of nervous tissue dorsal to notochord	Brain and spinal cord
Postanal tail	Posterior tail that extends past the anus	Present in embryo

MATERIALS

Per student:

- blunt probe

Per student pair:

- dissection microscope
- compound microscope, lens paper, a bottle of lens-cleaning solution (optional), and a lint-free cloth (optional)
- dissection pan

- preserved or mounted sea tunicates (sea squirts)
- preserved and plastic mounted lancelet specimens
- prepared slide of a whole mount of a lancelet
- prepared slide of a cross section of a lancelet in region of the pharynx
- boxes of different sizes of latex or vinyl gloves (optional)
- box of safety goggles (optional)

A. Tunicates (Subphylum Urochordata)

Tunicates are also called sea squirts. Both common names are descriptive of obvious features of these animals. A leatherlike "tunic" covers the adult, and water is squirted out of an excurrent siphon (Figure 20-13).

Sea squirt larvae resemble tadpoles in general body form and have a notochord confined to the postanal tail. The notochord and tail degenerate when the larva becomes an adult tunicate. The larva also has a rudimentary

b Body plan of the tadpole-like larva, shown midsagittal section.

c A new larva swims about for a brief period. Metamorphosis begins when its head attaches to a substrate. The notochord, tail, and most of the nervous system are resorbed (recycled to form new tissues). Slits in the pharynx wall multiply. Organs rotate until the openings through which water enters and leaves the pharynx are directed away from the substrate.

(Photo by Rick M. Harbo; after Starr and Taggart, 2001.)

Figure 20-13 (**a**) Adult form of a sea squirt. (**b**) A sea squirt larva. (**c**) Metamorphosis of a larva into the adult.

brain and sense organs. These structures undergo reorganization into a nerve ganglion and nerve net in the adult. The number of pharyngeal gill slits increases in the adult.

1. Examine a preserved or plastic mounted specimen of a sea squirt with a dissection microscope. These animals are small, inactive, and very common marine organisms that inhabit coastal areas of all oceans. The adult is a filter feeder, capturing organic particles into an incurrent siphon by ciliary action. Individuals either float freely in the water (singly or in groups) or are sessile, attached to the bottom as branching individuals or colonies.

2. Water enters a sea squirt through the *incurrent siphon*. It travels into the *pharynx*, where it seeps through *gill slits* to reach a chamber, the *atrium*. The water eventually exits through the *excurrent siphon*. Back in the pharynx, food particles are trapped in sticky mucus and then passed to the digestive tract. Undigested materials are discharged from the anus into the atrium, to be expelled with water out the excurrent siphon. Identify as many of these structures as possible.

B. Lancelets (Subphylum Cephalochordata)

The lancelets are distributed worldwide and are especially abundant in coastal areas with *warm, shallow waters. Amphioxus* (Figure 20-14) is the commonly studied representative of this subphylum. The word *Amphioxus* means "sharp at both ends," and this certainly describes its *elongate, fishlike body form.* Lancelets reach 50–75 mm in length as adults. Despite their streamlined appearance, these organisms are not very active. They spend most of their time buried in the sand with their heads projecting while they filter organic particles from the water.

1. Examine a preserved lancelet with the dissection microscope (Figure 20-15). Note that the lancelets are translucent, with a low, continuous dorsal and caudal (tail) **fin.** Trace the flow of water from the **mouth**

Figure 20-14 Cutaway view of a lancelet.

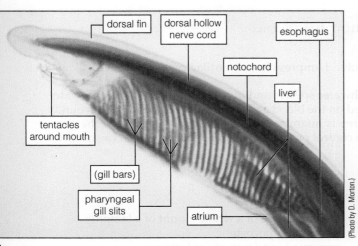

dorsal fin | dorsal hollow nerve cord | esophagus
notochord
liver
tentacles around mouth
(gill bars)
pharyngeal gill slits
atrium

(Photo by D. Morton.)

a

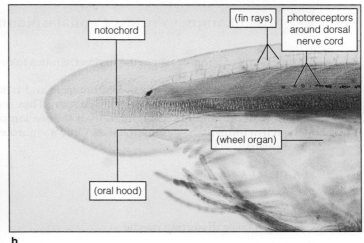

notochord | (fin rays) | photoreceptors around dorsal nerve cord
(wheel organ)
(oral hood)

(Photo by D. Morton.)

b

Figure 20-15   Whole mounts of (**a**) anterior end (30×) and (**b**) head (100×) of a lancelet.

(surrounded by **tentacles**), through the roughly 150 **pharyngeal gill slits** into the *atrium,* and out of the pore of the atrial cavity.

2. Now describe the capture of food and the path it takes through the digestive system, as was done previously for the tunicates. Unlike the tunicates, the *anus* in a lancelet opens externally.

    _____

    _____

    _____

    _____

    _____

3. Find the flexible **notochord** extending nearly the full length of the individual; this structure persists into the adult stage. There is a small brain, with a **dorsal hollow nerve cord** that bears light-sensitive cells (the *eyespot*) at its anterior end.

4. Examine a cross section of a lancelet with a compound microscope and identify the structures indicated in Figure 20-16.

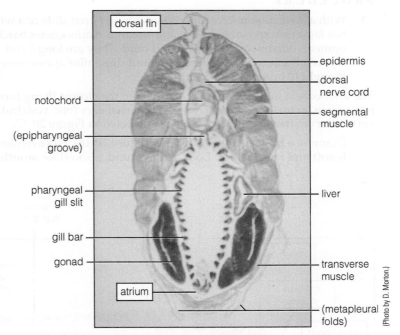

dorsal fin | epidermis
notochord | dorsal nerve cord
(epipharyngeal groove) | segmental muscle
pharyngeal gill slit | liver
gill bar
gonad | transverse muscle
atrium | (metapleural folds)

(Photo by D. Morton.)

Figure 20-16   Cross section of lancelet in region of pharynx (20×).

The ancestors of lampreys were the first vertebrates to evolve. Lampreys have a cartilaginous (made of cartilage), primitive skeleton.

Lampreys are represented by both marine and freshwater species and by some species that use seawater and fresh water at some point in their life span. They feed on the blood and tissue of fishes by rasping wounds in their sides. A landlocked population of the sea lamprey is infamous for having nearly decimated the commercial fish industry in the Great Lakes. Only a vigorous control program that targeted lamprey larvae restored this industry.

MATERIALS

Per student:

■ scalpel
■ blunt probe or dissecting needle

Per student pair:

■ dissection microscope
■ dissection pan

Per student group:

■ prepared slide of a whole mount of a lamprey larva or ammocoete
■ preserved specimen of sea lamprey

Per lab room:

■ boxes of different sizes of vinyl or latex gloves
■ box of safety goggles

PROCEDURE

1. With a dissection microscope, observe a prepared slide of a whole mount of a lamprey larva or ammocoete. Sea lampreys spawn in freshwater streams. Ammocoetes hatch from their eggs and, after a period of development, burrow into the sand and mud. They are long-lived, metamorphosing into adults after as long as 7 years. Because of their longevity and dissimilar appearance, adult lampreys and ammocoetes were long thought to be separate species.

The ammocoete is considered by many to be the closest living form to ancestral chordates. Unlike a lancelet, it has an eye (actually two median eyes), internal ears (otic vesicles), and a heart, as well as several other typical vertebrate organs. Identify the structures labeled in Figure 20-17.

2. Examine a preserved sea lamprey (Figure 20-18). Note its slender, rounded body. The skin of the lamprey is soft and lacks scales. Look at the round, suckerlike **mouth,** inside of which are circular rows of horny,

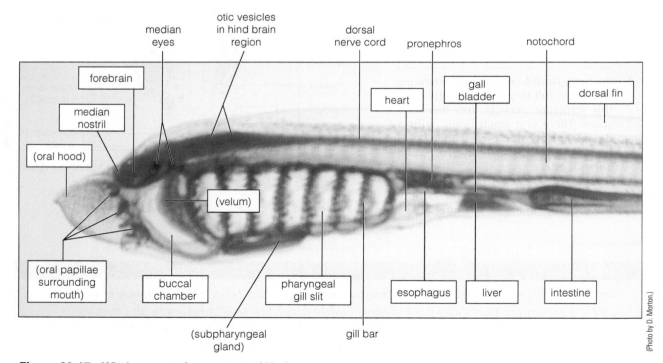

Figure 20-17   Whole mount of ammocoete (40×).

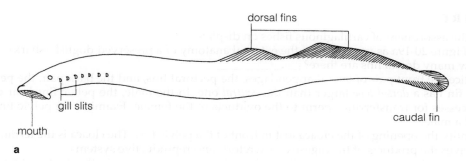

dorsal fins

gill slits

mouth

caudal fin

a

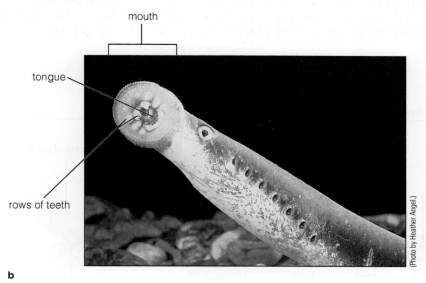

mouth

tongue

rows of teeth

(Photo by Heather Angel.)

b

Figure 20-18 (**a**) Side view and (**b**) oral disk of a sea lamprey.

rasping **teeth** and a deep, rasping **tongue**. Although there are no lateral, paired appendages, there are two **dorsal fins** and a **caudal fin** (tail fin). Count and record below the number of pairs of external **gill slits.**

20.4   Cartilaginous Fishes (Class Chondrichthyes) *(10 min.)*

The first vertebrates to evolve jaws and paired appendages, according to the fossil record, were the heavily armored *placoderms* (class Placodermi). These fishes arose about 425 million years ago. Current hypotheses suggest that the ancestors of placoderms relatively quickly gave rise to the cartilaginous fishes.

Members of the class Chondrichthyes are *jawed fishes* with *cartilaginous skeletons* and *paired appendages*. The evolution of jaws and paired appendages and the evolution of more efficient respiration and a better developed nervous system, including sensory structures, were critical events in the history of vertebrate evolution. Together these adaptations allowed cartilaginous fishes to chase, catch, and eat larger and more active prey. This mostly marine group includes the carnivorous skates, rays, and sharks.

MATERIALS

Per student:

- scalpel
- forceps
- dissecting scissors

Per student pair:

- dissection microscope
- dissection pan

Per student group:

- preserved specimen of dogfish (shark)

Per lab room:

- collection of
  preserved cartilaginous fishes
  shark jaw with teeth
- boxes of different sizes of vinyl or latex gloves
- box of safety goggles

PROCEDURE

1. Look at the assortment of cartilaginous fishes on display.
2. Refer to Figure 20-19a as you examine the external anatomy of a preserved dogfish (shark).

   (a) How many dorsal fins are there? _____

   (b) Notice the front pair of lateral appendages, the **pectoral fins,** and the back pair, the **pelvic fins.** The **tail fin** has a *dorsal lobe* larger than the *ventral* one. In the male, the pelvic fins bear **claspers,** thin processes for transferring sperm to the oviducts of the female. Examine the pelvic fins of a female and a male.

   (c) Identify the opening of the **cloaca** just in front of the pelvic fins. The cloaca is the terminal organ that receives the products of the digestive, excretory, and reproductive systems.

   (d) There are five to seven pairs of gill slits in cartilaginous fishes, six in the dogfish. Observe the most anterior gill slit, which is called the *spiracle,* located just behind the eye. Trace the flow of seawater in nature through the mouth, over the pharyngeal gills, and out of the gill slits.

a

b

Figure 20-19 (**a**) External appearance of the dogfish (shark), *Squalus acanthias.* (After S. Wischnitzer, *Atlas and Dissection Guide for Comparative Anatomy*, 3rd ed., © 1967, 1972, 1979, W. H. Freeman and Company. Used by permission.) (**b**) Shark jaw.

(e) Locate the **nostrils,** which open into blind olfactory sacs; they don't connect with the pharynx, as your nostrils do. They function solely in olfaction (smell) in the cartilaginous fishes. The **eyes** are effective visual organs at short range and in dim light. There are no eyelids.

(f) Find the dashed line that runs along each side of the body. This is called the **lateral line** and functions to detect vibrations in the water. It consists of a series of minute canals perpendicular to the surface that contain sensory hair cells. When the hairs are disturbed, nerve impulses are initiated; their frequency enables the fish to locate the disturbance.

(g) Placoid scales, toothlike outgrowths of the skin, cover the body. Run your hand from head to tail along the length of the animal. How does it feel?

_____

_____

Now run your hand in the opposite direction along the animal. How does it feel this time?

_____

_____

Cut out a small piece of skin with your scissors, pick it up with your forceps, and examine its surface with the dissection microscope. Draw what you see in Figure 20-20.

3. Examine the demonstration of a shark jaw with its multiple rows of teeth (Figure 20-19b).

Figure 20-20 Drawing of shark skin (_____×).

20.5　Bony Fishes (Class Osteichthyes) *(10 min.)*

The bony fishes, the fishes with which you are most familiar, inhabit virtually all the waters of the world and are the largest vertebrate group. They are economically important, commercially and as game species. The ancestors of cartilaginous fish gave rise to the first bony fishes about 415 million years ago. As their name suggests, the *skeleton* is at least *partly ossified (bony),* and the flat *scales* that cover at least some of the surface of most bony fishes are *bony* as well. Gill slits are housed in a common chamber covered by a bony movable flap, the **operculum.**

MATERIALS

Per student:

- scalpel
- compound microscope, lens paper, a bottle of lens-cleaning solution (optional), and a lint-free cloth (optional)
- clean microscope slide and coverslip
- dH₂O in dropping bottle
- forceps
- blunt probe or dissecting needle

Per student pair:

- dissection pan

Per student group:

- preserved specimens of yellow perch

Per lab room:

- collection of preserved bony fishes
- boxes of different sizes of vinyl or latex gloves
- box of safety goggles

PROCEDURE

1. Examine the assortment of bony fishes on display.
2. Examine a yellow perch as a representative advanced bony fish (Figure 20-21).
   (a) Identify the *spiny* **dorsal fin** located in front of the *soft* **dorsal fin.** Paired **pectoral** and **pelvic fins** are also present, and behind the **anus** is an unpaired **anal fin.** The **tail fin** consists of *dorsal* and *ventral lobes* of approximately equal size. The fins, as in the cartilaginous fishes, are used to brake, steer, and maintain an upright position in the water.

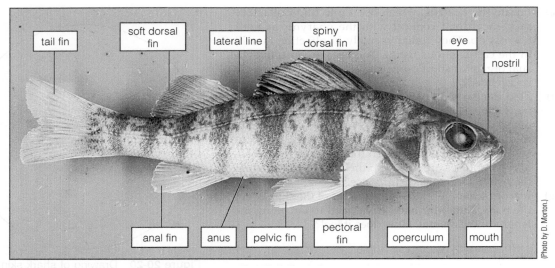

Figure 20-21 Preserved yellow perch.

(b) Note the double **nostrils,** leading into and out of *olfactory sacs.* The eyes resemble those in sharks, with no eyelids. With forceps, pry open the operculum to see the organs of respiration, the **gills.**

(c) Find the **lateral line.** This functions similarly to that of the shark.

(d) Bony scales cover the body. Using forceps, remove a scale, make a wet mount, and examine it with the compound microscope. Locate the *annual rings,* which indicate the age of the fish. How are the annual rings of the fish scale analogous to the annual ridges of the mussel or clam shell?

_____

_____

_____

Draw the scale in Figure 20-22.

Figure 20-22 Drawing of yellow perch scale (_____×).

20.6   Amphibians (Class Amphibia) *(30 min.)*

The *amphibians* were the first vertebrates to assume a terrestrial existence, having evolved about 370 million years ago from a group of lobe-finned fishes. The paired appendages are modified as legs, which support the individual during movement on land. Respiration by one species or another or by the different developmental stages of one species is by lungs, gills, and the highly vascularized skin and lining of the mouth. There is a *three-chambered heart,* compared to the two-chambered heart of fishes, with two *circuits for the blood circulation,* compared to one circuit in fishes. Reproduction requires water, or at least moist conditions on land. Fertilized eggs hatch in water, and larvae generally live in water. The skeleton is bonier than that of the bony fishes, but a considerable proportion of it remains cartilaginous. The *skin* is usually *smooth and moist,* with mucous glands; scales are usually absent. This group of vertebrates includes the frogs, toads, salamanders, and tropical, limbless, burrowing, mostly blind caecilians.

MATERIALS

Per student:

- forceps
- dissecting scissors
- blunt probe or dissecting needle
- dissection pins

Per student pair:

- preserved leopard frog

Per lab room:

- collection of preserved bony fishes
- collection of preserved amphibians
- skeleton of frog
- skeleton of human
- boxes of different sizes of vinyl or latex gloves
- box of safety glasses

PROCEDURE

1. Examine preserved specimens of a variety of amphibians.
2. The leopard frog illustrates well the general features of the vertebrates and the specific characteristics of the amphibians. Obtain a preserved specimen and after rinsing it in tap water, examine its external anatomy (Figure 20-23).
   - **(a)** Find the two *nostrils* at the tip of the head. These are used for inspiration and expiration of air. Just behind the eye locate a disklike structure, the *tympanum,* the outer wall of the middle ear. There is no external ear. The tympanum is larger in the male than in the female. Examine the frogs of other students in your lab.
     Is your frog a male or female?

   _____

   - **(b)** At the back end of the body, locate the *cloacal opening.*
   - **(c)** The forelimbs are divided into three main parts: the **upper arm, forearm,** and **hand.** The hand is divided into a **wrist, palm,** and **fingers** (digits). The three divisions of the hindlimbs are the **thigh, shank** (lower leg), and **foot.** The foot is further divided into three parts: the **ankle, sole,** and **toes** (digits).
3. Examine the internal anatomy of the frog.
   - **(a)** With the scissors, cut through the joint at both angles of the jaw. Identify the structures labeled in Figure 20-24. The region containing the opening into the **esophagus** and the **glottis** is the **pharynx** (throat). The esophagus leads to the stomach and the rest of the digestive tract; the glottis leads into the blind respiratory tract.
   - **(b)** Fasten the frog, ventral side up, with pins to the wax of a dissection pan. Lift the skin with forceps. Then make a superficial

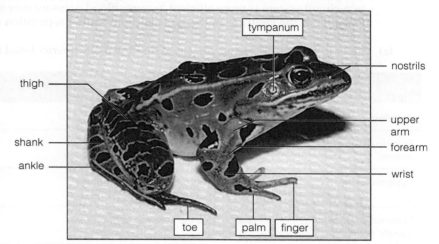

Figure 20-23   External anatomy of the frog. (Photo by D. Morton.)

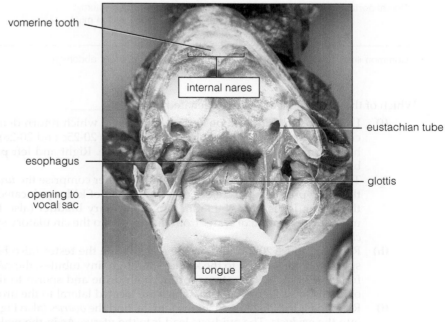

Figure 20-24   Oral cavity of the frog. (Photo by D. Morton.)

cut with your scissors from the lower abdomen forward, and just left or right of center, to the tip of the lower jaw. Pin back the skin on both sides to expose the large abdominal muscles. Lift these muscles with your forceps, and cut through the body wall with your scissors again from the lower abdomen to the tip of the lower jaw, cutting through the sternum (breastbone) but not damaging the internal organs. Pin back the body wall as you did the skin to expose the internal organs (Figure 20-25).

(c) Use Figure 20-25 to locate the *spleen* (Figure 20-25c) and the following organs of the digestive system: **stomach, small intestine, large intestine** (colon), **liver, gall bladder,** and **pancreas.** Trace the esophagus from its opening in the pharynx to the stomach. Parallel to its upper portion find the **bronchi** (the singular is *bronchus*), which lead toward the **lungs.** Are the bronchi dorsal or ventral to the esophagus?

_____

(d) Identify the two thin-walled **atria** and the thick-walled **ventricle** and the **conus arteriosus** of the heart along with and the right and left branches of the **truncus arteriosus** (Figure 20-9a). The latter structure carries blood to the paired **pulmocutaneous arches** and **systemic arches.** In frogs and other amphibians a *pulmocutaneous circuit* circulates blood to and from the lungs and the skin, and a *systemic circuit* services the rest of the body. Even though there is only one ventricle, because of the structure of the heart and its large arteries, most of the deoxygenated blood returning from the body is pumped into the pulmocutaneous circuit before the oxygenated blood is pumped into the systemic circuit. In comparison, a fish has a two-chambered heart with only one atrium and a one-circuit circulation. A two-circuit system is more efficient because blood pressure drops less after the blood is oxygenated. Partition of the ventricle of the heart and the further separation of the two circuits will continue in subsequent vertebrate classes.

(e) Refer to Figures 20-25 and 20-26 and find the major *arteries* listed in Table 20-2.

TABLE 20-2 Major Arteries of the Frog		
Arteries	**Location**	**Function Is to Convey Blood to**
Pulmocutaneous arches	First pair of vessels branching off truncus arteriosus	Lungs and skin
Systemic arches	Second pair of vessels branching off truncus arteriosus	The rest of the body
Common carotids (carotid arches)	Branch from the systemic arches	Head
Subclavians	Branch from the systemic arches	Arms
Dorsal aorta	Formed by the fusion of the systemic arches along dorsal body wall in mid abdomen	Lower half of the body
Common iliacs	Division of dorsal aorta in lower abdomen	Legs

Which of these arteries carries deoxygenated blood? _____

(f) Locate the **anterior** and **posterior vena cavae,** which return deoxygenated blood from the systemic circuit to the right atrium of the heart (Figures 20-25c and 20-26). Other veins return blood from the head, arms, and legs to one of the vena cavae. Right and left **pulmonary veins** return oxygenated blood from the lungs to the left atrium.

(g) The excretory and reproductive organs together comprise the *urogenital system* (Figure 20-27). Locate the urine-producing excretory organs, the pair of **kidneys** located dorsally in the body cavity. A duct, the **ureter,** leads from the kidney to the **urinary bladder** (also Figure 20-25a), an organ that stores urine for resorption of water from the urine into the circulatory system. The bladder empties into the *cloaca.*

(h) Refer to Figure 20-27a and, in the male, locate the **testes** (also Figure 20-25c); these organs produce sperm that are carried to the kidneys through tiny tubules, the *vasa efferentia.* The ureters serve a dual function in male frogs, transporting both urine and sperm to the cloaca. Find the vestigial female oviducts (also Figure 20-25b), which are located lateral to the urogenital system.

(i) Refer to Figure 20-27b and, in the female, find the *ovaries* (also Figure 20-25d); these organs expel eggs into the *oviducts.* The oviducts lead into the *uterus.* As in the male, the reproductive tract ends in the cloaca.

(j) Locate the *fat bodies* (Figures 20-25c and d), many yellowish, branched structures just above the kidneys. They store food reserves for hibernation and reproduction.

(k) The nervous system of vertebrates is composed of (1) the *central nervous system,* the brain and spinal cord, and (2) the *peripheral nervous system,* nerves extending from the central nervous system. Turn your frog over and remove the skin from the dorsal surface of the head between the eyes and along the vertebral column. With your scalpel, shave thin sections of bone from the skull, noting the shape and size of the *cranium,* until you expose the *brain.* Pick away small pieces of bone with your forceps to expose the entire brain. Use the same procedure to expose the vertebrae and *spinal cord.* Note the *cranial nerves* coming from the brain and the *spinal nerves* coming from the spinal cord. Spinal nerves are also easy to see running along the dorsal wall of the abdomen.

(l) Dispose of your dissected specimen in the large plastic bag provided for this purpose.

4. Comparison of frog and human skeleton.

(a) The skeleton of vertebrates consists of the following: (1) the **axial skeleton,** consisting of the bones of the **skull, sternum, hyoid bone, vertebral column,** and rib cage (when present); and (2) the **appendicular skeleton,** with the bones of its **girdles** and their appendages. The **pectoral girdle** consists of the paired **clavicle** and **scapula** bones (**suprascapular** in the bullfrog). The latter articulates—forms a joint—with the **humerus.** The **pubis, ischium,** and **ilium** bones form the pelvic girdle, which articulates with the femur. Compare the skeleton of the bullfrog and human (Figure 20-28), and identify the axial and appendicular portions of the skeleton.

(b) There are differences in the two skeletons, but their basic plan is remarkably similar. To a large extent, the size and shape of the different parts of the skeleton of a vertebrate correlate with body specializations and behavior. List some reasons for the differences in the girdles, appendages, and cranium of the frog and human skeletons.

_____

_____

_____

20.7 Reptiles (Class Reptilia) *(10 min.)*

Reptiles are the oldest group of vertebrates *adapted to living primarily on land,* although many do live in fresh water or seawater. They arose from the ancestors of amphibians about 300 million years ago. Their *skeleton* is bonier than that of amphibians. The *skin* is *dry* and covered by *epidermal scales.* There are virtually no skin glands. Reptiles lay *amniotic eggs* (Figure 20-29). Inside these eggs, embryos are suspended by fetal membranes in an internal aquatic environment surrounded by a shell to prevent their drying out.

There is no larval stage. The amniotic egg (characteristic of birds and some mammals as well as reptiles) and lack of larvae are adaptations to living an entire life cycle on land. The heart consists of two atria and a partially divided ventricle or two ventricles (in crocodiles). The nervous system, especially the brain, is more highly developed than that of amphibians.

Reptiles, like the fishes and amphibians, are largely **ectothermic,** without the capability to maintain a relatively high core-body temperature physiologically and with a greater dependence on gaining or losing heat from or to their external environment. Reptiles and other ectotherms have an adaptive advantage over endothermic mammals in warm and humid areas of the earth because they expend minimal energy on maintaining body temperature, which leaves more energy for reproduction. This advantage is reflected in the greater numbers of individuals and species of reptiles compared to mammals in the tropics. Mammals have the advantage in moderate to cold areas.

MATERIALS

Per student:

- scalpel

Per student pair:

- dissection pan

Per lab room:

- collection of preserved reptiles
- skeleton of snake
- turtle skeleton or shell
- boxes of different sizes of vinyl or latex gloves
- box of safety goggles

PROCEDURE

1. Examine an assortment of preserved reptiles and note their diversity as a group. This diverse group of vertebrates includes the turtles, lizards, snakes, crocodiles, and alligators.

Figure 20-25 Abdominal views of dissected frogs. (**a–c**) Male. (**d**) Female. *Continues.*

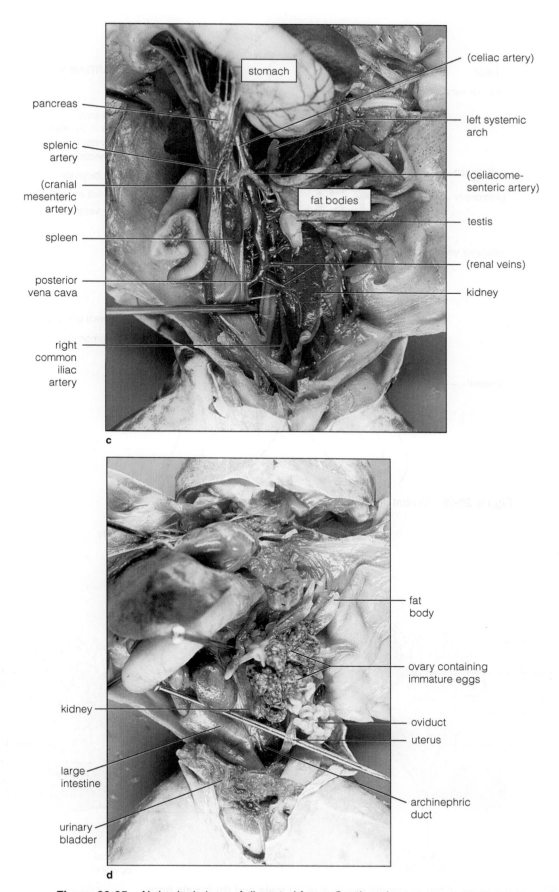

pancreas

splenic artery

(cranial mesenteric artery)

spleen

posterior vena cava

right common iliac artery

stomach

(celiac artery)

left systemic arch

(celiacome-senteric artery)

fat bodies

testis

(renal veins)

kidney

c

kidney

large intestine

urinary bladder

fat body

ovary containing immature eggs

oviduct

uterus

archinephric duct

d

Figure 20-25 Abdominal views of dissected frogs. *Continued.*

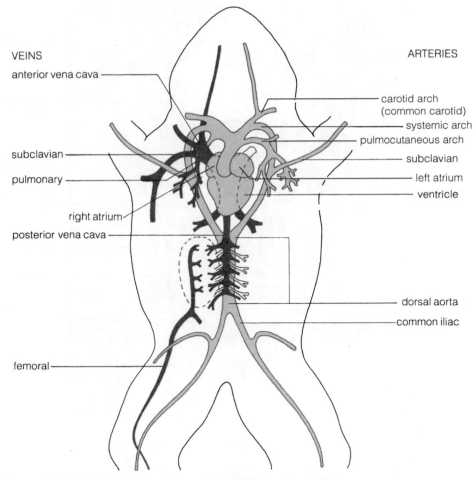

VEINS

ARTERIES

anterior vena cava

carotid arch
(common carotid)

systemic arch

pulmocutaneous arch

subclavian

subclavian

pulmonary

left atrium

ventricle

right atrium

posterior vena cava

dorsal aorta

common iliac

femoral

Figure 20-26   Ventral view of the major blood vessels of the frog.

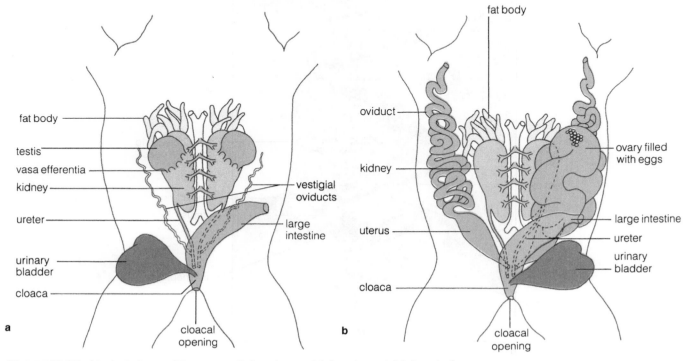

fat body

fat body

oviduct

testis

ovary filled
with eggs

vasa efferentia

kidney

kidney

vestigial
oviducts

ureter

large
intestine

uterus

large intestine

ureter

urinary
bladder

urinary
bladder

cloaca

cloaca

a

b

cloacal
opening

cloacal
opening

Figure 20-27   Ventral views of the urogenital systems of (a) male and (b) female frogs.

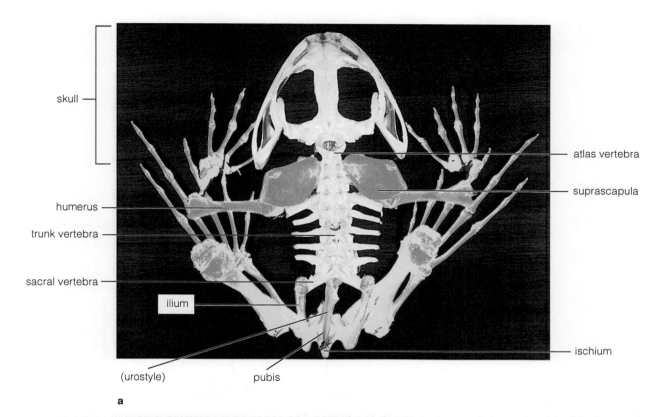

Labels for image a:
- skull
- atlas vertebra
- humerus
- suprascapula
- trunk vertebra
- sacral vertebra
- ilium
- (urostyle)
- pubis
- ischium

a

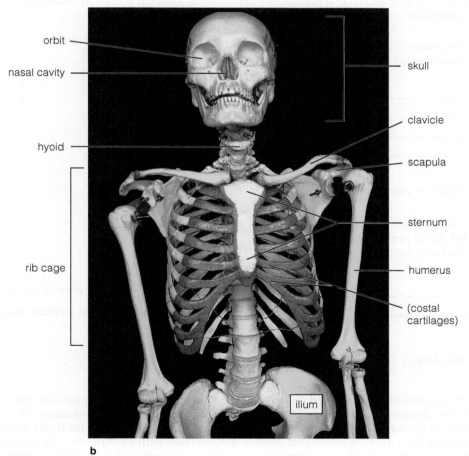

Labels for image b:
- orbit
- nasal cavity
- skull
- hyoid
- clavicle
- scapula
- rib cage
- sternum
- humerus
- (costal cartilages)
- ilium

b

Figure 20-28 Skeletons of (**a**) a bullfrog and (**b,c**) a human. The appendicular skeleton is colored yellow and the axial skeleton is uncolored. (Photos by D. Morton.) *Continues.*

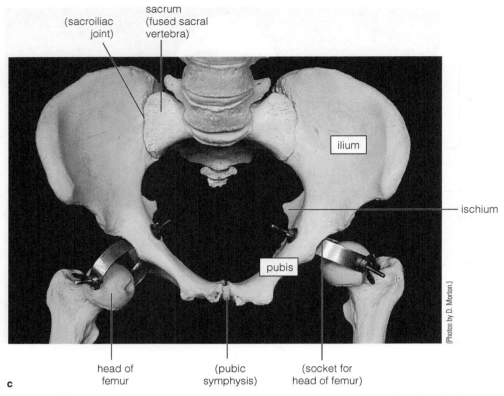

c

Figure 20-28 Skeletons of (**a**) a bullfrog and (**b,c**) a human. The appendicular skeleton is colored yellow and the axial skeleton is uncolored. *Continued.*

2. Compare the skeleton of a snake (Figure 20-30) with that of the frog. Describe any differences you see.

_____
_____
_____
_____
_____

Identify the axial and appendicular portions of the skeleton.

3. Look at the inside of the *carapace* (the upper portion) of a turtle shell. What portions of the skeleton are incorporated into the shell?

_____
_____
_____

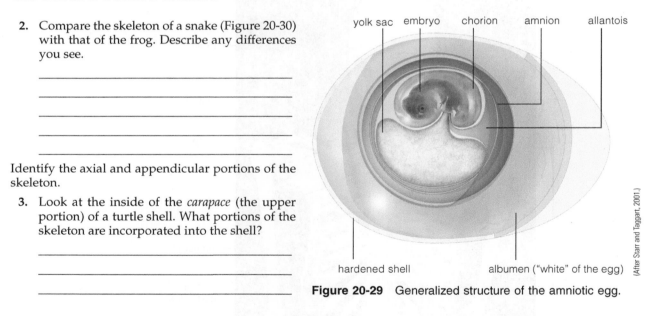

Figure 20-29 Generalized structure of the amniotic egg.

| 20.8 | **Birds (Class Aves)** *(10 min.)* |

Birds are likely descended from small bipedal (walked on two legs) reptiles about 160 million years ago and are thought to be closely related to dinosaurs. Their body is covered with *feathers;* and *scales,* reminiscent of their reptilian heritage, are present on the feet. The front limbs in most birds are modified as *wings* for flight. An additional internal adaptation for flight is the well-developed *sternum* (breastbone), with a *keel* for the attachment of powerful muscles for flight (Figure 20-31). Birds are **endothermic** vertebrates, capable of maintaining relatively high core-body temperatures physiologically.

numerous
free ribs
(no sternum)

unfused lower jaw and
other adaptations allow for
a flexible jaw mechanism

(Photo by D. Morton.)

Figure 20-30 Snake skeleton.

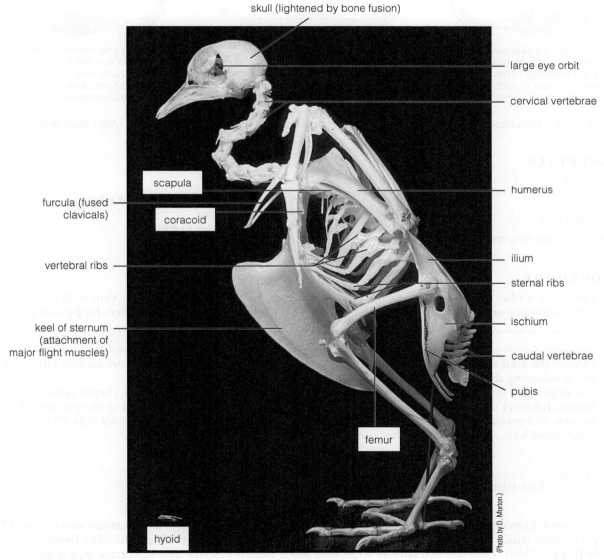

skull (lightened by bone fusion)

large eye orbit

cervical vertebrae

scapula

furcula (fused
clavicals)

coracoid

humerus

vertebral ribs

ilium

sternal ribs

ischium

keel of sternum
(attachment of
major flight muscles)

caudal vertebrae

pubis

femur

hyoid

(Photo by D. Morton.)

Figure 20-31 Bird skeleton.

The major *bones* of birds are *hollow* and contain *air sacs connected to the lungs.* Birds have a *four-chambered heart,* with two atria and two ventricles (Figure 20-32). This permits the complete separation of oxygenated and deoxygenated blood. Why is this circulatory arrangement an advantage for birds, as opposed to that found in amphibians and reptiles? (*Hint:* Recall that birds are endothermic and most can fly.)

_____

_____

_____

The nervous system resembles that of reptiles. However, the brain is larger, permitting more sophisticated behavior and muscular coordination; the optic lobes are especially well developed in association with a keen sense of sight.

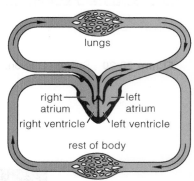

a In fishes, a two-chambered heart (atrium, ventricle) pumps blood in one circuit. Blood picks up oxygen in gills and delivers it to rest of body. Oxygen-poor blood flows back to heart.

b In amphibians, a heart pumps blood through two partially separate circuits. Blood flows to lungs, picks up oxygen, and returns to heart. It mixes with oxygen-poor blood still in heart, flows to rest of body, and returns to heart.

c In birds and mammals, the heart is fully partitioned into two halves. Blood circulates in two circuits: from the heart's right half to lungs and back, then from the heart's left half to oxygen-requiring tissues and back.

Figure 20-32 Circulatory systems of (**a**) fishes, (**b**) amphibians, and (**c**) birds and mammals. (After Starr and Taggart, 2001.)

MATERIALS

Per student:

■ scalpel

Per student pair:

■ dissection microscope

Per lab room:

■ an assortment of feathers, stuffed birds, or bird illustrations
■ several field guides to the birds

PROCEDURE

1. Examine a feather and identify the **rachis** (shaft) and **vane** (Figure 20-33). Examine the vane with the dissection microscope and note the **barbs** and **barbules**. What else do birds use their feathers for besides flight?

   _____

   _____

2. Identify the axial and appendicular portions of the skeleton (Figure 20-31). Note the various adaptations for flight, including the elongated wrists and ankles.

3. The upper and lower jaws are modified as variously shaped *beaks* or *bills,* with the shapes reflecting the feeding habits of the species. No teeth are present in adults. Examine the assortment of birds or bird illustrations and speculate on their food preferences by studying the configurations of their bills. Check your conclusions with a field guide or other suitable source that describes the food habits.

20.9   **Mammals (Class Mammalia)** *(10 min.)*

Mammals arose from an ancient branch of reptiles over 200 million years ago. The term *mammal* stems from the *mammary glands,* which all mammals possess. Female mammals feed their young milk produced by the mammary glands (Figure 20-34). The *brain* is relatively *larger than that of other vertebrates,* and its surface area is increased by grooves and folds (Figure 20-35). Behavior is more complex and flexible. *Hair* is present during some portion of the life span. Mammals are equipped with a variety of modifications and outgrowths of the skin in addition to hair, all made of the protein keratin. They include horns, spines, nails, claws, and hoofs. Mammalian dentition is intricate, with teeth specialized for cutting, grooming, wounding, tearing, slicing, and grinding. The teeth in the upper and lower jaws match up.

Like birds, mammals are *endothermic* and the *heart* is *four-chambered*. The ear frequently has a cartilaginous outer portion called the *pinna*, which functions to collect sound waves. In addition to mammary glands, there are three other types of skin glands: *sebaceous, sweat, and scent glands*.

MATERIALS

Per student:

- scalpel

Per lab room:

- stuffed mammals or mammal illustrations
- mammalian placentas and embryos (in utero)

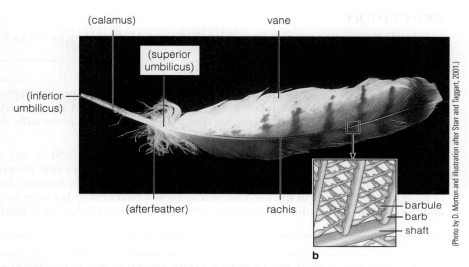

Figure 20-33   (a) Feather and (b) expanded view of the vane.

Figure 20-34   Female dog with nursing puppies.

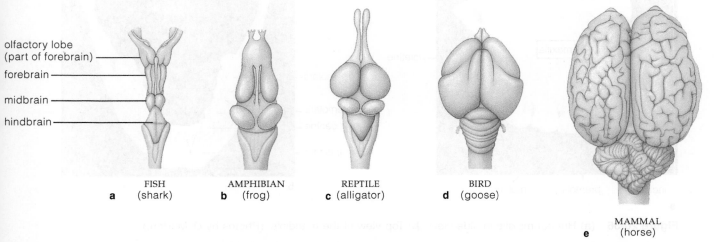

Figure 20-35   Evolutionary trend toward an expanded, more complex brain, as suggested by comparing the brain of existing vertebrates: (a) shark; (b) frog; (c) alligator; (d) goose; and (e) horse. These dorsal views are not to the same scale. (After Starr and Taggart, 2001.)

PROCEDURE

1. Study the assortment of mammals on display and list as many functions for hair as you can.

_____

_____

2. Except for two species of monotremes that lay eggs (platypus and spiny anteater), most mammals are **viviparous:** Females bear live young after supporting them in the uterus with a *placenta,* a connection between the mother and the embryo. The placenta exchanges gases with, delivers nutrients to, and removes wastes from the embryo, among other functions.

Some viviparous mammals (marsupials—kangaroos, opossums, and so on) give birth early, and along with spiny anteater hatchlings, continue development suckling milk in a skin pouch. Eutherian mammals give birth later, but the young of all mammals receive extended parental care. Examine the placentas and embryos in uteri of mammals on display in the lab. Can you suggest a relationship between the early development of mammals and the comparative sophistication of the nervous system and behavior of adult mammals?

_____

_____

3. Examine Figure 20-36 and identify the teeth present in the skull of the human skeleton. Fill in the numbers of each type in the upper and lower jaws and their functions in Table 20-3.

TABLE 20-3 Human Dentition			
Type of Tooth	Number in Upper Jaw	Number in Lower Jaw	Function
Incisors			
Canines			
Premolars			
Molars			

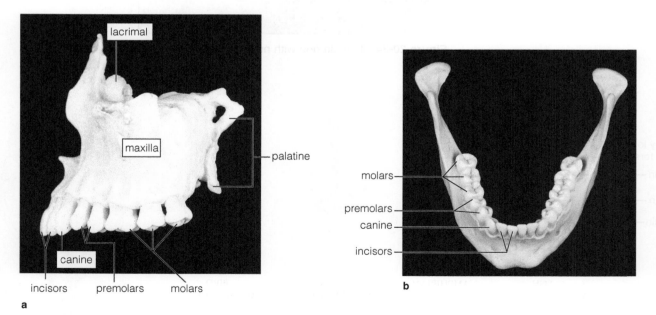

Figure 20-36 (**a**) Human maxilla in side view. (**b**) Top view of the mandible. (Photos by D. Morton.)

_____ **1.** Echinoderms and chordates are
(a) deuterostomes
(b) protostomes
(c) animals whose blastopore becomes a mouth
(d) both b and c

_____ **2.** The skin gills of sea stars are structures
(a) for the exchange of gases and excretion of ammonia
(b) of defense
(c) for movement
(d) that produce the skeletal elements

_____ **3.** The tube feet of a sea star
(a) bear tiny toes
(b) are located only at the tips of the arms
(c) function in movement
(d) protect the organism from predatory fish

_____ **4.** Aristotle's lantern is a tooth-bearing structure of the
(a) sea stars
(b) tunicates
(c) acorn worms
(d) sea urchins

_____ **5.** The sieve plate, stone canal, circular canal, and radial canals of a sea star are structures of the
(a) nervous system
(b) water-vascular system
(c) digestive system
(d) excretory system

_____ **6.** The dermal endoskeleton of echinoderms is made of
(a) cartilage
(b) bone
(c) calcium carbonate
(d) chitin

_____ **7.** Which structure is *not* a major diagnostic feature of the chordates?
(a) dorsal hollow nerve cord
(b) notochord
(c) pharyngeal gill slits
(d) vertebral column

_____ **8.** The sea squirts and lancelets have an inner chamber that expels water. This chamber is called the
(a) intestine
(b) bladder
(c) atrium
(d) nephridium

_____ **9.** Invertebrates
(a) do not have a vertebral column
(b) have a vertebral column
(c) are all members of the phylum Chordata
(d) do not include animals that are members of the phylum Chordata

_____ **10.** Which animal is a chordate?
(a) sea star
(b) sea cucumber
(c) acorn worm
(d) lancelet

_____ **11.** Animals that have the four basic characteristics of chordates plus a vertebral column are
(a) invertebrates
(b) hemichordates
(c) cephalochordates
(d) vertebrates

_____ **12.** The ammocoete is the larva of
(a) lampreys
(b) sharks
(c) bony fishes
(d) amphibians

_____ 13. Placoid scales are characteristic of class
     (a) Cephalaspidomorphi
     (b) Chondrichthyes
     (c) Osteichthyes
     (d) Reptilia

_____ 14. The bony movable flap that covers the gills and gill slits is called the
     (a) operculum
     (b) cranium
     (c) tympanum
     (d) colon

_____ 15. Which group of animals is endothermic?
     (a) fishes
     (b) mammals
     (c) reptiles
     (d) amphibians

_____ 16. The bones that surround and protect the brain are collectively called the
     (a) spinal cord
     (b) vertebral column
     (c) pelvic girdle
     (d) cranium

_____ 17. The lampreys are unusual vertebrates in that they have no
     (a) eyes
     (b) jaws
     (c) gill slits
     (d) mouth

_____ 18. The structure of the cartilaginous and bony fishes that detects vibrations in the water is the
     (a) anal fin
     (b) operculum
     (c) nostrils
     (d) lateral line

_____ 19. Amphibians have
     (a) a two-chambered heart
     (b) a three-chambered heart
     (c) a four-chambered heart
     (d) none of the above

_____ 20. The amniotic egg of reptiles, birds, and mammals is an adaptation to
     (a) carnivorous predators
     (b) a life on land
     (c) compensate for the short period of development of the young
     (d) protect the young from the nitrogenous wastes of the mother during the formation of the embryo

EXERCISE 20

Echinoderms, Invertebrate Chordates, and Vertebrates

POST-LAB QUESTIONS

Introduction

1. What characteristic of vertebrates is missing in all invertebrates?

2. List the basic characteristics of vertebrates.

20.1 Echinoderms (Phylum Echinodermata)

3. Describe the various structures on the aboral "spiny skin" of a sea star and discuss their functions.

4. Describe the various functions of tube feet.

5. Identify the following structures on this aboral view of the tip of a sea star arm.

a _____

b _____

c _____

(Photo by D. Morton.)

(78×).

6. Describe reproduction in the sea star.

7. List the structures in the water-vascular system of a sea star.

20.2 Chordates (Phylum Chordata)

8. List the four major characteristics of chordates.

9. Why are sea squirts and lancelets referred to as invertebrate chordates?

10. Compare the presence or absence of the four chordate characteristics in adult sea squirts and lancelets.

11. Compare arthropods, echinoderms, and chordates in terms of their similarities and differences.

Food for Thought

12. Hypothesize an evolutionary relationship among the bipinnaria larva of echinoderms, larval and adult tunicates, and lancelets.

20.3 Jawless Fishes (Class Cephalaspidomorphi)

13. What is an ammocoete? What is its possible significance to the evolution of vertebrates?

14. How do lampreys differ from other vertebrates?

20.4 Cartilaginous Fishes (Class Chondrichthyes)

15. Explain how the adaptations of cartilaginous fishes make them better predators.

20.5 Bony Fishes (Class Osteichthyes)

16. Identify this vertebrate structure. What do the rings represent?

(24×).

20.7 Reptiles (Class Reptilia)

17. Describe an amniotic egg. What is its evolutionary significance?

20.9 Mammals (Class Mammalia)

18. List the unique characteristics of mammals.

19. Describe the evolution of the heart in the vertebrates.

Food for Thought

20. About 65 million years ago, an asteroid impact may have caused a mass extinction, which led to the demise of dinosaurs and created new opportunities for surviving plants and animals, including mammals. Create a short evolutionary scenario for the next human-made or natural mass extinction event.

Plant and Animal Organization

After completing this exercise, you will be able to

1. define *vegetative, morphology, dicotyledon (dicot), monocotyledon (monocot), cotyledon, taproot system, node, internode, adventitious root, herb (herbaceous plant), woody (woody plant), heartwood, sapwood, growth increment (annual ring); tissue, organ, system, organism, histology, basement membrane, goblet cells, cilia, brush border of microvilli, keratinization, keratin, collagen fibers, elastic fibers, fibroblast, fat cells, lumen chondrocytes, lacunae, Haversian systems, osteocytes, actin filaments, myosin filaments, intercalated disk, neuron, cell body, axon, dendrites, neuroglia, body cavities*—*thoracic, abdominal, pleural, pericardial, pelvic, cranial* and *spinal;*

2. identify and give the function of the external structures of flowering plants (those in **boldface**);

3. identify and give the functions of the tissues and cell types of roots, stems, and leaves (those in **boldface**);

4. determine the age of woody branches;

5. discuss the high degree of organization present in animal structure and explain its significance;

6. recognize the four basic tissues and their common mammalian subtypes;

7. explain how the four basic tissues combine to make organs;

8. list each system of a mammal and its vital functions;

9. describe the basic plan of the mammalian body;

10. explain the layout of the body's major cavities;

11. locate the major organs in a mammal's body.

INTRODUCTION

Unicellular eukaryotic organisms contain organelles that carry on all functions vital to life. In multicellular organisms, each cell is specialized to emphasize certain activities, although most continue to carry on basic functions such as cellular respiration. In most animals, clusters of similarly specialized cells associate together along with any extracellular material they secrete and maintain to form **tissues.** Different subtypes from each of the four basic tissue types are combined much like quadruple-decker sandwiches to make the body's **organs.** Groups of related organs are strung together functionally, and usually structurally, to form **systems.** The levels of organization of an animal with systems can be summarized as follows:

Animal Organism

⋀

Systems (e.g., digestive, respiratory)

⋀

Organs (e.g., esophagus, stomach, trachea, lungs)

⋀

Epithelial, Connective, Muscular, and Nervous Tissues

⋀

Specialized Cells

⋀

Organelles

The first part of this exercise introduces you to the external and internal structure of the **vegetative organs**—those not associated with sexual reproduction—of flowering plants. The organs are the roots, stems, and leaves. Flowers are the sexual reproductive organs, and were considered in detail in Exercise 17. In the second part of this exercise, we examine animal tissues, organs, and organ systems.

Each organ is usually distinguished by its shape and form, its **morphology.** But the cells and tissues comprising these three organs are remarkably similar. Each organ is covered by the protective dermal tissue; each possesses vascular tissue that transports water, minerals, and the products of photosynthesis; and each contains ground tissue, that which is covered by the dermal tissue and in which the vascular tissue is embedded. Examine Figure 21-1, which illustrates these relationships.

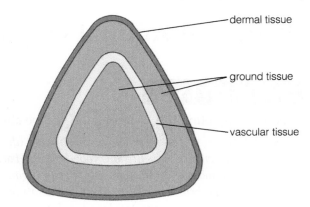

Figure 21-1 Model plant organ in cross section.

The organs of the plant body are more similar than they are dissimilar. In fact, for this reason the differences between a root and a stem or leaf are said to be *quantitative* rather than *qualitative*. That is, these differences are in the number and arrangement of cells and tissues, not the type. Consequently, the plant body is a continuous unit from one organ to the next.

We'll begin our study of plant and animal organization by examining the organs of two rather large assemblages of flowering plants, **dicotyledons** (dicots) and **monocotyledons** (monocots). **Cotyledons** are the leaves that are formed within the seed. Dicots have two seed leaves, monocots one. In addition to this fundamental difference, dicots and monocots have other dissimilarities, as shown in Figure 21-2. Refer to Figure 21-2 as you proceed through each section.

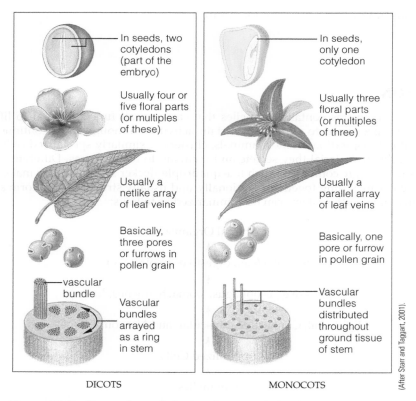

DICOTS   MONOCOTS

(After Starr and Taggart, 2001).

Figure 21-2 Comparison of dicot and monocot structure.

External Structure of the Flowering Plant *(About 15 min.)*

MATERIALS

Per student group (table):

- mature corn plant

Per lab room:

- living bean and corn plants in flats
- potted geranium and dumbcane plants
- dishpan half-filled with water

PROCEDURE

A. Dicotyledons

The common garden bean, *Phaseolus vulgaris*, is a representative dicot. Other familiar examples of dicotyledons (dicots) are sunflowers, roses, cucumbers, peas, maples, and oaks. Let's look at its external morphology. Label Figure 21-3 as you study the bean plant.

1. Obtain a bean plant by gently removing it from the medium in which it is growing. Wash the root system in the dishpan provided, not in the sink.

Figure 21-3   External structure of the bean plant.
Labels: root system, shoot system, primary root (taproot), lateral root, node, internode, axillary bud, terminal bud, cotyledon remnant, petiole, blade, simple leaf, compound leaf, leaflet

(After Starr and Taggart, 1984).

2. The plant consists of a **root system,** that portion usually below ground, and a typically aerial **shoot system.** Examine the root system first. The root system of the bean is an example of a **taproot system,** that is, one consisting of one large **primary root** (the **taproot**) from which **lateral roots** arise. Identify the taproot and lateral roots.
3. Now turn your attention to the shoot system, consisting of the stem and the leaves.
4. Identify the points of attachment of the leaves to the stem, called **nodes;** the regions between nodes are **internodes.**
5. Look in the upper angle created by the junction of the stem and leaf stalk to find the **axillary bud.** These buds give rise to branches and/or flowers.
6. Find the **terminal bud** at the very tip of the shoot system. The terminal bud contains an apical meristem that accounts for increases in length of the shoot system.

If lateral branches are produced from axillary buds, each lateral branch is terminated by a terminal bud and possesses nodes, internodes, and leaves, complete with axillary buds. As you see, the shoot system can be a highly branched structure.

7. Look several centimeters above the soil line for the lowermost node on the stem. If the plant is relatively young, you should find the **cotyledons** attached to this node. The cotyledons shrivel as food stored in them is used for the early growth of the seedling. Eventually the cotyledons fall off.

The cotyledons are sometimes called *seed leaves* because they are fully formed (although unexpanded) in the seed. By contrast, most of the leaves you're observing on the bean plant were immature or not present at all in the seed.

Now let's examine the other component of the shoot system, the foliage leaves (also called *true leaves* in contrast to the cotyledons). The first-formed foliage leaves (those nearest the cotyledons) are **simple leaves,** each leaf having one undivided blade.

8. Identify the **petiole** (leaf stalk) and **blade** on a simple leaf, and label it on Figure 21-3.

In bean plants, subsequently formed leaves are **compound leaves,** consisting of three **leaflets** per petiole. Each leaflet has its own short stalk and blade.

9. Identify a compound leaf, and label the petiole and leaflets in Figure 21-3.
10. Note the netted arrangement of veins in the blades. Veins contain vascular tissues—the xylem and phloem.
11. Identify the **midvein;** it is the largest vein and runs down the center of the blade, giving rise to numerous lateral veins.

B. Monocotyledons

Corn (*Zea mays*) is a **monocotyledon.** These plants have only one cotyledon (seed leaf). You're probably familiar with a number of monocots: lilies, onions, orchids, coconuts, bananas, and the grasses. (Did you realize that corn is actually a grass?)

Label Figure 21-4 as you study the corn plant.

1. Remove a single young plant from its growing medium and wash its root system in the dishpan. Note that the seed (technically this is a fruit called a "grain") is still attached to the plant.

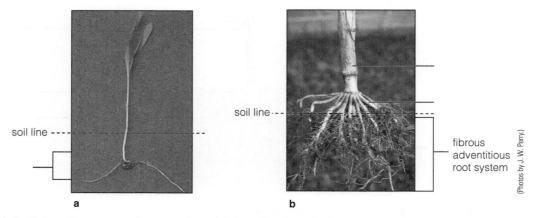

Figure 21-4 External structure of a corn plant. (**a**) Seedling (0.5×). (**b**) Lower portion of mature plant (0.1×). **Labels:** root system, prop root, leaf sheath

2. Identify the **root system.** Note that there is no one particularly prominent root. In most monocots, the primary root is short lived and is replaced by numerous **adventitious roots.** Adventitious roots are roots that arise from places other than existing roots.
3. Trace the adventitious roots back to the corn grain.

Where do they originate?

_____

As the roots branch, they develop into a **fibrous root system,** one particularly well suited to prevent soil erosion.

4. Examine the mature corn plant. Identify the large **prop roots** at the base of the plant.

Where do prop roots arise from?

_____

Would you classify these as adventitious roots? (yes or no) _____

5. The shoot system of a young corn plant appears somewhat less complex than that of the bean. There seem to be no nodes or internodes. Look at the mature corn plant again. You should see that nodes and inter-nodes do indeed exist. In your young plant, elongation of the stem has not yet taken place to any appreciable extent.
6. Strip off the leaves of the young corn plant. Keep doing so until you find the shoot apex. (It's deeply embedded.)
7. Examine the leaves of the corn plant in more detail. Note the absence of a petiole and the presence of a **sheath** that extends down the stem. The leaf sheath adds strength to the stem. Look at the veins, which have a parallel arrangement. (Contrast this to the petioled, netted-vein arrangement of the bean leaves.)

21.2   The Root System (About 15 min.)

MATERIALS

Per student:

- single-edged razor blade
- clean microscope slide
- coverslip
- prepared slide of buttercup (*Ranunculus*) root, c.s.
- prepared slide of corn (*Zea*) root, c.s.
- compound microscope

Per student pair:

- dH$_2$O in dropping bottles

Per lab room:

- germinating radish seeds in large petri dishes
- demonstration slide of Casparian strip in endo-dermal cell walls

PROCEDURE

A. Living Root Tip

1. Obtain a germinating radish seed. Identify the **primary root.** Its fuzzy appearance is due to the numerous tiny **root hairs** (Figure 21-5). Root hairs increase the absorptive surface of the root tremendously.
2. Using a razor blade, cut off the seed and discard it, then make a wet mount of the primary root. (Add enough water so that no air surrounds the root. *Do not* squash the root.)
3. Examine your preparation with the low-power objective of your compound microscope. (If you're having difficulty seeing the root clearly, increase its contrast by closing the microscope's diaphragm somewhat.) Locate the conical root tip.

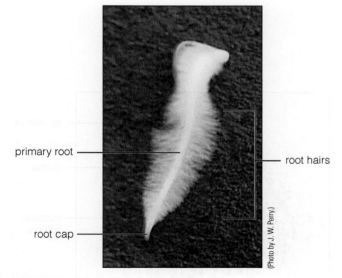

primary root — root hairs

root cap

(Photo by J. W. Perry.)

Figure 21-5 Living primary root (4×).

4. At the very end of the root tip, identify the protective **root cap** that covers the tip. As a root grows through the soil, the tip is thrust between soil particles. Were it not for the root cap, the apical meristem containing the dividing cells would be damaged.

5. Find the root hairs.

Do they originate all the way down to the root cap? (yes or no) _____

6. Examine the root hairs carefully.

What happens to their length as you observe them at increasing distance from the root tip?

_____

_____

      The youngest root hairs are the shortest. What does this imply regarding their point of origin and pattern of maturation?

_____

_____

B. Dicot Root Anatomy

Now let's see what the internal architecture of the root looks like.

1. Obtain a prepared slide containing a mature buttercup (*Ranunculus*) root in cross section. Refer to Figure 21-6 as you study this slide. Examine the slide first with the low-power objective of your compound microscope to gain an overall impression of the organization of the tissues present.
2. Starting at the edge of the root, identify the **epidermis.**
3. Moving inward, locate the **cortex** and the central **vascular column.** These regions represent the dermal, ground, and vascular tissue systems, respectively.
4. Switch to the medium-power objective for further study. Look at the outermost layer of cells, the **epidermis.**
5. Beneath the epidermis find the relatively wide **cortex,** consisting of parenchyma cells that contain numerous **starch grains.**

Based on the presence of starch grains, what would you suspect one function of this root might be?

_____

_____

6. Switch to the high-dry objective. Between the cells of the cortex, find numerous **intercellular spaces.**

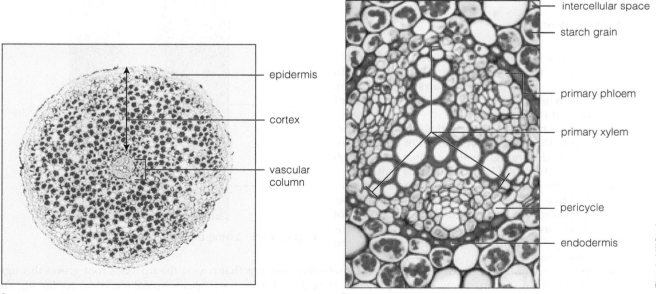

Figure 21-6 Cross section of buttercup (*Ranunculus*) root. (**a**) 45×. (**b**) Portion of cortex and vascular column (75×).

The innermost layer of the cortex is given a special name. This cylinder, a single cell thick, is called the **endodermis.**

7. Locate the endodermis on your slide and in Figure 21-6b.
8. Switch back to the medium-power objective, and focus your attention on the central vascular column. The cell layer immediately beneath the endodermis is the **pericycle.** Cells of the pericycle have the capacity to divide and produce lateral roots, like those you saw in the bean plant (Figure 21-3).
9. Finally, find the **primary xylem,** consisting of three or four ridges of thick-walled cells. (The stain used by most slide manufacturers stains the xylem cell walls red.) The xylem is the principal water-conducting tissue of the plant.
10. Between the "arms" of the xylem find the **primary phloem,** the tissue responsible for long-distance transport of carbohydrates produced by photosynthesis (known as photosynthates).

Primary xylem and phloem make up the *primary* vascular tissues, which are those produced by the apical meristems at the tips of the root and shoot. Later, we'll examine a *secondary* vascular tissue.

cell wall

toward cortex

toward vascular column

Casparian strip
(imagine that the cell wall is transparent; no cytoplasmic components are shown)

Figure 21-7 Diagrammatic representation of endodermal cells with Casparian strip.

xylem

cortex

Casparian strip in sectional view as part of radial wall of endodermal cell

Casparian strip in surface view as part of transverse wall of endodermal cell

(Photo by J. W. Perry.)

Figure 21-8 Endodermal cells showing Casparian strip (296×).

C. Monocot Root Anatomy

Now that you have an understanding of the internal structure of a dicot root, let's compare and contrast it with that of a monocot. Draw and label the monocot root in Figure 21-9 as you proceed with your study.

1. Obtain a prepared slide of a cross section of a corn (*Zea mays*) root. Examine it with the low-power objective of your compound microscope. Draw the general shape of the corn root in Figure 21-9.
2. Identify and draw the **epidermis.**
3. Next locate the **cortex.** Count the number of cell layers and draw the cortex.

Do you find any starch grains in the cortex of the corn stem? _____

4. Now locate the **endodermis.** If the root you have is a mature one, you will see that the endodermis has very thick walls on three sides.
5. The vascular column of a monocot is quite different from a dicot in several ways. First note that the center is occupied by thin-walled cells. These cells make up a region called the **pith.**
6. Draw the pith.
7. Next note that the **xylem** of this monocot root consists of scattered cells. Look at Figure 21-10, a high magnification photomicrograph of the xylem and phloem of this root.
8. Draw the xylem.

Figure 21-9 Drawing of a corn (monocot) root, c.s. (_____×).
Labels: epidermis, cortex, endodermis, pith, xylem, phloem

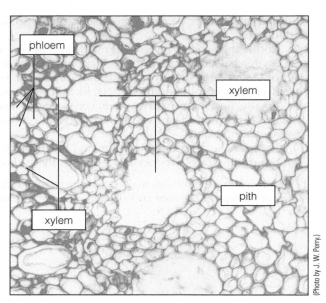

(Photo by J. W. Perry.)

Figure 21-10 Portion of a cross section of a corn (monocot) root showing vascular tissue (140×).

| 21.3 | **The Shoot System: Stems** *(About 25 min.)* |

MATERIALS

Per student:

- prepared slides of
    herbaceous dicot stem, c.s. (flax, *Linum*; or
    alfalfa, *Medicago*)
    monocot stem, c.s. (corn, *Zea*)
    woody stem, c.s. (basswood, *Tilia*)
- woody twig (hickory, *Carya*; or horse chestnut, *Aesculus*)
- metric ruler or meter stick
- compound microscope

Per student pair:

- cross section of woody branch (tree trunk)
- dissecting microscope

Per lab room:

- demonstration slide of lenticel

PROCEDURE

A. Dicot Stem: Primary Structure

Remember that the root and shoot are basically similar in structure; only the arrangement of tissues differs. Dicot stems have their vascular tissues arranged in a more or less complete ring of individual bundles of vascular tissue (called vascular bundles). Moreover, the ground tissue of dicots can be differentiated into two regions: **pith** and **cortex.**

You've probably heard the term *herb.* An *herb* is an **herbaceous plant,** one that develops no or very little wood. Herbaceous plants have only primary tissues. Woody plants develop secondary tissues—wood and bark.

Beans, flax, and alfalfa are examples of herbaceous dicots. Maples and oaks are woody dicots. Let's look at an herbaceous stem first.

1. Obtain a slide of an herbaceous dicot stem (flax or alfalfa). This slide may be labeled "herbaceous dicot stem." As you study this slide, refer to Figure 21-11, of a partial section of an herbaceous dicot stem.
2. Using the low- and medium-power objectives, identify the single-layered **epidermis** covering the stem, a multilayered **cortex** between the epidermis and **vascular bundles,** and the **pith** in the center of the stem.

3. Observe a vascular bundle with the high-dry objective (Figure 21-12). Adjacent to the cortex, find the **primary phloem.**
4. Just to the inside of the primary phloem, locate the thin-walled cells of the **vascular cambium.** (The vascular cambium is the lateral meristem that produces wood and secondary phloem, both secondary tissues. Despite your specimen being an herbaceous plant, a vascular cambium may be present. Generally, this meristem does not produce enough secondary tissue to result in the plant being considered woody.)
5. Locate the thick-walled cells of the **primary xylem.** The primary xylem is that vascular tissue closest to the pith. (The wall of the xylem cells is probably stained red.)

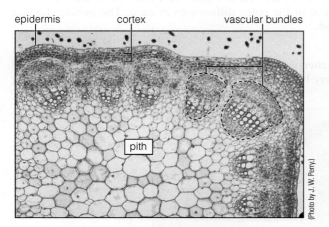

(Photo by J. W. Perry.)

Figure 21-11 Portion of a cross section of an herbaceous dicot stem (75×).

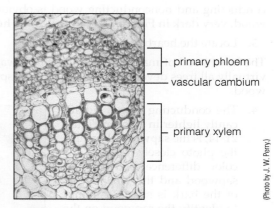

— primary phloem

— vascular cambium

— primary xylem

(Photo by J. W. Perry.)

Figure 21-12 Vascular bundle of an herbaceous dicot stem (192×).

B. External Features of Woody Dicot Stems

Woody plants are those that undergo secondary growth, producing the secondary tissues. Both roots and shoots may have secondary growth. This growth occurs because of activity of the two meristems near the edge of the plant—the vascular cambium and the cork cambium. The vascular cambium produces secondary xylem (wood) and secondary phloem, while the cork cambium produces a portion of the bark called the **periderm.**

1. Examine a twig of hickory (*Carya*) or buckeye (*Aesculus*) that has lost its leaves. Label Figure 21-13 as you study the twig.
2. Find the large **terminal bud** at the tip of the twig. If your twig is branched, each branch has its own terminal bud.
3. Identify the shield-shaped **leaf scars** at each **node.** (Remember, a node is the region where a leaf attaches to the stem.) Leaf scars represent the point at which the leaf petiole was attached on the stem.
4. Within each leaf scar, note the numerous dots. These are the **vascular bundle scars.** Immediately above and adjacent to most leaf scars should be an **axillary bud.**
5. In the **internode** regions of the twig, locate the small raised bumps on the surface; these are **lenticels,** the regions of the periderm that allow for exchange of gases.

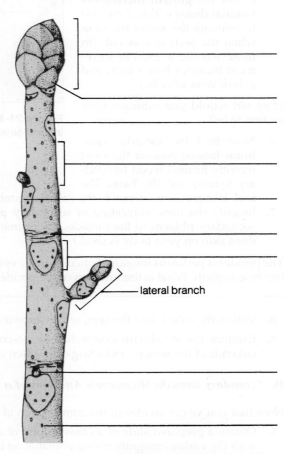

— lateral branch

Figure 21-13 External structure of a woody stem. **Labels:** terminal bud, leaf scar, node, vascular bundle scar, axillary bud, internode, lenticel, bud scale, terminal bud scale scars

1. Examine a cross section of a tree trunk (Figure 21-14; *trunk* is the nonscientific term for any large, woody stem). A tiny region in the center of the stem is the **pith.** Most of the trunk is made up of **wood** (also called *secondary xylem*). Locate the pith and the wood.
2. Now identify the **bark.**

As a woody stem grows larger, it requires additional structural support and more tissue for transport of water. These functions are accomplished by the wood. However, it is only the outer few years' growth of wood that is involved in water conduction. In some tree species, like that pictured in Figure 21-14, the distinction between conducting and nonconducting wood is obvious because of the color differences in each. The nonconducting wood, very dark in Figure 21-14, is called the **heartwood.**

3. Locate the heartwood in your stem.

The heartwood of many species, like black walnut or cherry, is highly prized for furniture making. Although virtually all trees develop heartwood, not all species have heartwood that is *visibly* distinct from the conducting wood.

4. The conducting wood, significantly lighter in color in Figure 21-14, is the **sapwood.** Examine the photo closely, because the color difference between the sapwood and the inner layers of the bark is subtle. Attempt to identify the sapwood on the stem you are examining.
5. Count the **growth increments (annual rings)** within the wood to estimate the age of the stem when the section was cut. (In most woods, a growth increment includes *both* a light and a dark layer of cells.)

Figure 21-14 Cross section of a woody locust stem. This stem was injured several years into its growth, causing the unusual shape (0.5×).

How old would you estimate your section to be? _____ years

6. Now find the **vascular cambium** located *between* the most recently formed wood (secondary xylem) and the **bark.** The bark is everything *external* to the vascular cambium.
7. Identify the bark, consisting of **secondary phloem** and **periderm.** (As the vascular cambium produces secondary phloem to the outside, the primary phloem, cortex, and epidermis are sloughed off, much as dead skin on your body is shed.)

The periderm performs the same function as the epidermis before the epidermis ruptured as a result of the stem's increase in girth. What is the function of the periderm?

_____

8. Within the wood, find the **rays,** which appear as lines running from the center toward the edge of the stem.
9. Examine the wood with a dissecting microscope and locate the numerous holes in the wood. These are the cut ends of the water-conducting cells, often called **pores.**

D. Secondary Growth: Microscopic Anatomy of a Woody Dicot Stem

Now that you've got an idea of the composition of a woody stem, let's examine one with the microscope.

1. Obtain a prepared slide of a cross section of a woody stem (basswood, *Tilia*, or another stem). Examine it with the various magnifications available on the dissecting microscope. Use Figure 21-15 as a reference.
2. Starting at the edge, identify the **periderm** (darkly stained cells). Depending on the age of the stem, **cortex** (thin-walled cells with few contents) may be present just beneath the periderm. Now find the broad band of **secondary phloem** (consisting of cells in pie-shaped wedges). Identify the **vascular cambium** (a narrow band of cells separating the secondary phloem from secondary xylem), **secondary xylem (wood),** and pith

periderm
cortex
secondary phloem
— bark

vascular cambium

secondary xylem (wood)

lenticel

one annual ring

vessel member (pore)

ray

(Photo by J. W. Perry.)

Figure 21-15 Cross section of a woody dicot stem (15×).

(large, thin-walled cells in the center). Count the number of growth increments (annual rings). Note the largest, thick-walled cells in the wood. These are the pores.

How old is this section? _____ years

3. Find the **rays** running through the wood. Rays are parenchyma cells that carry water and photosynthates *laterally* in the stem. (For the most part, the xylem and phloem carry substances *vertically* in the plant.)

Recall that the periderm replaces the epidermis as secondary growth takes place. The epidermis had stomata, which allowed the exchanging of gases between the plant and the environment. When the epidermis was shed, so were the stomata. But the need for exchange of gases still exists because the living cells require oxygen for respiration (Exercise 10). The plant has solved this problem by having special regions, **lenticels,** in the periderm. Lenticels are groups of cells with lots of intercellular space, in contrast to the tightly packed cells in the rest of the periderm.

4. Identify a lenticel on your slide. If none is found, examine the *demonstration* slide, specifically chosen to demonstrate this feature.

E. Structure of a Monocot Stem

Monocot and dicot stems differ in several ways. Monocot stems lack differentiation of the ground tissue into cortex and pith. Unlike the dicot stem whose vascular tissues are arranged in a ring, the vascular bundles of monocots are scattered throughout the ground tissue.

As you study the monocot stem, draw what you see in Figure 21-16.

1. Obtain a prepared slide of a monocot (corn, *Zea mays*) stem cross section. Observe the slide first using the low-power objective of your compound microscope, or perhaps even a dissecting microscope.
2. Draw its general appearance in Figure 21-16, labeling the **epidermis** on the outside, the thin-walled cells comprising the **ground tissue,** and the numerous **vascular bundles** scattered within the vascular tissue.
3. Switch to the medium-power objective of your compound microscope to study a single vascular bundle more closely. Draw the detail of one vascular bundle in Figure 21-17. (The vascular bundles of monocots look a lot like the face of a human or other primate.)

Figure 21-16 Drawing of a corn (monocot) stem, c.s. (_____×).
Labels: epidermis, ground tissue, vascular bundles

Figure 21-17 Drawing of the vascular bundle of a corn (monocot) stem, c.s. (_____×).
Labels: bundle sheath, xylem, phloem

4. Observe the thick-walled cells surrounding the vascular bundle. These cells make up the bundle sheath. (The walls of these cells are often stained red.)
5. Note the very large cells that give the impression of the vascular bundle's "eyes, nose, and mouth." These cells make up the water-conducting xylem. (The cell walls are often stained red.) Draw and label these xylem.
6. Finally, find the phloem, located on the vascular bundle's "forehead." (Phloem cell walls are typically stained green or blue.)

21.4   The Shoot System: Leaves *(About 20 min.)*

Leaves make up the second part of the shoot system. You examined the external morphology of the leaves in Section 21.1. Now let's look inside leaves, starting with a typical dicot leaf.

MATERIALS

Per student:

- prepared slide of dicot leaf, c.s. (lilac, *Syringa*)
- prepared slide of monocot leaf, c.s. (corn, *Zea*)
- compound microscope

PROCEDURE

A. Dicot Leaf Anatomy

1. Obtain a prepared slide of a cross section of a dicot leaf (lilac or other). Refer to Figure 21-18 as you examine the leaf.
2. Examine the leaf first with the low-power objective to gain an overall impression of its morphology. Note the size and orientation of the **veins** within the leaf. The veins contain the xylem and phloem.

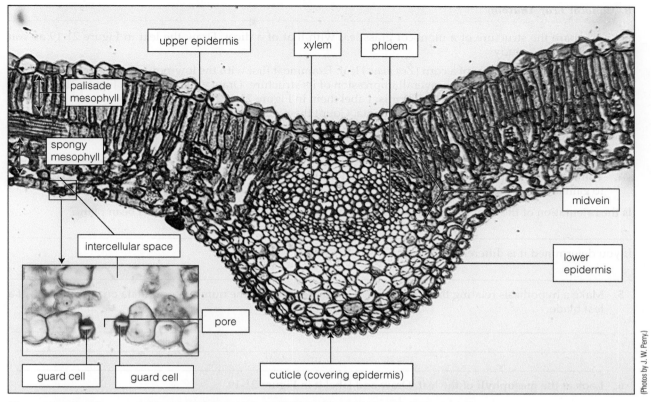

Figure 21-18 Cross section of a dicot leaf with midrib (105×); inset of a stoma (480×).

(Photos by J. W. Perry.)

3. Find the centrally located **midvein** within the **midrib,** the midvein-supporting tissue. You might think of the midvein as the major pipeline of the leaf, carrying water and minerals to the leaf and materials produced during photosynthesis to sites where they will be used during respiration.

4. Use the high-dry objective to examine a portion of the blade to one side of the midvein. Starting at the top surface of the leaf, find the **cuticle,** a waxy, water-impervious substance covering the **upper epidermis.** The epidermis is a single layer of tightly appressed cells.

5. The ground tissue of the leaf is represented by the **mesophyll** (literally "middle leaf"). In dicot leaves, the mesophyll is usually divided into two distinct regions; immediately below the upper epidermis, find the two layers of **palisade mesophyll.** These columnar-shaped cells are rich in chloroplasts.

6. Below the palisade mesophyll, find the loosely arranged **spongy mesophyll.** Note the large volume of **intercellular air space** within the spongy mesophyll.

Does the spongy mesophyll contain any chloroplasts? (yes or no) _____

What is one function that occurs within the spongy mesophyll? _____

7. In the **lower epidermis,** find a **stoma** (plural: *stomata*) with its **guard cells** and the **pore** (inset, Figure 21-18). Large **epidermal hairs** shaped somewhat like mushrooms are usually found on the lower epidermis.

Is the lower epidermal layer covered by a cuticle? _____

8. Compare the abundance of stomata within the lower epidermis with that in the upper epidermis.

Which epidermal surface has more stomata? _____

9. Examine the midvein in greater detail. Find the thick-walled xylem cells (often stained red).
10. Below the xylem, locate the **phloem** (usually stained green).
11. Now identify and examine the smaller veins within the lamina (blade). Note that these, too, contain both xylem and phloem.

B. Monocot Leaf Anatomy

Let's compare the structure of a monocot grass leaf with that of a dicot. Draw the leaf in Figure 21-19 as you proceed with your study.

1. Obtain a prepared slide of a corn (*Zea mays*) leaf. Examine it first with the low-power objective of your compound microscope to gain an overall impression of its structure. Draw what you see in Figure 21-19.
2. Identify the **upper** and **lower epidermis.** Label them in Figure 21-19.
3. Search on both epidermal layers for **stomata.** Count them on each layer.

Are there more, fewer, or about the same number on the upper epidermis versus the lower?

_____

4. Think about the orientation of the leaf blade on the plant. (If necessary, examine a living or dried corn plant to gain an impression of the orientation.)

Is the orientation of the corn leaves the same or different from that of a dicot, such as the bean plant?

_____

If you determined it is different, in what way is it different?

_____

5. Make a hypothesis relating the orientation of the leaf blade and the number of stomata on each surface of a leaf blade.

_____

_____

_____

6. Look at the **mesophyll** of the leaf. Draw and label it in Figure 21-19.

Figure 21-19 Drawing of a corn (monocot) leaf, c.s. (_____×).
Labels: cuticle, epidermis, stoma, guard cells, mesophyll, bundle sheath, xylem, phloem

Is the mesophyll divided into palisade and spongy layers? (yes or no) _____

7. Note the **intercellular air spaces** within the mesophyll. Draw and label the intercellular air spaces.
8. Note that the bundle sheath cells are tightly packed, with no intercellular spaces separating them. The bundle sheath serves a function like that of the endodermis in the root.
9. Finally, identify the larger **xylem** cells and **phloem** cells within the vascular bundle. Draw and label these tissues in Figure 21-19.

21.5   Tissues *(50 min.)*

The study of tissues is called **histology.** The four basic tissues types are **epithelial tissue, connective tissue, muscle tissue,** and **nervous tissue.** Each type has subtypes. In your study of these subtypes, you will examine a variety of tissues and organs, all permanently mounted on glass microscope slides. Most slides have sections of tissues and organs, usually 6–10 μm thick. Other slides have whole pieces of organs that are either transparent or are teased (gently pulled apart) and spread on the surface of the slide until they are thin enough to see through. Some organs are simply smeared onto the surface of slides.

These prepared slides have been chosen to show not only the characteristics of each tissue but also how variations in the basic structure of each allows for the related but distinct functions of its subtypes. For the sake of simplicity, this exercise includes only the common subtypes of adult mammalian tissues.

MATERIALS

Per student:

- compound microscope, lens paper, a bottle of lens-cleaning solution (optional), a lint-free cloth (optional), a dropper bottle of immersion oil (optional)
- prepared slides of
  - whole mount of mesentery (simple squamous epithelium)
  - section of the cortex of the mammalian kidney
  - section of trachea
  - small intestine c.s. (preferably of the ileum)
  - section of esophagus
  - section of mammalian skin
  - sections of contracted and distended urinary bladders

teased spread of loose (areolar) connective tissue
tendon, l.s.
compact bone ground c.s.
section of white adipose tissue
sections of the three muscle types
smear of the spinal cord of an ox (neurons)

Per lab room:

- demonstration of intercalated disks in cardiac muscle tissue
- 50-mL beaker three-fourths full of water
- 50-mL beaker three-fourths full of immersion oil
- 2 small glass rods

PROCEDURE

A. Epithelial Tissues

Epithelial tissues are widespread throughout the body, covering both the body's outer (epidermis of skin) and inner surfaces (ventral body cavities), and lining the inner surfaces of tubular organs (the small intestine, for example). Their main functions are *protection* and *transport* (such as secretion and absorption). Specialized functions include sensory reception and the maintenance of the body's gametes (egg and developing sperm).

Epithelial cells carry on rapid cell division in the adult, and various stages of mitosis are often seen in this tissue type. As a consequence, epithelia have the highest rates of cell turnover among tissues. For example, the lining of the small intestine replaces itself every 3–4 days. Epithelial tissues don't have blood vessels and are attached to the underlying connective tissue by an extracellular **basement membrane** that is difficult to see if it is not specially stained. Use the following questions to identify most subtypes of epithelial tissue:

QUESTION 1. What is the shape of the outermost cells?

There are three answers: *squamous* (scalelike or flat), *cuboidal*, or *columnar*. These choices describe the shape of the cells when viewed in a section perpendicular to the surface. In surface view, all three types are polygonal.

QUESTION 2. How many layers of cells are there?

Epithelial tissues are *simple* if there is one layer of cells; they are *stratified* if there are two or more. Figure 21-20 applies these definitions to squamous epithelia. *Pseudostratified* epithelial subtypes appear stratified but

simple
squamous
epithelium

a

stratified
squamous
epithelium

b

Figure 21-20 Squamous epithelia. (**a**) Simple.
(**b**) Stratified.

cilia

columnar
epithelial
cells

basement
membrane

Figure 21-21 Pseudostratified columnar
epithelium. It is columnar because of the
shape of the cells that reach the free surface.

really are not because their cells all rest on the basement membrane (Figure 21-21). As only the tallest cells reach the free surface, cell nuclei lie at different levels, giving the false appearance of several layers of cells.

In addition, the epithelium that lines the inside of the urinary bladder (and parts of other nearby urinary system organs) changes its subtype as it fills or empties with urine. This epithelium is called *transitional* to avoid confusion.

There are six common subtypes of epithelia: *simple squamous, simple cuboidal, simple columnar, pseudostratified columnar, stratified squamous,* and *transitional.* Refer to Figures 21-40, 21-41, and 21-42 as you find and examine these subtypes in the following slides.

1. *Whole mount of mesentery* (Figure 21-41). The mesentery is a fold of the abdominal wall and holds the intestines in place. This slide is a surface view of the **simple squamous epithelium,** which lines the inside of the ventral body cavities and the organs within.

What is the shape of the surface cells? _____
Draw what you see in Figure 21-22 and note the total magnification of the compound microscope you're using. Repeat this procedure for each subsequent drawing.

2. *Kidney* (Figure 21-42). With the help of Figure 21-23, find a *renal corpuscle.* A renal corpuscle is composed of a tuft of capillaries surrounded by a hollow capsule formed from the cup-shaped end of one of the kidney's functional units, the nephron. Identify a side view of the simple squamous epithelium that comprises the outer wall of the capsule. Around the renal corpuscle, you can see a number of transverse and oblique sections of the tubular portion of the nephron. Their walls are composed of **simple cuboidal epithelium.** The main function of the nephrons and the entire kidney is the production of urine.

3. *Trachea* (Figure 21-40). The trachea is a tubular organ that conveys air to and from the lungs. Note that its inner surface is lined by **pseudostratified columnar epithelium** (Figure 21-24). Locate the unicellular glands, which are called **goblet cells** because of their shape. They secrete mucus that is difficult to see unless it is specifically stained. Using high power, do you see the numerous hairlike structures that project from the surface of the columnar epithelial cells? These are **cilia,** which in life move synchronously, sweeping mucus, trapped bacteria, and debris up the trachea to the throat. When you clear your throat, you collect this mucus and swallow it.

Figure 21-22 Drawing of a surface view
of simple squamous epithelium (____×).

Figure 21-23 Sections of the cortex of the kidney, **(a)** low-power (25×) and **(b)** medium-power (183×) views.

(Photos by D. Morton.)

4. *Small intestine* (Figure 21-41). The small intestine is a tubular organ that connects the stomach to the large intestine. Its inner surface is lined with **simple columnar epithelium** (Figure 21-25). Note that *goblet cells* are present. Don't confuse the relatively thinner **brush border of microvilli** with the cilia from the previous slide. Microvilli are primarily responsible for the large surface area of the small intestine. Individual microvilli can best be seen at the electron-microscopic level (Figure 21-26).

5. *Esophagus* (Figure 21-40). The tubular esophagus connects the throat to the stomach. Examine the epithelium lining the inner surface of the esophagus (Figure 21-27).

Is the shape of the outermost cells squamous, cuboidal, or columnar? _____

Are there one or many layers of cells in this tissue? _____

Name this subtype of epithelial tissue. _____

6. *Skin*. The skin is divided into three layers (Figure 21-28). The *epidermis* is composed of stratified squamous epithelium, while the *dermis* and *hypodermis* (or subcutaneous layer) are connective tissue and will be studied later.

The epidermis is the most extreme example of a protective epithelium. The process of keratinization, whereby the cells transform themselves into bags of the protein keratin, causes strata in the epidermis. It is this substance that gives skin its tough, flexible, and water-resistant surface.

At one of the free edges of your section of mammalian skin, locate the **keratinized stratified squamous epithelium.** It will be stained bluer than the predominately pink connective tissue layers. Hair follicles and multicellular sweat glands may be present in the connective tissue layers. These structures grow into the connective tissue layers from the epidermis during the development of the skin.

7. *Urinary bladder* (Figure 21-42). Figure 21-29 shows two sections, one from a contracted bladder, the other from a distended bladder. Locate the **transitional epithelium** at the surface of each section. The transitional epithelium from the contracted bladder appears like stratified cuboidal epithelium. In the distended bladder, the transitional epithelium is thinner and looks like stratified squamous epithelium. Draw a high-power view of these two extremes in Figure 21-30.

B. Connective Tissue

Connective tissues occur in all parts of the body. They contain a large amount of material external to the cells, called the *extracellular matrix*. This matrix consists of *fibers* embedded in *ground substance*. Two basic kinds of fibers exist: collagen and elastic. Collagen fibers are tough, flexible, and inelastic, whereas elastic fibers stretch when pulled, returning to their original length when the pull is removed. Except for cartilage, connective tissues contain blood vessels. Similar to epithelia, connective tissue cells are capable of cell division in the adult, but at a reduced rate. Table 21-1 lists most connective tissue subtypes along with their matrix characteristics.

basement membrane

pseudostratified coumnar epithelium

mucosa

(glands)

submucosa

tracheal cartilage (hyaline variety)

a

cilia

columnar epithelial cells

pseudostratified columnar epithelium

nucleus of a goblet cell

basal epithelial cells

loose connective tissue

(Photos by D. Morton.)

b

collagen fiber   nucleus of fibroblast

Figure 21-24   Sections of the inner surface of the trachea, (**a**) low-power (100×) and (**b**) oil immersion (1000×) views.

(capillary)

(lacteal)

loose
connective tissue

villus

simple
cuboidal
epithelium

goblet cell

(lacteal)

intestinal gland

a

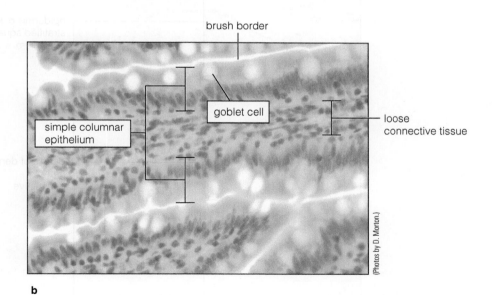

brush border

goblet cell

simple columnar
epithelium

loose
connective tissue

(Photos by D. Morton.)

b

Figure 21-25 Sections of the inner surface of the small intestine, (**a**) medium-power (250×) and (**b**) high-power (400×) views.

Figure 21-26 Scanning electron microscopic view of the surface of the small intestine: MA—small microvilli on surface of absorptive cells, Mv—longer, larger microvilli on surface of a goblet cell, and arrows indicate droplets of mucus (12,220×).

stratified squamous epithelium

loose connective tissue

Figure 21-27 Section of the epithelial tissue lining the inner surface of the esophagus (300×).

epidermis of keratinized stratified squamous epithelium

dermis of dense irregular connective tissue

hypodermis

Figure 21-28 Section of skin (30×).

contracted transitional epithelium

distended transitional epithelium

(Photos courtesy Biodisc, Inc.)

a

b

Figure 21-29 Sections of (**a**) contracted and (**b**) distended urinary bladders (89×).

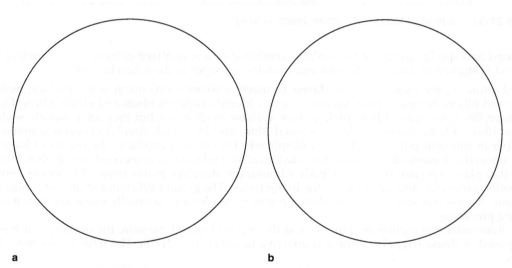

a

b

Figure 21-30 Drawings of high-power views of transitional epithelia from (**a**) contracted and (**b**) distended urinary bladders (_____×).

TABLE 21-1	Connective Tissue Groups and Common Subtypes	
Group	**Subtypes**	**Matrix Contains**
Soft	Loose (also called areolar)	Few collagen and elastic fibers arranged apparently randomly
	Dense irregular	Many collagen or elastic fibers arranged apparently randomly
	Dense regular	Many collagen or elastic fibers arranged in a parallel fashion
Hard	Cartilage	Many collagen or elastic fibers and polymerized (or jellylike) ground substance
	Bone	Many collagen fibers and mineralized ground substance
Special	Adipose	Delicate collagen fibers
	Blood	Plasma

collagen fibers

elastic fibers

fibroblasts

(Photo by D. Morton.)

Figure 21-31   Spread of loose connective tissue (450×).

The hard and special groups are sometimes combined as a specialized category of connective tissue sub-types. Blood is studied in Exercise 25. Find and examine subtypes in the following slides.

1. *Teased spread of loose connective tissue.* **Loose connective tissue** forms much of the packing material of the body and fills in the spaces between other tissues. Identify **collagen fibers** and **elastic fibers** (Figure 21-31). Collagen fibers are stained light pink and are variable in diameter, but they are generally wider than the elastic fibers. Elastic fibers are darkly stained, thin, and branched. Areolar connective tissue contains a number of different cell types. To see a **fibroblast**—the cell that produces the matrix of loose and other soft connective tissues—look for an elongated, oval-shaped nucleus associated with a fiber. Many kinds of cells that play important roles in the body's immune system live in this tissue. The spaces between fibers and cells contain ground substance in the living tissue. The ground substance of all soft connective tissues consists of a viscous soup of carbohydrate-protein molecules and is usually extracted from tissue sections during processing.

2. *Skin.* Reexamine the section of skin. Look at the second layer of the skin, the dermis, which is primarily composed of **dense irregular fibrous connective tissue** (Figure 21-28). The term *fibrous* refers to collagen fibers.

The dermis cushions the body from everyday stresses and strains. Note that the looser irregular connective tissue of the hypodermis has a lower concentration of collagen fibers and islands of fat cells. It functions as a shock absorber, as an insulating layer, and as a site for storing water and energy. In animals that move their skin independently of the rest of the body (like cats), skeletal muscle tissue also is found in the hypodermis.

3. *Tendon.* A tendon connects a skeletal muscle organ to a bone organ. Tendons are composed predominantly of **dense regular fibrous connective tissue.** Examine a longitudinal section of a tendon (Figure 21-32).

Describe the density and arrangement of the fibers.

_____

_____

_____

This design makes tendons very strong, much like a rope composed of braided strings, which in turn are made of even smaller fibers. How are the fibroblasts oriented relative to the arrangement of the fibers?

_____

_____

4. *Trachea* (Figure 21-40). Re-examine the section of the trachea. Find a portion of one of the supporting carti-lages, which prevent the wall from collapsing and closing the **lumen** (the space within any hollow organ). These cartilaginous structures are composed of **hyaline cartilage** tissue (Figure 21-33). Look for the **chon-drocytes** (cartilage cells) that are located in small holes in the matrix called **lacunae** (singular, *lacuna*).

collagen fibers

nuclei of fibroblasts
aligned in a row
between collagen fibers

(Photo by D. Morton.)

Figure 21-32 Dense regular fibrous connective tissue from a longitudinal section of tendon (500×).

chondrocytes

lacunae

new hyaline
cartilage
being added
by appositional
growth

isogenous
group of
lacunae
resulting from
interstitial
growth

(Photo by D. Morton.)

Figure 21-33 Section of hyaline cartilage in the wall of the trachea (250×).

Although invisible, many collagen fibers are embedded in the polymerized ground substance. They cannot be seen because the indices of refraction of these two matrix components are similar. Your instructor has set up a demonstration of this phenomenon. Observe the two labeled beakers, one filled with immersion oil and the other with water. Look at the glass rod placed in each of them. The index of refraction is about 1.58 for glass, about 1.33 for water, and about 1.52 for immersion oil. In which fluid is it easier to see the glass rod?

In locations where cartilage has to be more durable (intervertebral disks, for example), the collagen content is higher and the fibers are visible. In other sites (such as outer ear flaps), large numbers of elastic fibers are present. Elastic cartilage is deformed by a small force and returns to its original shape when the force is removed.

5. *Bone.* Living bones are amazingly strong. Bone organs are predominantly composed of hard yet flexible **bone** tissue. Its hardness is due to minerals (predominantly calcium-phosphate salts called hydroxyapatites) deposited in the matrix. Its flexibility comes from having the highest collagen content of all connective tissues.

Examine the cross section of compact bone tissue (Figure 21-34). Grinding a piece of the shaft of a long bone with coarse and then finer stones until a thin wafer remains has produced this preparation. Although only the mineral part of the matrix is present, the basic architecture has been preserved. Compact bone tissue is primarily composed of longitudinally arranged **Haversian systems** (also called *osteons*). Locate a Haversian system and identify its *central canal, lamellae* (singular, *lamella*), *lacunae, and canaliculi*—little canals that you see connecting lacunae with each other and with the central canal.

In living bone, blood vessels and nerves are present in central canals, concentric layers of matrix form the lamellae, and the intervening rings of *lacunae* contain bone cells called **osteocytes.** In young living bone, the canaliculi contain the cytoplasmic processes of osteocytes. Thus, the osteocytes can easily exchange nutrients, wastes, and other molecules with the blood. By comparison, substances in cartilage have to diffuse across the

Figure 21-34 Ground cross section of the shaft of a long bone showing compact bone tissue (100×).

capillaries   fat cells

(Photo by D. Morton.)

Figure 21-35   Section of white adipose tissue (450×).

matrix between chondrocytes and blood vessels in the surrounding soft connective tissue. Which tissue, bone or cartilage, will heal quicker? Explain why you made this choice.

_____

_____

_____

6. *White adipose tissue.* As you see in Figure 21-35, **white adipose tissue** consists mainly of **fat cells.** However, careful examination of the section using high power shows them to be surrounded by delicate collagen fibers, fibroblasts, and capillaries. Because the fat has been lost during the slide preparation, the fat cells look empty. The primary function of this tissue is energy storage.

C. Muscle Tissue

Muscle tissue is contractile. Its cells (fibers) can shorten and produce changes in the position of body parts, or they try to shorten and produce changes in tension. Contraction results from interactions between two types of protein filaments: **actin** and **myosin.** Like epithelial tissue, muscle tissue is primarily cellular; but unlike both epithelial and connective tissues, its cells (fibers) do not normally divide in the adult. Therefore, dead fibers are typically not replaced. There are three subtypes of muscle tissue: *skeletal, cardiac,* and *smooth.*

Skeletal muscle tissue is under *voluntary control.* This means that your conscious mind can order skeletal muscles to contract, although most of their contractions are actually involuntary. Cardiac muscle and smooth muscle tissues are always under *involuntary control.* Involuntary control means contractions are directed at the unconscious level.

Examine your slide with sections of all three subtypes (Figure 21-36). Identify their characteristics (see Table 21-2). In skeletal and cardiac muscle fibers, actin and myosin filaments overlap to produce the alternating pattern of light and dark bands (cross or transverse striations) seen in these tissues. Only cardiac muscle cells are

TABLE 21-2   Characteristics of Muscle Tissue Subtypes

Subtypes	Organ Location	Position and Number of Nuclei in Fibers	Cross-Striated Fibers	Special Fiber Features
Skeletal	Skeletal muscles	Peripheral and many	Yes	Long cylindrical shape
Cardiac	Heart	Central and usually one	Yes	Branches and intercalated disks
Smooth	Walls of internal organs	Central and one	No	Shape tapers at both ends

multiple nuclei per cell

muscle cells in cross section

muscle cells in longitudinal section

fibroblasts in connective tissue between fibers

a

striations

intercalated disks

nucleus of cardiac muscle cell

branch

(Photos by D. Morton.)

b

Figure 21-36 Sections of muscle tissue: (**a**) Skeletal (400×), (**b**) cardiac (1000×). *Continues.*

nuclei of smooth muscle cells

(Photos by D. Morton.)

c

Figure 21-36 *Continued.* Sections of muscle tissue: (c) smooth (400×).

branched. Where the branch of one fiber joins another, the cells are stuck together and in direct communication through a complex of cell-to-cell junctions. The complex is called an **intercalated disk.** Find an intercalated disk in your section, but if you have trouble seeing it, look at the demonstration set up by your instructor.

D. Nervous Tissue

Nervous tissue is found in the brain, spinal cord, nerves, and all of the body's organs. Its function is the point-to-point transmission of information. Messages are carried by impulses that travel along the functional unit of the nervous system, the **neuron** (or nerve cell). Like muscle cells, neurons do not divide in the adult, and therefore natural replacement is impossible.

The largest cells in Figure 21-37 are *motor neurons,* which connect the spinal cord to muscle fibers or glands. Find a similar cell in your smear of an ox spinal cord. The motor neuron has a **cell body**

smaller nuclei of numerous or neuroglial accessory cells

cell bodies of somatic motor neurons

nuclei of neurons

(Photo by D. Morton.)

Figure 21-37 Smear of spinal cord showing nervous tissue (100×).

and a number of slender cytoplasmic extensions called *neuron processes,* including one long **axon** and several shorter **dendrites.** The dendrites and cell body are stimulated within the spinal cord, and the axon conducts impulses out of it. The cells with smaller nuclei are accessory cells called **neuroglia.** Accessory cells help neurons function and make up about half the mass of nervous tissue.

21.6   Observation: Mouse Dissection *(50 min.)*

There are 11 systems in mammals, and each one contains a number of organs. In this portion of the exercise, you will identify the vital functions of these systems and many of their constituent organs. Many of these organs are located in or near the major **body cavities.** The *ventral* (located toward the belly surface) and *dorsal* (located toward the back surface) *body cavities* of humans are typical of mammals. A muscular *diaphragm* separates the **thoracic cavity** and **abdominal** cavities. The thoracic cavity is further subdivided into two lateral (away from the midline) **pleural cavities** and a medial (at or near the midline). Preservation of animals for dissection changes the appearance and consistency of the body and its organs. There are obvious advantages to observing the insides of a mammalian body much as a surgeon does during an operation.

MATERIALS

Per group (4):

- scalpel
- dissecting scissors
- 4 dissecting pins
- dissecting needle
- blunt probe
- freshly euthanized mouse
- squeeze bottle containing 0.9% saline solution
- cotton balls
- dissection pan

- small plastic bag for disposal of organs and soiled cotton balls during the dissection

Per lab section:

- large plastic bag for disposal of the small plastic bags and the carcasses at the end of the exercise

Per lab room:

- demonstration dissection of the nervous system of the mouse
- boxes of different sizes of latex gloves

PROCEDURE

A. External Features

1. Work in groups of four unless otherwise directed by your instructor. After putting on a pair of latex gloves, obtain a freshly euthanized mouse and place it in the dissection pan.
2. Referring to Figure 21-38, identify the four major body regions—the *head, neck, trunk,* and *tail*—and the two major surfaces—the *dorsal surface* (back) and the *ventral surface* (belly).
3. The trunk is divided into a ventral (anterior in humans) portion, the *thorax* (supported by the rib cage), and a dorsal (posterior in humans) portion, the *abdomen*. Feel the rib cage and the soft abdomen.
4. Observe the four *appendages* attached to the trunk. The two *arms* are attached to the thorax, and the two *legs* are attached to the abdomen. Each appendage has three segments. The arm is divided into the *upper arm, forearm,* and *front foot,* and the leg is divided into the *thigh, shank,* and *hind foot.* There are five *digits* at the end of each appendage, although the thumb is reduced in size and has a *nail* rather than a *claw*.
5. Note that most of the mouse's body is covered by hair, which traps air and forms an insulating layer. Most of the human body surface is sparsely covered by hair and has sweat glands in the skin that secrete sweat onto its surface for cooling via evaporation. Mice have sweat glands only on the pads of their feet.
6. Find the following openings on the body surface: *mouth* (entrance to the digestive system), two *external nostrils* (openings of the respiratory system), two *external auditory canals* (in ears), and *anus* (exit from the digestive system)
7. If you have a male mouse (see Figure 21-39b), note the *preputial opening*. A portion of the copulatory organ, the *penis*, protrudes from this depression. Feel the rest of the penis under the skin of the preputial opening. At the tip of the penis is the *urethral opening*, which is shared by the reproductive and urinary systems.
8. If you have a female mouse (see Figure 21-39a), note the *vulva*. This opening of the reproductive system is in front of the anus on the ventral surface. The *urethral opening* is the exit of the urinary system and is located underneath the protruding *clitoris*, which is immediately in front of the vulva. The clitoris has a common developmental origin with the penis.
9. If you have a male, locate the saclike *scrotum*, which covers the anus ventrally. Feel for the paired testes in the scrotum. Each *testis* produces the male sex hormone and sperm. Unlike human males, the testes of the mouse may be withdrawn into the abdomen. The function of the scrotum and the muscles that attach to each testis is temperature regulation. The ideal temperature for sperm production is slightly less than body temperature.

If you have a mature female, find the well-developed teats of the *mammary glands*. How many do you count?

10. Exchange your mouse for one of the opposite sex from another group and examine the differences in external features.

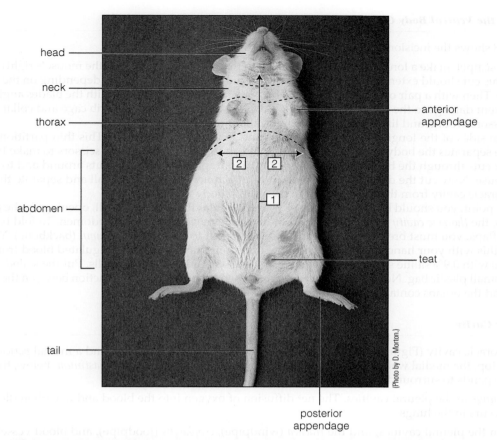

head

neck

thorax

abdomen

tail

anterior
appendage

teat

posterior
appendage

(Photo by D. Morton.)

Figure 21-38 How to open the ventral body cavities. The numbered arrows indicate incisions.

tip of penis
protruding through
preputial opening

clitoris

vulva

anus

scrotum

(Photo by D. Morton.)

a

b

Figure 21-39 Posterior halves of the ventral surfaces of (**a**) female and (**b**) male mice.

B. Opening the Ventral Body Cavities

Figure 21-38 shows the incisions (cuts) necessary to open the ventral body cavities.

1. With a scalpel, make a longitudinal incision through the skin just to the right (the mouse's right) of the midline. This cut should extend from the neck to the preputial opening or clitoris, depending on the sex of your mouse. Then with a pair of scissors pierce the body wall just below the ribs. With the blades angled upward to prevent damage to the internal organs, cut along the incision through the rib cage and collar bone. Turn the scissors around and likewise cut through the abdominal muscles.

2. Pull the sides of the longitudinal incision apart and look for the *diaphragm*. This thin partition of skeletal muscle separates the body cavities of the thorax and abdomen. Again use the scissors to make two perpendicular cuts through the body wall just below the diaphragm. Extend these cuts around and to the back of the mouse. Now cut the diaphragm away from its attachment to the body wall and separate the organs of the thoracic cavity from their attachment to the ventral body wall.

3. At this point, you should be able to fold back four triangular flaps of body wall, opening up the *ventral body cavities*, the *thoracic cavity* in the thorax, and the *abdominopelvic cavity* in the abdomen. To fold back the two upper flaps, you must break the ribs near their attachment to the *vertebral column* (backbone). You can easily do this with your hands. Pin the flaps to the dissecting tray. Rinse any coagulated blood from the body cavities with 0.9% saline solution and remove any excess fluid with cotton balls. Put the soiled cotton balls in the small plastic bag. Note that a thin, wet serosal membrane that reduces friction between the inner body wall and the organs contained therein lines each body cavity.

C. Thoracic Cavity

1. The thoracic cavity (Figure 21-40) is comprised of two lateral *pleural cavities* and a medial *pericardial cavity*. At the top, the medial walls of the pleural sacs join to form a septum, the *mediastinum*. Below, the mediastinum expands to surround the pericardial sac.

Locate the *lungs* in the pleural cavities. The net diffusion of oxygen into the blood and of carbon dioxide out of the blood occurs in the lungs.

2. Between the pleural cavities, find the *trachea* (windpipe), *esophagus* (foodpipe), and blood vessels traveling to and from the head in the mediastinum. Especially in young mice, you must remove the *thymus*, which

Figure 21-40 Ventral view of organs in thoracic cavity (2×).

covers the mediastinum. The thymus is important in the development of the immune defenses. The size and function of the thymus decrease with age. Dispose of the thymus in the small plastic bag.

3. Open the pericardial sac and examine the pump of the circulatory system, the *heart*. Just above and behind the heart, find where the trachea divides into a right and left *bronchus*. During the process of inspiration, the bronchi carry air from the trachea toward the lungs. Under the trachea and pericardial sac is the esophagus. Do you see where it pierces the diaphragm, passing into the abdominopelvic cavity?

D. Abdominopelvic Cavity

1. Referring to Figure 21-41, observe just posterior to the diaphragm the body's largest gland, the *liver*. It has several lobes. Lift them and look for a reddish brown sac, the *gall bladder*. The gall bladder stores *bile* secreted by the liver. When the gall bladder contracts, bile is squirted through a duct into the small intestine to aid in the digestion of fats.

2. Locate the *stomach* in the left side of the abdominopelvic cavity, under the liver. The stomach helps process swallowed food. Can you discover where the esophagus joins the stomach at its anterior end? Examine the *spleen*, a dark red organ located just to the left of the stomach. The spleen filters the blood, removes old blood cells, and plays a role in immunity.

3. Note where the *small intestine* arises from the lower end of the stomach. The small intestine completes the digestion of food and is the main site for absorption of the end products of digestion. It is the longest organ in the body, and its convolutions fill most of the abdominopelvic cavity. A double membrane, the mesentery, attaches the small intestine to the dorsal body wall.

4. To observe the *pancreas*, look for a diffuse organ in the first loop of the small intestine. This gland produces enzymes for the digestion of food and, as part of the endocrine system, secretes *insulin* and other hormones into the blood.

5. Find the lower end of the small intestine, the place where it empties into the *large intestine*. The large intestine is shaped like an upside-down U. To see it, lift the small intestine. Follow the large intestine until it joins the short *rectum*, which terminates at the anus. Return to the junction between the small and large intestines. Note the blind sac extending in the direction opposite from the large intestine. This is the *cecum*, which in humans is a relatively small structure. In humans a blind twisted tube, the *vermiform appendix*, is attached to the cecum.

6. Carefully remove the abdominal portion of the digestive tract by cutting (a) the esophagus between the diaphragm and stomach, (b) the dorsal mesentery, and (c) the descending portion of the large intestine (the third arm of the upside-down U). Do not disturb the urinary bladder, which lies in front of the cecum. Also, if you have a female, do not disturb the reproductive system, which is situated under the small intestine and in front of the rectum.

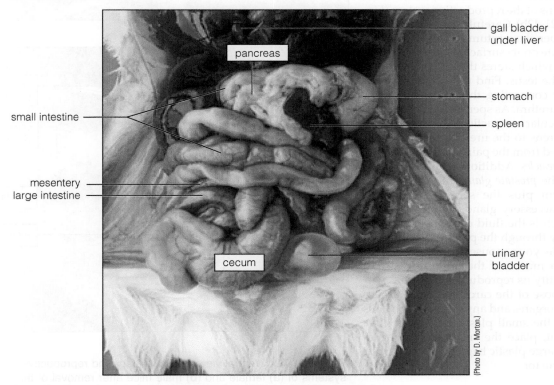

Figure 21-41 Ventral view of organs of abdominopelvic cavity (2×).

Stretch out the length of the small intestine and measure it.

Length of small intestine = _____ cm

Now measure the mouse from the tip of the nose to the base of the tail.

Length of head and body of mouse = _____ cm

How many times the length of the mouse is its small intestine? _____ times

Dispose of the stomach and intestines in the small plastic bag.

7. The *urinary bladder* stores urine delivered via two *ureters* from the paired *kidneys* (Figure 21-42). Find the kidneys, which are located on the dorsal body wall under the serosal membrane, which in this location is called the *peritoneum*. With a dissecting needle, tear away the serosal membrane above one kidney. Each kidney is like a thick C, with the indentation pointing toward the midline of the body. The ureter arises from the center of this concave surface. Trace the ureter to the urinary bladder. At the lower end of the urinary bladder find the *urethra,* the duct that conveys urine out of the body when the bladder contracts.

8. If your mouse is male, skip to step 9. If you have a female mouse, examine the organs of the reproductive system (Figure 21-42a). Find the *body of the uterus* immediately behind the urinary bladder. Trace the body of the uterus upward until it branches into two *uterine horns*, which pass under the ureters and extend almost to the kidneys. Here each uterine horn joins a short *oviduct*, which expands to help form a sac surrounding the *ovary*. The paired ovaries are the source of female sex hormones and eggs. If the mouse is pregnant, the uterine horns will be quite large. Follow the uterus in the other direction and see where it joins the *vagina*, which in turn opens into the vulva.

   Skip step 9 and go on to step 10.

9. If you have a male mouse, examine the organs of the reproductive system (Figure 21-42b). Carefully use your scissors to open the scrotum and expose a *testis*. Locate on its surface the coiled *epididymis*, which stores the sperm produced by the testis. Find the *vas deferens*, the tube connecting the epididymis with the urethra. As sperm are propelled by muscular contractions through the vas deferens to the urethra, secretions are added from the paired, glandular *seminal vesicles*. Additional fluid is secreted by the *prostate gland* into the urethra. Sperm plus the secretions of these sex accessory glands comprise *semen*, which is the fluid ejaculated from the body through the penis.

10. Trade your mouse to another group for a mouse of the opposite sex and identify its reproductive organs.

11. Dispose of the carcass, cut-out tissues and organs, and any soiled cotton balls into the small plastic bag. After closing it, place the small plastic bag in the large plastic bag provided by your instructor.

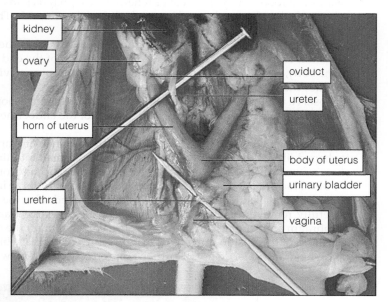

a

b

(Photos by D. Morton.)

Figure 21-42 Ventral views of the urinary and reproductive systems of (**a**) female and (**b**) male mice after removal of the digestive system (3×).

_____ 1. The study of a plant's structure is
  (a) physiology
  (b) morphology
  (c) taxonomy
  (d) botany

_____ 2. A plant with two seed leaves is
  (a) a monocotyledon
  (b) a dicotyledon
  (c) exemplified by corn
  (d) a dihybrid

_____ 3. A taproot system lacks
  (a) lateral roots
  (b) a taproot
  (c) both of the above
  (d) none of the above

_____ 4. Which structure is not part of the shoot system?
  (a) stems
  (b) leaves
  (c) lateral roots
  (d) axillary buds

_____ 5. An axillary bud
  (a) is found along internodes
  (b) produces new roots
  (c) is the structure from which branches and flowers arise
  (d) is the same as a terminal bud

_____ 6. The endodermis
  (a) is the outer covering of the root
  (b) is part of the vascular tissue
  (c) contains the Casparian strip, which regulates the movement of substances
  (d) is none of the above

_____ 7. Meristems are
  (a) located at the tips of stems
  (b) located at the tips of roots
  (c) regions of active growth
  (d) all of the above

_____ 8. To determine the age of a woody twig, one counts the
  (a) nodes
  (b) leaf scars
  (c) lenticels
  (d) regions between sets of terminal bud scale scars

_____ 9. The midrib of a leaf
  (a) contains the midvein
  (b) contains only xylem
  (c) is part of the spongy mesophyll
  (d) contains only phloem

_____ 10. The bundle sheath in a monocot leaf
  (a) is filled with intercellular space
  (b) is the location of stomata
  (c) is covered with a cuticle to prevent water loss
  (d) functions in a manner somewhat similar to the root endodermis

11. Histology is the study of
   (a) cells
   (b) organelles
   (c) tissues
   (d) organisms

12. A collection of similarly specialized cells and any extracellular material they secrete and maintain describes
   (a) an organ
   (b) a system
   (c) a tissue
   (d) organelles

13. Organs strung together functionally and usually structurally form
   (a) organs
   (b) systems
   (c) tissues
   (d) organelles

14. _____ are constructed of all four basic tissue types.
   (a) organs
   (b) systems
   (c) cells
   (d) organelles

15. An epithelial tissue formed by more than one layer of cells and with columnlike cells at the surface is called
   (a) simple squamous
   (b) stratified squamous
   (c) simple columnar
   (d) stratified columnar

16. The middle layer of the skin
   (a) is called the dermis
   (b) is primarily connective tissue
   (c) contains collagen fibers
   (d) is all of the above

17. To which subtype of muscle tissue does a fiber with cross striations and many peripherally located nuclei belong?
   (a) skeletal
   (b) cardiac
   (c) smooth
   (d) none of the above

18. In which tissue would you look for cells that function in point-to-point communication?
   (a) connective
   (b) epithelial
   (c) muscle
   (d) nervous

19. The ventral body cavities include
   (a) the thoracic cavity
   (b) the cranial cavity
   (c) the abdominopelvic cavity
   (d) both a and c

20. The cranial cavity contains
   (a) the lungs and heart
   (b) the spinal cord
   (c) the brain
   (d) both b and c

EXERCISE 21

Plant and Animal Organization

POST-LAB QUESTIONS

Introduction

1. In the correct order from smallest to largest, list the levels of organization present in most animals.

21.1 External Structure of the Flowering Plant

2. What type of root system do you see on the dandelion at the right?

(0.25×).

21.3 The Shoot System: Stems

3. On the figure below, identify structures **a**, **b**, and **c**.

a _____

b _____

c _____

(0.5×).

4. Identify the structures labeled **a** and **b** on the figure below.

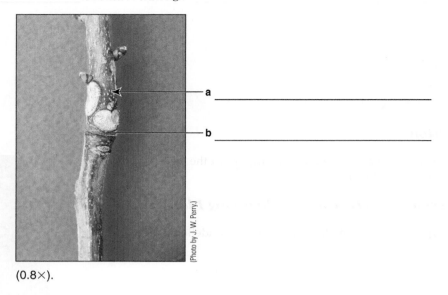

a _____

b _____

(0.8×).

5. What feature(s) would you use to determine the age of a woody twig?

6. Label the diagram using the following terms: bark; heartwood; sapwood; secondary phloem; vascular cambium.

7. The photo shows the microscopic appearance of maple wood. Using your knowledge of the woody stem section, identify cell type **a** and the "line" of cells at **b**. (Note: The outside of the tree from which this section was taken is shown in the photo that accompanies question 8.)

a _____

b _____

(Photo by J. W. Perry.)

(58×).

8. A section cut from an ash branch is shown below.

 a. Identify region **a**.

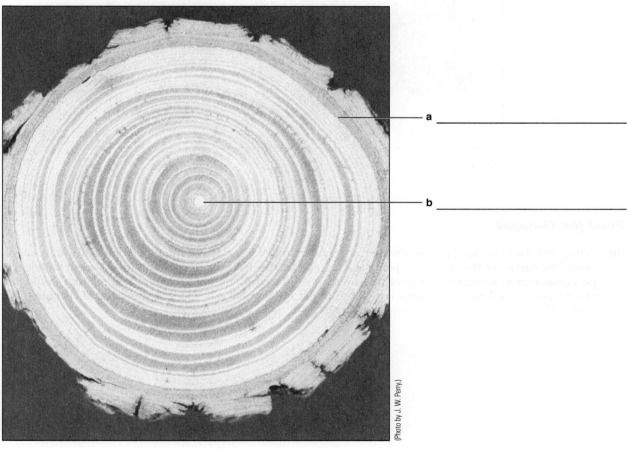

a _____

b _____

(Photo by J. W. Perry.)

(1×).

b.   Which meristem is located at **b**?

c.   Within ±3 years, how old was this branch when cut?

21.4 The Shoot System: Leaves

9.   The following photo shows a section of a leaf from a dicot that is adapted to a dry environment. Its lower epidermis has depressions, and the stomata are located in the cavities. Even though it's different from the leaf you studied in lab, identify the regions labeled **a, b,** and **c.**

(75×).

Food for Thought

10.   A major problem for land plants is water conservation. Most water is lost through stomata due to evaporation at the surface of the leaf. Many plants, including lilac (the leaf section you examined), orient their leaves perpendicular to the drying force of the sun's rays. What did you observe about the relative abundance of stomata in the lower epidermis versus the upper epidermis? Why do you think this distribution has evolved?

21.5 Tissues

11. Describe the main structural characteristics of the four basic tissues.

    a. epithelial tissue

    b. connective tissue

    c. muscle tissue

    d. nervous tissue

12. Describe the main functions of the four basic tissues.

    a. epithelial tissue

    b. connective tissue

    c. muscle tissue

    d. nervous tissue

13. Identify the following tissues.

(186×).

a _____

space within nephron tubule

(480×).

(Photos by D. Morton.)

b _____

21.6 Observation: Mouse Dissection

14. Identify the following structures.

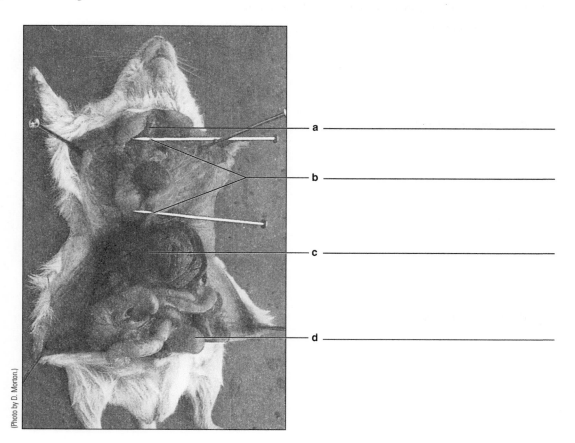

(Photo by D. Morton.)

a _____

b _____

c _____

d _____

Food for Thought

15. Bone is a subtype of connective tissue and bones are organs. How are the two related yet different from each other? Can you think of another tissue/organ pair that potentially creates a similar confusing situation?

16. Search the phrase "tissue engineering" on the World Wide Web. List two sites and briefly summarize their content.

http://

http://

The Natural Arsenal: An Experimental Study of the Relationships Between Plants and Animals

OBJECTIVES

After completing this exercise, you should be able to

1. define *herbivore, plant secondary compound, allelochemical, bioactive, cytotoxic, bioassay;*

2. explain the ecological role of many plant toxins and their potential effects on herbivores, pathogens, or competitors;

3. describe the nature of the chemical "arms race" between plants and herbivores;

4. state scientific hypotheses and predictions, design a simple experiment with proper controls and replication, evaluate the results, and reach conclusions based on the evidence provided by the experiment.

INTRODUCTION

"NO! Don't touch that leaf!" . . . "Don't eat that berry!" Sound like something your parents said to you and your siblings when you were young? Why shouldn't we eat the berries of American yew bushes, or any part of the foxglove plant? Why is one nightshade species called "deadly"? Why have so many of us learned to identify poison ivy ("leaves of three, let it be")? Because they're "poisonous," right?

So why do plants produce chemicals that are harmful to people or other animals? Recall that plants occupy the producer trophic level. They use solar energy to build organic molecules from water and carbon dioxide in the process of photosynthesis, and also incorporate into their tissues mineral nutrients absorbed via their roots. Plants therefore compete with each other for crucial resources and occupy the base of most food webs, with animals and other **herbivore** consumers (herbivores are organisms that eat plants) eating them in order to acquire the nutrients and energy stored in the plant body.

Plants would seem to be at a distinct disadvantage in the predation and competition relationships we just described. The vast majority are rooted in the earth; certainly plants aren't able to evade predators by moving away. Nor can they physically move to more advantageous locations for gathering sunshine or minerals. Nonetheless, they are not defenseless against the vast array of herbivores and competitors. In addition to various physical defenses like thorns and tough tissues, most plants have highly effective chemical weapons.

All higher plants have **secondary compounds.** These are chemicals that do NOT fall into the major chemical groupings of carbohydrates, proteins, fats, or nucleic acids. They occur irregularly, with most secondary compounds occurring in a few kinds of plants but not in others. More importantly, most secondary substances have no known role in the metabolism of the plants in which they occur. Rather, they seem to perform a variety of functions, including that of chemical defense agent.

The secondary chemical compound signals that are active between different species are called **allelochemicals.** Caffeine, nicotine, strychnine, organic cyanide compounds, and curare are just a few of the "weapons" in the chemical arsenal that plants have evolved to defend themselves against animal consumers, plant competitors, and pathogenic (disease-causing) microbes. For example, tannins in the leaves of oaks and other plants combine with leaf proteins and digestive enzymes in an insect's gut, inhibiting protein digestion by the insect. Thus tannins considerably slow the growth of most caterpillars and other herbivores.

Of course, herbivores may counter such toxic effects through the evolutionary modification of their own biochemistry or physiology. (Toxins react with specific cellular components to kill cells or alter growth or development in harmful ways.) Herbivore species that coevolve detoxification mechanisms of secondary chemicals may be able to specialize on plant hosts that are poisonous to most other species.

One familiar example is the Monarch butterfly. The adult female lays eggs on milkweed (*Asclepias*) plants. The eggs hatch into an immature stage called a *larva*, which we know as the "caterpillar." The larvae eat the milkweed leaves and eventually complete their developmental cycle. What makes the Monarch/milkweed relationship so intriguing is that milkweed plants contain potent heart poisons that deter virtually all herbivore feeding. Monarch butterflies have evolved metabolic pathways, however, to detoxify the milkweed poison. In fact, Monarch larvae store the milkweed toxin in their tissues and thereby protect themselves from predators such as birds!

Not all allelochemicals act as toxins that reduce herbivore survival. Some alter the development of insects by interfering with the production of crucial hormones, while others act as repellants that prevent feeding. Still others have antibiotic effects that inhibit infections by pathogens.

In this exercise, you will investigate the harmful effects of some plant compounds on animals and other plants, focusing especially on those bioactive compounds that may be **cytotoxic,** or poisonous to specific cell types. You'll work in groups to design and conduct bioassays to identify potentially **bioactive** compounds, that is, molecules that have a targeted biological effect on survival, growth, or reproduction. A **bioassay** is a method of screening for potentially active substances by exposing a test population of living organisms to the substance in a controlled environment. A bioassay provides an evaluation by measuring the quantity of a substance that results in a defined effective dose.

Bioassays are used for a variety of purposes. They enable researchers to find plant chemicals that show biological activity on selected research organisms. For example, botanists and biochemists use bioassays to screen unstudied plants for potentially useful, naturally occurring drugs. The National Institutes of Health, the National Cancer Institute, and several major U.S. pharmaceutical companies have launched intensive bioassay "chemical prospecting" efforts in tropical rainforests to find new sources of drugs in the fights against cancer, AIDS, heart disease, and many other health problems.

Bioassays are also used by the pharmaceutical industry in other ways. Some pharmaceuticals are cytotoxic agents; chemotherapy agents, for example, are toxic to cancer cells. Certain side effects of chemotherapy are due to the chemical's cytotoxic effect on other body cells as well. Cytotoxic effects are due to interactions with specific biochemical pathways. Therefore, these chemicals are toxic to cells that utilize the specific pathway, but have little to no effect on other cells that don't use the pathway.

While it's unlikely that you will discover an unidentified cancer-fighting chemical or natural herbicide in the plants in your lab, you might very well find cytotoxic agents. It's important to keep in mind that the reason those chemicals exist in the first place is the result of coevolution between plants and their herbivores, competitors, and pathogens. The more we know about what organisms make these chemicals, why they are made, how they are made, and the consequences of the secondary compounds to the parties involved, the more we will know about the evolutionary process and about potential practical uses of such chemicals for our own benefit.

You will use two test organisms in your bioassays. The first, *Artemia,* or brine shrimp, is a small crustacean inhabitant of salty lakes like the Great Salt Lake. *Artemia* are filter feeders that sweep algae and other tiny food particles into their mouths as they swim. They therefore occupy a primary consumer position in aquatic ecosystems. One bioassay will look for effects on *Artemia* cells as a general indication of the presence of cytotoxic compounds in a plant extract.

You may have used the second bioassay organism, Wisconsin Fast Plants™ (*Brassica rapa*), in a previous bioassay (see Exercise 1). Fast Plants™ are small, very fast-growing plants of the cabbage family. A bioassay with Fast Plants™ serves to identify potential herbicides (plant-killing compounds) or plant-growth stimulants by looking at the effect of a plant extract on seed germination and plant growth over 1 day.

27.1 Experimental Design

Work in groups of four to explore the effects of plant secondary compounds on cell survival of *Artemia,* and/or the effects on seed germination and growth of Fast Plants™. Your instructor will direct you to the plant materials that are available for testing.

Develop an hypothesis that you will test. Your hypothesis might relate to differences between extracts of different plant species with respect to effects on *Artemia* cell survival. Or you might wish to test the effect that a single plant extract has on *Artemia* cell survival versus its effect on Fast Plant™ germination and growth.

Remember, there is no *single* correct hypothesis.
The hypothesis we will test is

_____

_____

_____

Design an experiment using the materials available in the lab and the following bioassay procedures to test your hypothesis.
Our experimental design is

_____

_____

_____

_____

What will be your control treatment(s)? What is the purpose of a control treatment?

_____

_____

How will you provide replication to improve the reliability of your results?

_____

_____

Write a prediction for your experiment.

_____

_____

List the possible general outcomes of your experiment. What does each tell you about your prediction and hypothesis?

_____

_____

_____

_____

Develop a work plan to carry out your experiment so that each group member has specific tasks to accomplish and contribute to the overall group effort. For example, if your experiment will test the differences between extracts of two plant species with respect to their ability to harm _Artemia_, two group members might prepare the bioassay for one species, and the other two might run the bioassay for the second plant species. You also might divide up the work of collecting data for the duration of the bioassay.

27.2   Bioassay Procedures

A. Preparation of Plant Extract _(About 20 min.)_

MATERIALS

Per student group:

- 25-mL graduated cylinder
- two 20-mL beakers
- 50-mL beaker
- small mortar and pestle
- spatula
- plant material of your choice
- glass stirring rod

Per lab room:

- several electronic balances calibrated to weigh in 0.1-g increments
- weighing papers or boats
- liquid nitrogen (optional)

PROCEDURE

1. Grind about 1 g of the plant tissue to a fine paste with the mortar and pestle. (If liquid nitrogen is available, carefully pour a small amount over the plant material to instantly freeze it.)

Caution

Liquid nitrogen is extremely cold and will cause cryogenic burns. DO NOT touch the liquid or allow any to splash onto your skin.

If using leaf tissue, try not to include large veins; if using root tissue, wash off all soil very well. Grind the tissue _for at least 5 minutes._ The goal is to rupture virtually all the plant cells to mix their contents in the bioassay liquid. When you think you've ground the tissue adequately, continue grinding for two more minutes.

2. Use the balance to measure out two 0.1-g samples of the paste onto two pieces of weighing paper or two weighing boats.

3. Measure 10 mL of prepared brine into one labeled 20-mL beaker, and 10 mL of distilled water into a second labeled 20-mL beaker. Mix a 0.1-g sample of plant paste into each beaker, being careful to scrape off ALL plant material, and stir to create uniform suspensions. This extract has a concentration of 0.1-g plant material/ 10 mL, or 10 mg/mL. (Recall that 1000 mg = 1 g.) You will use the brine mixture with brine shrimp bioassays, and the dH$_2$O mixture for Fast Plant™ bioassays.

B. Artemia Bioassay (About 1 hr)

MATERIALS

Per student group:

- glass microscope slides
- coverslips
- fine-pointed water-resistant marker (Sharpie® or similar) or wax pencil
- wide-mouth plastic graduated transfer pipets
- razor blade or scalpel
- trypan blue stain in dropping bottle
- acetic acid in dropping bottle

- dissecting needle
- compound microscope
- plant extract(s) prepared in brine in part A

Per lab room:

- live *Artemia* in aquarium or beaker
- plant extracts
- paper towels

PROCEDURE

1. Label one microscope slide "Negative control" and a second microscope slide "Positive control."
2. Obtain a number of brine shrimp and brine in the 50-mL beaker.
3. Place a brine shrimp onto each slide, transferring only a little brine. Blot excess brine with a paper towel. The brine shrimp should be surrounded in a small brine droplet.
4. Swirl the trypan blue stain bottle to suspend the stain mixture evenly. Place a couple drops of stain atop the brine shrimp on each slide. The brine shrimp should not be able to swim, but should be covered by the liquid. Blot excess stain with a paper towel.
5. Place the negative control slide on the microscope stage and focus on the brine shrimp at low magnification. Observe the structure of the animal, locating the point where the "tail" emerges behind the main body. (See Figure 27-1.)
6. Using a sharp scalpel, cut about ¹/₂ to ²/₃ of the tail off the brine shrimp.
7. Put a coverslip over the severed tail sections. Observe the cut ends of the tail. Amoebocytes, the small roundish cells that ooze out of the tail cavity, are excellent bioassay subjects. They respond to cytotoxic agents in much the same way that human cells do. Healthy cells exclude trypan blue stain and appear colorless, but damaged and dead cells will take up the stain and appear blue (Figure 27-2). Do not confuse clumps of dye crystals with the very round cells.
8. Find a field of view where the amoebocytes aren't being moved by liquid movements. Count the number of cells that are colorless in appearance, and the number that are blue for a total of about 25 cells total. Calculate the percentage of dead cells. This number represents the "background" rate for dead cells. Record your data in Table 27-1.
9. Repeat steps 4–5 for the positive control brine shrimp.
10. Add a drop of acetic acid to the severed tail section for the positive control treatment and mix with a dissecting needle. (Acetic acid is a potent cytotoxin.) Add a coverslip and wait a couple minutes before observing with the microscope.
11. Count unstained and stained cells (about 25 total), and calculate the percentage of dead cells. This number illustrates the effects of a strong cytotoxin on *Artemia* amoebocytes. If you see no stained cells, wait up to 30 minutes for a cytotoxic effect to become visible. Record your data in Table 27-1.
12. Test your plant extract(s) similarly by cutting off a brine shrimp tail in a drop of trypan blue stain on a clean slide, then adding 1–2 drops of plant extract. Add a coverslip, wait a couple minutes, then count stained (dead) and unstained (living) cells (about 25 total). Record your data in Table 27-1.

Figure 27-1 *Artemia*, or brine shrimp.

Figure 27-2 (a) Healthy (unstained) cells, (b) dead (stained) cells (500×).

(Photos by J. W. Perry.)

TABLE 27-1 Effect of Plant Extracts on *Artemia* Amoebocytes

Treatment	Droplet Order on Slide	Number Unstained (Live) Cells	Number Stained (Dead) Cells	Percentage Dead Cells
Negative control	Brine + trypan blue			
Positive control	Brine + trypan blue + acetic acid			
Plant extract 1	Brine + trypan blue + plant extract 1			
Plant extract 2	Brine + trypan blue + plant extract 2			
Plant extract 3	Brine + trypan blue + plant extract 3			

C. Fast Plant™ Bioassay *(About 30 min.)*

MATERIALS

Per student group:

- fine-pointed water-resistant marker (Sharpie® or similar)
- 35-mm film canister with lid prepunched with 4 holes
- 4 microcentrifuge tubes with caps
- 4 paper-towel wicks

- disposable pipets and bulb
- forceps
- 8 Wisconsin Fast Plants™ seeds
- 15-cm plastic ruler
- dH₂O in dropping bottle
- plant extract(s) prepared in dH₂O in Part A

PROCEDURE

1. Using a fine-pointed, water-resistant marker, label the caps and/or sides of the four microcentrifuge tubes 10.0, 1.0, 0.1, and C (for Control).
2. Place 10 drops of the previously prepared plant extract into the tube labeled 10.0. This tube now contains 10 mg/mL of the test extract. You will now make *serial dilutions* of the solution, producing concentrations of 1.0 mg/mL and 0.1 mg/mL of the test substance:

(a) Add 9 drops of dH$_2$O to tubes 1.0 and 0.1.

(b) From tube 10.0, remove a small quantity of the solution with the disposable pipet and place *one* drop into tube 1.0. Mix the contents thoroughly by "thipping" the side of the microcentrifuge tube (flicking the sides of the bottom of the tube with the index finger of your dominant hand while holding the sides of the top of the tube between the index finger and thumb of your other hand). Return any solution remaining in the pipet to tube 10.0. Tube 1.0 now contains a concentration 10% of that in tube 10.0, or 1.0 mg/mL.

(c) Now, from tube 1.0, remove a small quantity of the solution with another disposable pipet and place *one* drop in tube 0.1. Mix the contents thoroughly and return any solution left in the pipet to tube 1.0. Tube 0.1 now contains a 1% concentration of the original, or 0.1 mg/mL.

3. From the dropping bottle, place 10 drops of dH$_2$O into tube C. This is the control for the experiment, containing none of the test solution.

4. Insert a paper-towel wick into each microcentrifuge tube (Figure 27-3). With your forceps, place two RCBr seeds near the top of each wick. Close the caps of the tubes.

> ### Caution
>
> *Do not allow any of the wick to protrude outside the cap.*

5. Carefully insert the microcentrifuge assay tubes through the holes in the film canister lid (Figure 27-4). Set the experiment aside in the location indicated by your instructor.

(Photo by J. W. Perry.)

Figure 27-3   One of the four bioassay tubes.

(Photo by J. W. Perry.)

Figure 27-4   Experimental apparatus for Fast Plant™ bioassay.

6. After 24 hours or more, examine your bioassay to see how many and which seeds germinated. Record your results in Table 27-2. Rather than simply recording the response as "germinated" (G) or "did not germinate" (DNG), also indicate the extent of any germination by measuring and recording the length in millimeters (mm) of the roots and shoots of seed 1 (S1) and seed 2 (S2) for each treatment. If you are testing a second plant extract, record those results in Table 27-3.

TABLE 27-2   Effect of _____ on Germination of Fast Plant™ Seeds

Tube	Germination		Length of Roots (mm)		Length of Shoots (mm)	
	Seed 1	Seed 2	Seed 1	Seed 2	Seed 1	Seed 2
Control (dH$_2$O)						
0.1 mg/mL extract						
1.0 mg/mL extract						
10.0 mg/mL extract						

TABLE 27-3   Effect of _____ on Germination of Fast Plant™ Seeds

Tube	Germination		Length of Roots (mm)		Length of Shoots (mm)	
	Seed 1	Seed 2	Seed 1	Seed 2	Seed 1	Seed 2
Control (dH₂O)						
0.1 mg/mL extract						
1.0 mg/mL extract						
10.0 mg/mL extract						

27.3   Analysis of Results

Do your results indicate any cytotoxicity of the plant extract(s) you tested? _____

If yes, do your results indicate cytotoxicity toward plant cells, animal cells, or both? _____

Using your experimental results, make a conclusion regarding the effect of the plant extract(s) on your test organism.

_____

_____

Does your conclusion support your prediction or prove it unsound? Is your hypothesis supported or falsified by your conclusion? Explain.

_____

_____

_____

_____ 1. Plant secondary compounds are chemicals that
   (a) have no known metabolic function in the plant
   (b) are required for enzyme function
   (c) are generally carbohydrates or proteins
   (d) are important in cell division

_____ 2. Allelochemicals are active in preventing
   (a) herbivore feeding
   (b) germination of plant competitors
   (c) infection by pathogens
   (d) all of the above

_____ 3. Chemicals that are poisonous to specific cell types are said to be
   (a) hazardous
   (b) cytotoxic
   (c) allelochemicals
   (d) bioactive

_____ 4. Bioassays
   (a) are performed in a test tube using killed cells
   (b) expose a population of living organisms to a test substance
   (c) are used for chemotherapy
   (d) are none of the above

_____ 5. Artemia, brine shrimp,
   (a) are aquatic organisms
   (b) live in salty ecosystems
   (c) are filter-feeding primary consumers
   (d) are all of the above

_____ 6. Plant defenses against herbivore grazing include
   (a) thorns
   (b) plant secondary compounds
   (c) mobility
   (d) both a and b

_____ 7. Trypan blue is
   (a) taken up by living cells
   (b) taken up by dead cells
   (c) taken up by both living and dead cells
   (d) used to identify plant cells

_____ 8. Dead Artemia cells that have been treated with trypan blue appear
   (a) colorless
   (b) blue
   (c) red
   (d) indistinguishable from living treated cells

_____ 9. The dH$_2$O-only treatment in the Fast Plant™ bioassay provides
   (a) a control
   (b) moisture for seed germination
   (c) dilution of potential cytotoxins
   (d) none of the above

_____ 10. Artemia and Fast Plant™ bioassays can be used to identify
   (a) cytotoxins
   (b) herbicides
   (c) plant growth stimulators
   (d) all of the above

EXERCISE 27

The Natural Arsenal: An Experimental Study of the Relationships Between Plants and Animals

POST-LAB QUESTIONS

Introduction

1. Why have plants evolved secondary compounds?

2. Describe how a pharmaceutical company might use a bioassay to identify potential drugs in rainforest plants.

3. Would a chemical that is cytotoxic to brine shrimp cells necessarily have the same effect on Fast Plant™ cells? Explain.

27.1 Experimental Design

4. How can replication be increased in the *Artemia* bioassay to improve reliability of results?

27.2 Artemia Bioassay

5. What was the purpose of the *Artemia* slide prepared with droplets of

   a. brine and trypan blue only?

   b. brine, trypan blue, and acetic acid?

Fast Plant™ Bioassay

6. If seed germination took place in 100% of plants at the 1.0 mg/mL concentration, and no germination was observed at the 0.1 mg/mL concentration, how would you modify a second experiment to determine the actual effective concentration?

Food for Thought

7. If you found no cytotoxic effects with your plant extract, does this prove the extract is not cytotoxic? Explain.

8. If you found no cytotoxic effects with your plant extract, does this prove that the plant species from which the extract was made has no cytotoxic allelochemicals? Explain.

9. How might you alter the two bioassay procedures to provide more information?
   a. *Artemia* bioassay:

   b. Fast Plant™ bioassay:

10. What other kinds of tests could you perform to provide more information about possible cytotoxicity of a plant extract?

Ecology: Living Organisms in Their Environment

1. define *ecology, population, community, ecosystem, producer, consumer, trophic level, primary consumer, secondary consumer, tertiary consumer, decomposer, parasite, herbivore, carnivore, omnivore, survivorship curve;*

2. construct a food web;

3. determine an organism's trophic level;

4. identify the three basic types of survivorship curves and describe the trends exhibited by each.

INTRODUCTION

Ecology. The word certainly brings to mind groups who advocate for a clean environment, who lobby the government to prevent loss of natural areas, or who protest the policies or actions of other groups. To the biologist, however, this is *not* what ecology as a science is all about. Rather, these activities are environmental concerns that have grown out of ecological studies.

The word *ecology* is derived from the Greek *oikos,* which means "house," so ecology can be thought of as the study of a "home"—be it the earth, a neighborhood, our house, or a pond. Less broadly defined, **ecology** is the study of the interactions between living organisms and their environment. Individuals, whether they are bacteria or humans, do not exist in a vacuum. Rather, they interact with one another in complex ways. As such, ecology is an extremely diverse and complex study. There are so many aspects of ecology that it's difficult to pick one, or even a few, to represent the entire science.

Let's look at the levels of organization considered in an ecological study.

A **population** of organisms is a group of individuals of the same species occupying a given area at a given time. For example, you and your colleagues in the lab at this moment are a population; you are all *Homo sapiens.* Your population consists of humans in biology class right now. The place you occupy, the lab room, is your *habitat.* Of course, you share your habitat with other organisms; unseen bacteria, fungi, and possibly insects are present in the room as well. Maybe plants decorate the lab room; if so, these too, comprise yet another population in your habitat.

A **community** consists of *all* the populations of species that occupy a given area at a given time. To use our simple example, your lab community consists of humans, bacteria, fungi, insects, and plants.

Our community exists in a physical and chemical environment. The combination of the community and its environment comprise an **ecosystem.** Your lab ecosystem consists of humans, bacteria, insects, plants, an atmosphere, lab benches, walls, floors, light, heat, humidity, and so on. As you can see, an ecosystem has both living and nonliving components.

In this exercise, we will introduce some of the principles of ecology. You will study three concepts that demonstrate how ecological studies are performed: food webs, energy flow through ecosystems, and survivorship curves.

28.1   Food Webs *(About 25 min.)*

Let's consider the community of organisms in any environment. Each population of organisms plays a different role in the community, that is, each community has organisms that are producers and organisms that are consumers.

Producers are autotrophic organisms, so most plants and a few microorganisms are producers. They utilize the energy of the sun or chemical energy to synthesize organic (carbon-containing) compounds from inorganic compounds. Photosynthetic producers form the base of nearly all food chains and food webs.

Consumers are heterotrophic organisms that feed on other organisms. In ecological studies, consumers are usually classified into feeding levels (**trophic levels**) by what they eat, as follows:

■ **Primary consumers,** known as **herbivores,** are animals that eat plant material. Primary consumers thus consume producers.

- **Secondary consumers** are organisms that eat primary consumers. These organisms are called **carnivores,** animals that consume other animals.
- **Tertiary consumers** consume secondary consumers. They are also called carnivores.
- Sometimes feeding strategies cross trophic levels. **Omnivores** are organisms that eat either producers or consumers. They thus consume at various trophic levels depending on the particular food item eaten.
- **Parasites**—organisms that absorb nutrients from a living host organism for a period of time—might be considered primary, secondary, or tertiary consumers depending on whether they are living on a producer or another consumer.
- **Decomposers** include fungi, most bacteria, and some protistans that break down dead organic material from organisms of *all* trophic levels into smaller molecules. The decomposers then absorb the nutrients and ultimately play a crucial role by recycling the nutrients back into the ecosystem. Decomposers operate at virtually all trophic levels.

How would you classify yourself with respect to your feeding strategy and trophic level?

_____

_____

PROCEDURE

Below you will find a partial listing of species in a forest community and some of their source(s) of energy. In the blanks provided, list the *most specific* trophic level from the descriptions earlier.

- Human (black raspberries, hickory nuts, deer, rabbits) _____
- Black raspberry (sun) _____
- Deer (black raspberries) _____
- Bear (black raspberries, deer) _____
- Coyote (deer, rabbits, black raspberries) _____
- Caterpillar (living hickory leaves) _____
- Bacterial species 1 (living black raspberry leaves) _____
- Bacterial species 2 (dead skin cells of deer) _____
- Bacterial species 3 (dead hickory trees, dead black raspberries, dead humans, dead black bears, dead deer) _____
- Weasels (young rabbits) _____
- Mosquito (blood of living humans, deer, and bears) _____
- Hickory tree (sun) _____
- Fungal species 1 (living black raspberry stems) _____
- Fungal species 2 (dead black raspberries) _____
- Rabbit (black raspberries) _____

Now, in Table 28-1, construct a *food web* by placing the organisms in their appropriate trophic levels. Leave space around the names if more than one organism occupies a trophic level. Then connect lines from the organisms to their energy source(s) to complete the food web.

Example: Secondary consumer (carnivore)   mountain lion
 |
 Primary consumer (herbivore)   deer
 |
 Producer   grass

TABLE 28-1 A Simplified Food Web	
Trophic Level	**Organism(s)**
Decomposer:	
Secondary consumer (carnivore):	
Secondary consumer (parasite):	
Primary consumer (herbivore):	
Primary consumer (parasite):	
Omnivore:	
Producer:	

Suppose a new parasite species that kills black raspberry plants is introduced from another part of the world into this forest community. Speculate on the consequences of loss of black raspberries for the rabbit population.

_____

_____

How might the elimination of black raspberries affect the coyote populations? The weasel population?

_____

_____

What if pesticide spraying unintentionally kills both fungal species? What effect might these species losses have on both the raspberry and rabbit populations?

_____

_____

_____

28.2   Flow of Energy Through an Ecosystem (*About 15 min.*)

Ecologists have learned through careful measurement that the amount of energy captured decreases at each succeeding trophic level relative to the initial sunlight falling on the ecosystem. Of the total amount of sunlight falling on a green plant, the plant captures—at best—1% of this energy. That is, only a small fraction of the light energy falling on the surface of a leaf is converted to the chemical energy of ATP. A primary consumer on average only captures about 10% of the energy stored in a green plant. A secondary consumer usually captures only about 10% of the energy stored in the body of the animal that *it* eats, and so on.

What percentage of the energy contained in plant foods has been captured by the secondary consumer that feeds on an herbivore (primary consumer)? _____

A tertiary consumer eats the first (herbivore-eating) secondary consumer. Assuming a similar flow of energy, how much of the sun's *original* energy does this secondary consumer gain? _____

Suppose an omnivore can obtain all the nutritional requirements necessary for life by eating either plant material or animal material. From an energetics standpoint, which route will allow the omnivore to capture the greater amount of the sun's energy? _____

What other routes would enable this organism to obtain equal amounts of the sun's energy? _____

_____

_____

28.3   Survivorship*

Within a population, some individuals die very young while others live into old age. To a large extent, the *pattern* of survivorship is species dependent. Generally, **survivorship** takes on one of three patterns, which we summarize using **survivorship curves,** graphs that plot the pattern of mortality (death) in a population.

Humans in developed countries with good health-care services are characterized by a Type I curve (see Figure 28-4), in which there is high survivorship until some age, then high mortality. The insurance industry uses this information to determine risk groups. The premiums they charge are based on an individual's risk group, with risk of death (and cost of premiums) highest for the oldest purchasers of insurance.

While survivorship curves for humans are relatively easy to generate, similar information on other species is much more difficult to determine. It can be quite a trick to determine the age of an individual plant or animal, let alone track an entire population over a period of years. However, survivorship rates can be demonstrated in the laboratory using nonliving objects.

In this section, you will study the "populations" of dice and soap bubbles, using them to model real populations and to construct survivorship curves. You will subject these populations to different kinds of stress to determine their effects on survivorship curves.

_____

*Adapted from an exercise courtesy J. Shepherd, Mercer University, personal communication.

MATERIALS

Per student:

- 15-cm ruler

Per student group (4):

- bucket containing 50 dice
- soap bubble solution and wand
- stopwatch or digital watch

Per lab room:

- 1–2 survivorship frames (see Figure 28-1)
- overhead transparency of Figures 28-2 and 28-3
- 1 set of red, blue, black, and green pens (Sharpie® or similar marker)
- overhead projector
- projection screen

PROCEDURE

A. Dice Survivorship *(About 30 min.)*

Work in a group of four. One person should be assigned to dump the dice, another to record data, and the other two to count.

Population 1

1. Empty the bucket of 50 dice onto the floor.
2. Assume that individuals who come up as 1's die of heart disease. All others survive.
3. Pick up all the 1's, set them aside (in the cemetery), and count the number of individuals who have survived. Record the number of *survivors* in this generation (generation 1) in the left-hand column of Table 28-2.
4. Return the survivors to the bucket.
5. Dump the survivors onto the floor again and remove the deaths (1's) that occur during this second generation.
6. Count and record the number of survivors.
7. Continue this process until all the dice have "died" from heart disease.
8. Now determine the percentage of survivors for each generation using the following formula and record in Table 28-2:

$$\text{percentage surviving} = \frac{\text{number surviving}}{50} \times 100\%$$

Population 2

1. Start again with a full bucket of 50 dice. Assume that 1's die of heart disease and 2's die of cancer. Proceed as described for population 1, recording the counts in Table 28-2, until all dice are "dead."
2. Again determine the percentage of survivors for each generation with the following formula:

$$\text{percentage surviving} = \frac{\text{number surviving}}{50} \times 100\%$$

How does adding another cause of death affect the survivorship rate?

_____

_____

_____

Do you think this activity models human survivorship well? Why or why not?

_____

_____

_____

TABLE 28-2 Survival Rates of Dice Populations

Generation	Population 1 Survivors (Heart Disease Only)		Population 2 Survivors (Cancer & Heart Disease)	
	Number	Percentage	Number	Percentage
0	50	100%	50	100%
1	_____	_____	_____	_____
2	_____	_____	_____	_____
3	_____	_____	_____	_____
4	_____	_____	_____	_____
5	_____	_____	_____	_____
6	_____	_____	_____	_____
7	_____	_____	_____	_____
8	_____	_____	_____	_____
9	_____	_____	_____	_____
10	_____	_____	_____	_____
11	_____	_____	_____	_____
12	_____	_____	_____	_____
13	_____	_____	_____	_____
14	_____	_____	_____	_____
15	_____	_____	_____	_____
16	_____	_____	_____	_____
17	_____	_____	_____	_____
18	_____	_____	_____	_____
19	_____	_____	_____	_____
20	_____	_____	_____	_____
21	_____	_____	_____	_____
22	_____	_____	_____	_____
23	_____	_____	_____	_____
24	_____	_____	_____	_____
25	_____	_____	_____	_____

Work in groups of four. One person blows bubbles, a second person times the "life" of the bubble, a third observes survivorship, and the fourth records data in Table 28-3.

Bubbles are "alive" as long as they are intact, but "die" when they burst. You will be following bubbles and timing how long they "live."

Different student groups in your lab section will create three different populations of soap bubbles. Your group will be assigned one population to work with during this exercise:

Population 1. Once the bubble leaves the wand, group members wave, blow, or fan in an effort to keep the bubble in the air and prevent it from breaking (dying) as long as possible.

Population 2. Group members do nothing to interfere with the bubbles or keep them up in the air once the bubbles leave the wand.

Population 3. This group uses a wand mounted on a wooden frame (Figure 28-1). The person blowing bubbles stands at the wand facing the frame, dips the wand in the soap solution, and tries to blow the bubbles through the opening in the frame. *Bubbles that break on the paper "hazard" or any other part of the frame rather than passing through the frame are timed and included in the data. Bubbles that fall to the side without passing through or breaking on the frame are ignored (not counted in the data). Do not attempt to manipulate the frame in any way so as to increase the chances that the bubbles will pass through it.*

1. Practice blowing bubbles for a few minutes until you can generate them with the single end of the wand. Even though you may generate several bubbles, follow only one at a time to measure its life span.
2. The timer should start the watch once the bubble is free of the wand. When the bubble bursts, the timer notes the time and checks the age at death in Table 28-3.
3. Measure the life span of 50 bubbles.
4. Summarize your data as follows:
   (a) Count the number of checks (number of bubbles dying) at each age. Record the number in the column marked "Total."
   (b) To determine the number surviving at each age, subtract the number dying at each age from the number surviving at the previous age. So, if 5 bubbles break (die) at age 1 second, then $50 - 5 = 45$ survive at least 1 second. If 10 more bubbles die at age 2 seconds, then $45 - 10 = 35$ survive at least 2 seconds.
   (c) Calculate the percentage surviving at each age. Since at birth (the moment the bubble leaves the wand) 50 bubbles are alive, 100% are alive at age 0. Use the following formula:

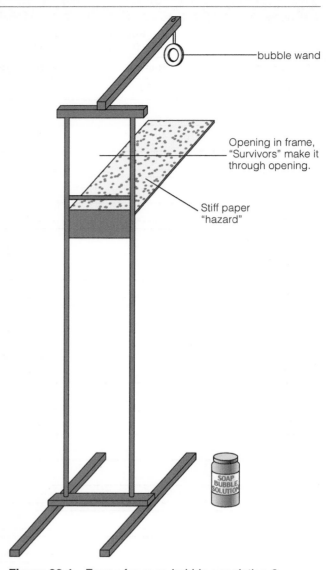

Figure 28-1 Frame for soap bubble population 3.

$$\textbf{percentage surviving to this age} = \frac{\textbf{number surviving at age}}{50} \times 100\%$$

TABLE 28-3 Survivor Data for Soap Bubble Population

Age at Death (sec)	Bubbles Dying at This Age		Bubbles Surviving to This Age	
	Number (✔ = 1)	Total	Number	Percentage
0	0	0	50	100%
1	_____	_____	_____	_____
2	_____	_____	_____	_____
3	_____	_____	_____	_____
4	_____	_____	_____	_____
5	_____	_____	_____	_____
6	_____	_____	_____	_____
7	_____	_____	_____	_____
8	_____	_____	_____	_____
9	_____	_____	_____	_____
10	_____	_____	_____	_____
11	_____	_____	_____	_____
12	_____	_____	_____	_____
13	_____	_____	_____	_____
14	_____	_____	_____	_____
15	_____	_____	_____	_____
16	_____	_____	_____	_____
17	_____	_____	_____	_____
18	_____	_____	_____	_____
19	_____	_____	_____	_____
20	_____	_____	_____	_____
21	_____	_____	_____	_____
22	_____	_____	_____	_____
23	_____	_____	_____	_____
24	_____	_____	_____	_____
25	_____	_____	_____	_____
26	_____	_____	_____	_____
27	_____	_____	_____	_____
28	_____	_____	_____	_____
29	_____	_____	_____	_____
30+	_____	_____	_____	_____

PROCEDURE

Work alone for this activity.

1. Use Figure 28-2 to make an *arithmetic plot* of survivorship of the dice and soap bubble populations. Note that the horizontal lines are the same distance apart on this graph.

Using open circles to indicate the percentage of *dice* surviving at each age, plot the percentage surviving data from Table 28-2. Using closed circles to indicate the percentage of *soap bubbles* surviving at each age, plot the percentage surviving data from Table 28-3. Use a ruler to connect the data points from each population.

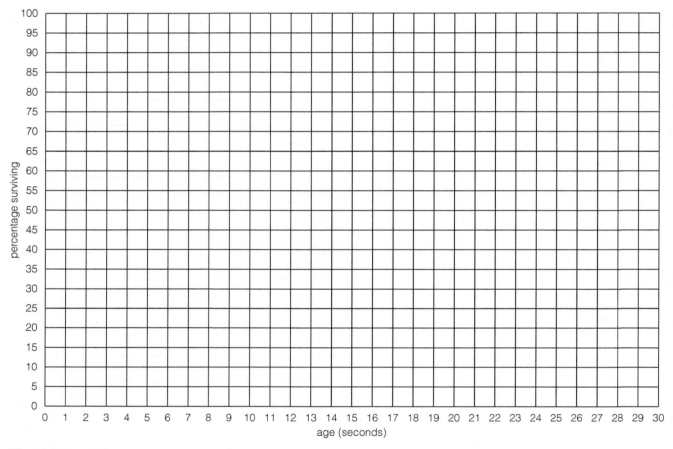

Figure 28-2   Arithmetic plot of survivorship.

2. Now you will use Figure 28-3 to make a *logarithmic plot* of survivorship. Note that on this *semilog* paper, the horizontal lines become closer together toward the top of the page.

If you've never used semilog paper, examine Figure 28-3 more closely. The scale on the vertical axis runs from 1 at the bottom to 9 near the middle, then from 1 to 9 near the top; there is a 1 at the topmost line. The lines are spaced according to the *logarithms* of the numbers.

The 1 at the top represents 100%, the 9 below it 90%, and so on. This means that the 1 in the middle of the page is 10%, while the 9 below it represents 9%; the 8, 8%; and so forth until the 1 at the bottom, which represents 1%.

Plot the survivorship of the dice and soap bubbles that your group generated, using the percentage surviving data from Tables 28-2 and 28-3. Open circles indicate the percentage of dice surviving and closed circles the percentage of soap bubbles surviving. Use a ruler to connect the points, forming a curve for each population.

After you've plotted your data, copy your plots onto the overhead transparency your instructor has for this purpose, using the pens provided. Different colored pens are available so that each population will have a separate color.

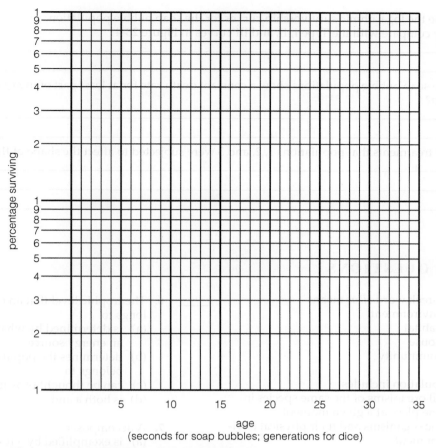

Figure 28-3 Logarithmic plot of survivorship.

Interpreting the Survivorship Curves *(About 15 min.)*

First examine the plots from the dice populations. In population 1 (heart disease only), a constant one-sixth, or 17%, of the population dies on average at each age. In population 2, two-sixths, or 33%, dies on average at each age. As you can see, on the *arithmetic plot* these data form a smooth curve, while on the *logarithmic plot* they form a straight line.

Both types of graphs provide useful information. A straight line on a logarithmic plot indicates the death rate is *constant*, but it's easier to see that more individuals die at a young age than at older ages in the arithmetic plot.

In natural populations, three basic trends of survivorship affecting population size have been identified. These are shown in Figure 28-4 and summarized in Table 28-4.

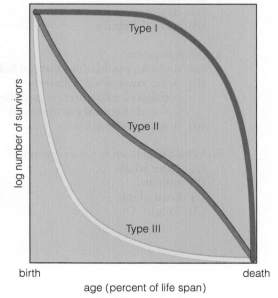

Figure 28-4 Three basic types of survivorship curves.

TABLE 28-4 Survivorship Curves

Type	Trend
I	Low mortality early in life, most deaths occurring in a narrow time span at maturity
II	Rate of mortality fairly constant at all ages
III	High mortality early in life

Now examine the logarithmic survivorship curves for the soap bubble population. How do they compare with the Type I, II, and III curves in Figure 28-4?

_____

_____

Do any of the soap bubble populations show a constant death rate for at least part of their life span? If so, for which population?

_____

_____

How did the treatments that populations 1, 2, and 3 were subjected to affect the shape of the curves?

_____

_____

_____

PRE-LAB QUESTIONS

_____ 1. The Greek word *oikos* means
(a) environment
(b) habitat
(c) house
(d) community

_____ 2. A population includes
(a) all organisms of the same species in one place at a given moment
(b) the organisms and their physical environment
(c) the physical environment in which an organism exists
(d) all organisms within the environment at a given moment

_____ 3. The place that an organism resides is
(a) its community
(b) its habitat
(c) its population
(d) all of the above

_____ 4. An ecosystem
(a) includes populations but not habitats
(b) is the same as a community
(c) consists of a community and the physical and chemical environment
(d) is none of the above

_____ 5. Which organism is *not* a consumer?
(a) killer whale
(b) human
(c) bean plant
(d) fungus

_____ 6. The trophic level that an organism belongs to
(a) is determined by what it uses as an energy source
(b) determines the population it belongs to
(c) can be thought of as its feeding level
(d) is both a and c

_____ 7. A decomposer
(a) is exemplified by a fungus
(b) is the same as a parasite
(c) feeds on living organic material
(d) feeds on primary consumers only

_____ 8. An herbivore
(a) eats plant material
(b) eats primary producers
(c) is exemplified by a deer
(d) is all of the above

_____ 9. Which term best describes a human being?
(a) omnivore
(b) herbivore
(c) carnivore
(d) parasite

_____ 10. A survivorship curve shows
(a) the number of individuals surviving to a particular age
(b) the cause of death of an individual
(c) the place an organism exists in its environment
(d) the organism's trophic level

EXERCISE 28

Ecology: Living Organisms in Their Environment

POST-LAB QUESTIONS

Introduction

1. Define the terms *herbivore, carnivore, omnivore.*

2. Define the terms *producer, primary consumer, secondary consumer.*

3. Characterize yourself, using the terms listed in questions 1 and 2. Justify your answer.

28.1 Food Webs

4. Examine the food web you constructed in Table 28-1. Suppose a severe outbreak of rabies occurs in the coyote population, resulting in the death of the entire population. Draw a rough graph that describes the impact of the loss of this predator on the rabbit, deer, and raspberry populations over time, and explain your reasoning.

5. You've probably read newspaper articles about the so-called ozone "hole" over Antarctica and other areas of the planet, as well as health-care cautions that destruction of the earth's protective ozone layer will allow harmful ultraviolet (UV) light to reach the surface. Already, a significant increase in skin cancer is being noticed, a disease known to be caused by excessive exposure to UV light (including that produced by tanning lights). Perhaps not so well known is the damage UV light causes to the photosynthetic machinery of green plants and protists.

    Explain what would happen over time to the populations of organisms of your food web (Table 28-1) if ozone depletion becomes massive.

28.2 Flow of Energy Through an Ecosystem

6. You may have heard the advice to "eat low on the food chain." Explain how choosing a soybean-protein "burger" rather than a beef burger for lunch is energy efficient with respect to energy flow and utilization in trophic levels.

28.3 Survivorship

7. Would you expect a population in which most members survive for a long time to produce few or many offspring? Which would be most advantageous to the population as a whole?

8. Suppose a human population exhibits a Type III survival curve. What would you expect to happen to the curve over time if a dramatic improvement in medical technology takes place?

9. Return to the survivorship model you created using dice: You found that the chance of dying from heart disease is approximately one-sixth for each die, indicating that survivorship is essentially the same for each age group. Relate what happened in your model with a realistic projection showing at what ages most humans die of heart disease.

Food for Thought

10. Ecologist Aldo Leopold, the father of American conservation, said, "The last word in ignorance is the man who says of an animal or plant: 'What good is it?' . . . If the biota, in the course of aeons, has built something we like but do not understand, then who but a fool would discard seeming useless parts? To keep every cog and wheel is the first precaution of intelligent tinkering."

These are strong words indeed. How do they relate to what you've explored in this exercise?

Habitat Resource Partitioning in a Woodpecker Guild

Abstract

Elucidating how coexisting species partition resources is a fundamental aim of ecological research. Our research focused on determining how coexisting woodpecker species partition habitat space within a complex landscape mosaic. We found a statistically significant association between woodpecker species and habitat type, indicating that woodpecker species do differ in their use of habitat. Further studies focusing on more finely tuned data collection at the microhabitat level are discussed.

Introduction

A central goal within ecology is an assessment of the relationships between and among coexisting species. The competitive exclusion principle states that when resources are limited, coexisting species partition the resources such that the species never totally overlap in their use of the limiting resources (Diamond and Case 1986). Partitioning of resources may occur in several ways. Most simply, species may occupy different ranges of habitats with no co-occurrence at the same time. When species do have overlapping ranges, partitioning may occur on a local habitat (i.e., macrohabitat) level. For example, the thrashers of North America, *Mimidae*, all occupy some type of scrub habitat. However, each species is generally found to individually occupy a homogeneous vegetation type that has no overlap of use with the other species (Cody 1974). When species co-occur within a local habitat, partitioning may occur by species differing in their spatial and behavioral use of the habitat. This can occur in a vertical, horizontal, or temporal dimension. For example, MacArthur (1958) documented that separate foraging sites within a single habitat, the Maine spruce forests, were used by different species of *Dendroica* warblers. Yet another way in which co-occurring species may partition resources is through differences in the types of food taken. An example of this is provided by several species of European tits. All co-occur in a single local habitat type, oak woodland, but each species takes food items of slightly different sizes (Betts 1955).

Woodpeckers offer an excellent opportunity to explore the ways in which closely related species partition resources in order to coexist. Woodpeckers belong to the "trunk and branch foraging" guild, a predominantly insectivorous guild whose members primarily search for food on or in the trunks and branches of trees (De Graaf, Tilghman, and Anderson 1985). We chose to examine how woodpecker species coexist in the scrub-pine habitats of central Florida. The landscape is characterized by a complex mosaic of different vegetation associations. We quantified individual species' responses to the diversity of vegetation associations in order to understand how this woodpecker guild is able to coexist. Our objective was to determine whether woodpecker species differ in their use of *macrohabitat space* (herein defined as one of the major vegetation association types within the landscape).

Materials and Methods

Our study site was located at Archbold Biological Station (ABS), 12 kilometers south of Lake Placid in Highlands County, Florida. ABS includes the following vegetation associations: southern ridge sandhill (RS), sand pine scrub (SS), scrubby flatwoods (SF), flatwoods (FL), swale, bayhead, and seasonal ponds. Detailed descriptions of these habitats are given by Abrahamson et al. (1984). The vegetational structure and composition of these habitats is in large part determined by fire and drainage. As a result, a mosaic of habitats with different fire histories as well as different vegetation associations exists on the ABS property. To determine how the woodpecker species coexist within this mosaic of habitats, we chose three sites representing the predominant vegetation associations: RS, SS, and SF. The three sites chosen were of roughly the same size and shape (based on aerial photographs and GIS maps).

The species of woodpecker found on the ABS property include: the downy woodpecker, the red-cockaded woodpecker, the hairy woodpecker, the red-headed woodpecker, the red-bellied woodpecker, the pileated woodpecker, the yellow-bellied sapsucker, and the yellow-shafted flicker. As noted, these species belong to the trunk-and-branch foraging guild (De Graaf, Tilghman, and Anderson 1985). Their foraging behavior is predominately directed on and around the trunks and branches of trees. Of this guild, we observed and collected data on five species: the downy, flicker, hairy, red-bellied, and red-headed woodpecker species. We did not encounter the other members of the guild.

Our method of collecting data involved walking throughout the particular vegetation association site in such a manner as to ensure full coverage of the site. Each investigator covered a separate site so that all three sites were visited simultaneously. We spent a total of two hours canvassing each site. Data were recorded on each species encountered, and attempts were made to ensure that individuals were not counted more than once (by visual identification using binoculars). Data were compiled into a 3×5 contingency table and analyzed for habitat preferences of the five species using the chi-square test (Fowler, Cohen, and Jarvis 1998). Our null hypothesis stated that there was no association between habitat type and woodpecker species; our alternative hypothesis was that there is an association between habitat type and woodpecker species.

Results

We found a statistically highly significant association between woodpecker species and type of habitat ($X^2 = 44.59$, $P < 0.01$). We therefore rejected the null hypothesis and accepted the alternative hypothesis. To determine which woodpecker species are associated with which habitat type, we compared observed and expected frequencies of each species by habitat type. We found more red-headed woodpeckers than expected in scrubby flatwoods, more downy woodpeckers than expected in sandpine scrub, and more than expected numbers of the remaining three species (the yellow-shafted flicker and the hairy and red-bellied woodpeckers) in ridge sandhill (Table 1).

TABLE 1 Contingency Table of Frequencies for Woodpecker Species by Habitat Type

	Downy	Flicker	Hairy	Red-Bellied	Red-Headed	Total
Scrubby Flatwoods						
Observed	2	6	2	7	13	30
Expected	5.2	6.6	7.2	5.4	5.4	30
% within habitat	6.7	20.0	6.7	23.3	43.3	100
Sandpine Scrub						
Observed	22	10	16	8	11	67
Expected	11.7	14.8	16.2	12.1	12.1	67
% within habitat	32.8	14.9	23.9	11.9	16.4	100
Ridge Sandhill						
Observed	2	17	18	12	3	52
Expected	9.1	11.5	12.6	9.4	9.4	52
% within habitat	3.8	32.7	34.6	23.1	5.8	100

Discussion

This initial investigation into the ways in which closely related species partition resources has revealed that the woodpeckers co-occurring on the ABS property differ in the ways in which they use the habitat mosaic. Although all five species were found in all habitat types, they differed in their frequencies of occurrence within these habitats. None of the five species sampled was found to be using only one habitat category to the exclusion of the others. It may be that, by distributing their habitat use across more than one habitat, no two species come into severe enough competition for deleterious consequences to develop. Previous research has shown that woodpeckers are opportunistic foragers that use a variety of substrates (Short 1982). Habitat mosaics may allow enough partitioning of resources across the landscape such that the species avoid severe competition. One area for future research would be determining the size of the landscape mosaic of habitats that would be needed to support a large woodpecker species guild.

Alternatively, even though species co-occur within a macrohabitat category, they may actually be partitioning the resources at the level of the microhabitat. Studies could be designed that observe focal individuals. Data that could be collected include bird species, foraging behavior, substrate used (trunk, branch, or ground), tree species used, height on the tree, and whether the tree was live or dead. Bird foraging behavior could be divided into the following relevant categories: peering and poking, probing and drilling, scaling, and hawking. Additional investigations could examine the types of insects and other food sources used by species.

The results of studies such as the one reported here as well as those suggested will advance our understanding not only of how species coexist but also how species respond to environmental conditions such as food availability and habitat space. This type of data is necessary for making sound management decisions, especially decisions regarding landscape management and restoration activities.

Citations

Abrahamson et al. 1984

Betts, M. M. 1955. The food of titmice in oak woodland. *Journal of Animal Ecology* 24: 282–323.

Cody, M. L. 1974. *Bird communities*. Princeton, NJ: Princeton University Press.

De Graaf, R. M., N. G. Tilghman, and S. H. Anderson. 1985. Foraging guilds of North American birds. *Environmental Management* 9(6): 493–536.

Diamond, J., and T. J. Case (Eds.). 1986. *Community ecology*. New York: Harper & Row.

Fowler, J., L. Cohen, and P. Jarvis. 1998. *Practical statistics for field biology*. Chichester, UK: Wiley & Sons.

MacArthur, R. H. 1958. Population ecology of some warblers of northeastern coniferous forests. *Ecology* 39(4): 599–619.

Short, L. L. 1982. *Woodpeckers of the world*. Monographs Series No. 4. Greenville, DE: Delaware Museum of Natural History.

Human Impact on the Environment: Stream and Pond Ecology

OBJECTIVES

After completing this exercise, you will be able to

1. define *stream, pool, riffle, abiotic, biotic, watershed, point source pollution, nonpoint source pollution, pH, dissolved oxygen, nitrates, phosphates, chlorides, coliform bacteria, macroinvertebrate, larvae, Stream Quality Index;*
2. explain why most aquatic invertebrates are found in riffles;
3. describe how sediment pollution occurs and its major effects on the stream ecosystem;
4. describe the effects of organic pollutants and nutrient pollution on stream organisms;
5. explain the importance of dissolved oxygen in stream water;
6. describe how aquatic macroinvertebrates present in a stream can indicate water quality;
7. indicate the significance of finding coliform bacteria or bacteria identified via a PathoScreen test in a water sample;
8. discuss limitations and strengths of standard chemical water tests, as well as the Stream Quality Index;
9. discuss some of the ways in which human activity in a watershed can affect stream water quality.

INTRODUCTION

Global warming, extinction of species, damage to the stratospheric ozone layer, toxic chemical spills, ground water contamination, and deforestation. This partial list of environmental effects attributed to the activities of our exploding human population is diverse and alarming. Each of these issues is a complex problem with scientific, economic, philosophical, sociological, and political aspects, and no single exercise (or entire course!) can fully address any of these concerns. However, this exercise, which focuses on some of the ways humans affect streams and rivers, the arteries of our planet, will give you an idea of how scientists build the data base they use to assess environmental problems.

A **stream** is a body of running water flowing on the earth. Streams range from shallow, narrow brooks tumbling down mountainsides to broad, deep rivers like the Mississippi. Regardless of its size, every stream has distinct major habitat types that influence the types of organisms living there. Relatively slow-moving, deep waters are called **pools,** while **riffles** are shallow areas with fast-moving current bubbling over rocks (Figure 29-1).

a

b

(Photos by E. F. Benfield.)

Figure 29-1 Stream habitats. **(a)** Pool leading into a riffle, **(b)** closer look at a riffle.

Riffles are places where stream water tumbling over rocks and gravel bottom recharges the water with oxygen. Because of the higher dissolved oxygen levels and the rocks and gravel that provide habitat, most stream inhabitants live in riffles. The rapid current brings oxygen for cellular respiration as well as a steady supply of food from upstream. Pools, on the other hand, are still areas with lower oxygen content. Pools tend to have muddy beds, catch organic matter from upstream, and are areas of decomposition and nutrient recycling.

Gaseous, liquid, and solid substances enter the stream and either dissolve in the water or are carried along as suspended particles. The current thus transports these substances to where they may affect organisms downstream. The current speed, type of bottom structure, temperature, and dissolved substances are the **abiotic** components of the stream ecosystem. These abiotic components influence the life and habits of the organisms inhabiting the flowing water, the **biotic,** or living, components of the stream ecosystem.

The single most important factor influencing the abiotic and biotic components is the character of the **watershed,** all the surrounding land area that serves as drainage for a stream. A watershed may cover a few acres of land surrounding a very small stream, or include tens of thousands of square kilometers for a large river. You can think of a watershed as a bowl, with the stream flowing across the bottom. Water that falls on the higher elevations (the sides of the bowl) of a watershed eventually flows into the stream.

Your instructor will provide you with information about the boundaries and terrain of the watershed of the stream you will study.

The quality of a stream depends on its watershed and the human activities that occur there. In general, a stream is of the highest quality when the watershed and streamside vegetation remain in a natural state, while most human influences tend to be detrimental to stream quality. These human-induced effects can be lumped under the general term *pollution.* The most common types of water pollutants are

- *Human pathogens,* disease-causing agents, such as bacteria, viruses, and protists.
- *Toxic chemicals,* both organic (carbon-containing) and inorganic. Toxic chemicals can harm humans, and fish and other aquatic life. They include acids, heavy metals, petroleum products, pesticides, and detergents.
- *Organic wastes,* such as sewage, food-processing and paper-making wastes, and animal wastes. Organic wastes can be decomposed by bacteria, but the process uses up oxygen dissolved in the water. The decomposition of large quantities of organic wastes can deplete the water of oxygen, causing fish, insects, and other aquatic oxygen-requiring organisms to die.
- *Plant nutrients,* such as nitrates and phosphates, that can cause too much growth of algae and aquatic plants. When the masses of algae and plants die, the decay process can again deplete the critical dissolved oxygen in the water.
- *Sediments,* or suspended matter, the particles of soil or other solids that become suspended in the water. Sediment originates where soil has been exposed to rainfall, most often from construction sites, forestry operations, and agriculture. This is the biggest pollutant by weight, and it can reduce photosynthesis by clouding the water and can carry pesticides and other harmful substances with the soil particles. When sediment settles, it can destroy fish feeding and spawning areas and clog and fill stream channels, lakes, and harbors.
- *Heat,* or thermal pollution. Heated water holds less dissolved oxygen than colder water, so the addition of heated water by industries must be closely monitored to ensure that dissolved oxygen isn't driven to too low levels.

All these substances enter water as either "point" or "nonpoint" pollution. **Point source pollution** occurs at a specific location where the pollutants are released from a pipe, ditch, or sewer. Examples of point sources include sewage treatment plants, storm drains, and factory discharges. Point sources are relatively easy to identify, regulate, and monitor. Federal and state governments regulate the type and quantity of some types of pollutants for each point source discharge.

Nonpoint source pollution enters streams from a vast number of sources, with no specific point of entry contributing a large amount of pollutants. Most nonpoint source pollution results when rainfall and runoff carry pollutants from large, poorly defined areas into a stream. Examples of nonpoint source pollution include the washing of fertilizers and pesticides from lawns and agricultural fields, and soil erosion from construction sites. Because sources of nonpoint pollution are difficult to identify and define, it is much more difficult to regulate.

What human activities can you name that might be affecting your study stream? _____

_____

_____

_____

What activities might have affected your study stream in the past that are unlikely to occur today?

_____

_____

_____

A. Observations *(About 20 min.)*

MATERIALS

Per student group (4):

- clear glass jar or beaker
- map or aerial photo of watershed area (optional)

PROCEDURE

The first step in the quality analysis of your stream, as in so many scientific endeavors, is observation. Record your observations on the Stream Environment Characterization Data Sheet using the instructions and questions immediately following the data sheet for guidance.

B. Physical and Chemical Sampling *(About 1 hr.)*

MATERIALS

Per student:

- disposable plastic gloves (optional)

Per student group (4):

- nail clippers or scissors
- plastic beaker
- plastic sample bottles
- watch or clock

Per lab room:

- thermometer
- portable pH meter or pH indicator paper
- Hach or other dissolved oxygen test kit
- Hach or other nitrate test kit
- Hach or other chloride test kit
- Hach or other phosphate test kit
- dH$_2$O
- paper towels

PROCEDURE

In this section, you will take several streamside measurements, and collect water samples for analysis. Your class will divide into groups, with each group performing different tasks. As a class you will measure the temperature and pH of the water, plus determine several nutrient/pollutant levels. Additionally, you will collect macroinvertebrates for classification and sample the water for the presence of potentially pathogenic (disease-causing) bacteria.

1. **Temperature.** Stream organisms are typically more sensitive to higher temperatures. In addition to affecting the metabolic rate of the cold-blooded aquatic organisms, cooler water holds more dissolved oxygen than warmer water.

Measure the water temperature holding a thermometer about 10 cm below the water surface, if possible. Keep the thermometer in the water for approximately 1 minute so the temperature can equilibrate. Record the temperature measurements from 3 locations here, then total them and calculate the average temperature. Enter the average temperature in Table 29-1.

Temperature: _____ ; _____ ; _____

2. **pH.** pH is a measure of the concentration of hydrogen ions in the water. In essence, pH signifies the degree of acidity or alkalinity of water. The pH scale ranges from 0 (most acidic) to 14 (most basic), as indicated in Figure 29-2. A solution with a pH of 7 is neutral. A change of only 1 on the scale means a tenfold change in the hydrogen ion concentration of the water.

The bedrock in the watershed influences the pH of the stream water as does the pH of rainwater and discharges into the stream. pH values between 6.0 and 8.5 occur naturally in streams. A pH value below 6.0 indicates acid mine drainage, acid precipitation, or some other acid source, unless the stream drains a naturally acidic environment such as a swamp or bog.

    pH that is too low can damage fish gills. Low water pH can also cause some minerals, such as aluminum, in the streambed to go into solution and become toxic. The higher the pH, the more carbonates, bicarbonates, and salts are dissolved in the water. Streams with moderate concentrations of these substances are nutritionally rich and support abundant life.

STREAM ENVIRONMENT CHARACTERIZATION DATA SHEET

(circle appropriate choice for each)

Riparian Zone

Predominant Surrounding Land Use:

Forest/Overgrown field   Agricultural/Pasture   Residential

Commercial   Industrial   Other

Streambank Erosion:

None   Moderate   Severe

Local Nonpoint Source Pollution:

No evidence   Potential sources   Obvious sources

Canopy Cover:

Open   Little shade (40%)   Moderate shade (40–80%)

Shady (>80%)

Stream Corridor

Sediment Odors:

Normal   Sewage   Petroleum

Chemical   Anaerobic   Other

Sediment Deposits:

Sludge   Sawdust   Sand   Relict shells   Other

Streambed:

Green filamentous algae   Blue-green algae

Yellow-orange coating

Water Odors:

Natural   Sewage   Petroleum

Chemical   Other

Water Surface Oils and Foams:

None   Flecks   Globs   Sheen   Slick

Turbidity:

Clear   Slightly turbid   Turbid   Opaque

Water Color: _____

Instructions and Background

STREAM ENVIRONMENT CHARACTERIZATION INSTRUCTIONS AND BACKGROUND

Predominant land use: Look up and downstream on both banks and observe how land adjacent to the stream is being used. Also note any minor uses (for example, small corn field, parking lot, unpaved road) that may have an impact on the stream.

Streambank erosion: Observe the condition of the land adjacent to the streambank. Is the land highly vegetated and stable? Are there any gullies eroding the streambank or is the bank being undercut?

Local watershed nonpoint source pollution: Observe any sources of pollution aside from sedimentation. Are there roads close to the stream bank? Are there farms near the stream? Is the site adjacent to a golf course or residential or commercial area?

Canopy cover: Stand in the center of the stream and look up at the sky. What percentage of the stream is shaded? Is the entire stream covered with tree canopy or is the vegetation predominantly shrubs or herbs? Shaded streams have cooler water than unshaded. Warmer water also contains less dissolved oxygen than colder, and so may limit the kinds of organisms that can survive.

Sediment odors: Carefully take a handful or sediment from the site. Can you detect any odors? Indicate any odor on the data sheet even if it is not listed. *Note:* Anaerobic (without oxygen) sediments contain hydrogen sulfide and smell like rotting eggs. Anaerobic conditions can occur naturally in a marsh but can also indicate the presence of sewage pollution in a stream.

Sediment deposits: Are any sediment deposits found at the site? Are the undersides of any loosely embedded rocks blackened? This indicates an anaerobic condition unfavorable to benthic (bottom-dwelling) invertebrates.

Streambed: Green filamentous algae may indicate the presence of organic pollutants or excessive nutrients if they colonize more than 10% of the streambed. Dark-colored blue-green algae (more properly called "cyanobacteria") are more tolerant of pollution and may indicate pollution by organic materials such as sewage, liquid released from sanitary landfills, and/or animal wastes. A yellow to orange-red coating on the streambed may indicate a high soil erosion rate, industrial pollution, or polluted water draining from a mine.

Water odors: Sniff the stream waters and record any detectable odor. If no odor is recognizable, answer "natural."

Water surface oils and foams: Note the presence of any oils on the surface of the water. In streams, oils are usually seen as a rainbowlike sheen when in sunlight. Are oils widespread? Or are they only in isolated areas, perhaps surrounding leaves? (Plants naturally release oils as they decay.)

The presence of extensive white-colored foam more than 7 cm high indicates pollution from detergents.

Turbidity: Take a sample of water in a clear container and hold it up to a light background. Note the amount of turbidity (cloudiness) present. Turbidity is caused by the suspension of solid matter, including sediment and plankton. Determining turbidity will aid in evaluating water color.

Water color: Collect a water sample in a clear container and hold it up against a white background. What color does the water appear? Often a stream looks dark brown, tan, or green, but is actually clear, with the water color resulting from the stream bottom material. If any strange colors are observed, indicate whether they appear throughout the stream or in isolated areas, such as below a discharge pipe.

TABLE 29-1 Stream Measurements and Water Quality Standards

Physical/Chemical Measurement	Average Value	Water Quality Standards		Probable Cause of Degradation[a]
		General[b]	Trout Stream	
Temperature		< 32°C	< 20–23°C	Lack of shade
pH		6.0–8.5	6.5–8.5	Acid drainage
Dissolved oxygen (DO)		> 5 mg/L	> 6 mg/L	Organic and nutrient sources
Nitrate (NO_3^-)		< 2 mg/L	< 10 mg/L[3]	Organic and nutrient sources, fertilizers
Phosphate (PO_4^-)		< 0.1 mg/L		Organic and nutrient sources, fertilizers
Chloride (Cl^-)		< 30 mg/L		Road salt, sewage, agricultural chemicals
Total coliform bacteria			0 colonies[c]	Sewage, animal wastes
PathoScreen waterborne pathogens			0 colonies[c]	Sewage, animal wastes

[a] Probable cause(s) of values failing to meet standards.
[b] Standards for swimming and to protect general aquatic life. (*Source*: Wisconsin Department of Natural Resources.)
[c] Standards for drinking water. (*Source*: Wisconsin Department of Natural Resources.)

Use the pH meter or indicator paper to determine the pH of your stream water. Try to sample both riffle and pool areas. Determine and record the average pH in Table 29-1.

pH: _____ ; _____ ; _____

Perform each following chemical analysis on at least three locations, average your readings, and record the average concentration in Table 29-1. Follow the instructions provided with each test kit.

3. **Dissolved oxygen (DO).** Aquatic animals, like most living organisms, require oxygen for their metabolic processes. This oxygen is present in dissolved form in water. If much organic matter (for example, sewage) is present in water, microorganisms use the **dissolved oxygen** in the process of decomposing the organic matter. In that case, the level of dissolved oxygen might fall too low to be available for aquatic animals. How much DO an aquatic organism needs depends on its species, its physiology, water temperature, pollutants present, and other factors. However, many studies suggest that 4−5 parts per million (ppm) is the minimum needed to support a diverse fish population. The DO of good fishing waters generally averages about 9 ppm. When DO levels drop below 3 ppm, even pollution-tolerant fish species may die.

4. **Nitrate (NO_3^-).** Nitrogen (N) is a nutrient required for plant life. Nitrogen in the form of **nitrates** (NO_3^-) is a common component of the synthetic fertilizers used on lawns, golf courses, and farm fields to stimulate plant growth. Surface runoff and infiltration through the soil water from these sources is the most common route for nitrates to enter streams. Leaking sewage tanks, municipal wastewater treatment plants, manure from livestock and other animals, and discharges from car exhausts are all sources of stream nitrates. Excessive nitrates in streams can cause overgrowth of algae and other plant life. This plant growth may decrease the light available to other stream life, but eventually dies and decays. The decay process can deplete water of the vital dissolved oxygen.

5. **Phosphate (PO_4^-).** Phosphorous (P), another element crucial to plant life, is also a common component of commercial fertilizers in the form of **phosphates** (PO_4^-). When it rains, varying amounts of phosphates wash from farm fields and other fertilized areas into nearby waterways. Like nitrates, phosphate enrichment also causes nutrient problems in streams. Excessive levels indicate pollution by nutrient sources or organic substances (fertilizers, sewage, detergents, animal wastes).

6. **Chloride (Cl^-).** The chloride ion (Cl^-) has very different properties from chlorine gas (Cl_2), which is used as a disinfectant. **Chloride** is one of the major ions in sewage; it also enters waterways when washed from roadways that have been treated with salt (NaCl, sometimes $CaCl_2$) in wintertime to melt ice and snow. Agricultural chemicals are another source of chloride in water. Water with high chloride content is toxic to plant life.

MATERIALS

Per student:

- hip boots or footwear that can get wet
- forceps or tweezers

Per student group (4):

- sterile water sample collection bottles or containers
- kickseine
- white enamel pan
- bottle of alcohol
- sample collecting jars

Per lab room:

- Presence/Absence ampoule
- 100-mL plastic beaker
- 2 Whirl-Pak™ bags
- PathoScreen powder pillow
- nail clipper

PROCEDURE

1. **Total coliform bacteria.** **Coliform bacteria** are tiny, rod-shaped bacteria found in soil and water. Certain coliform bacteria, notably *Escherichia coli,* live in the intestines of humans and all warm-blooded animals, and these fecal coliform bacteria pass out of the body with feces. They can cause human disease if they enter a drinking water supply such as a private well or a river, and they are also associated with other kinds of pathogenic bacteria. While municipal water treatment plants routinely treat water to kill many potential pathogens, people who rely on private wells don't usually have that protection. Other coliform bacteria are common soil inhabitants but tend to associate in water with the more dangerous fecal coliforms. You will sample the water of your stream to determine whether any coliform bacteria are present. The presence of coliform bacteria suggests contamination with sewage or animal wastes.

    (a) Break a Presence/Absence ampoule and pour the contents into one Whirl-Pak™ bag. Be careful not to touch the inside of the bag or otherwise contaminate the contents. See Figure 29-3.

    (b) Collect at least 100 mL of stream water for each sample. Pour the water carefully into the Whirl-Pak™ bag, again being careful not to contaminate the inside of the sterile container with anything other than stream water. Swirl to mix well. Record the appearance of the liquid.

    (c) Incubate the sample at 35–40°C for 24 hours. A color change from purple to orange indicates the presence of coliform bacteria.

pH Value	Examples of Solutions and Effects
0	Hydrochloric acid (HCl)
1	
2	Lemon juice (2.3)
3	Toxic to all fish
4	Perch spawning inhibited
5	Rock bass, northern pike, sunfish disappear (4.7) Spawning inhibited in many fish
6	Walleye, smallmouth bass, lake trout disappear Walleye spawning inhibited (6.5)
7	Neutral, pure water
8	Seawater
9	Phosphate detergents, chlorine bleach
10	Soap solutions
11	Nonphosphate detergents
12	
13	Oven cleaner
14	Sodium hydroxide (NaOH)

Figure 29-2 The pH scale.

Figure 29-3 Use of sterile Whirl-Pak™ bag.

2. **PathoScreen for waterborne pathogens.** The PathoScreen test allows us to detect common human pathogens *other than* coliform bacteria. These bacteria may also be associated with fecal contamination, and include the organisms responsible for causing some kinds of dysentery, *Salmonella* poisoning, and other illnesses.

   (a) Clip the corner off a PathoScreen powder pillow and dump contents into a Whirl-Pak™ bag. Be careful not to touch the inside of the bag or otherwise contaminate the contents. (See Figure 29-3.)

   (b) Collect at least 100 mL of stream water for each sample. Pour the water carefully into the Whirl-Pak™ bag. Swirl to mix well. Record the appearance of the liquid.

   (c) Incubate the sample at 35−40°C for 24 hours. A color change from orange to black, accompanied by a strong sulfur odor, indicates the presence of potential pathogens.

3. **Aquatic Macroinvertebrates. Macroinvertebrates,** animals that are large enough to be seen with the naked eye and that lack a backbone, are an important part of the stream ecosystem. Nearly all of the macroinvertebrates present in the water are immature insects, called **larvae,** which mature and then spend their adult lives on land or in the air. Most aquatic larvae feed on decaying organic matter, but some graze on algae or pursue other animals. Other aquatic macroinvertebrates include mollusks (shelled organisms such as snails and clams), arthropods (relatives of shrimp and lobsters such as crayfish and scuds), and various types of worms.

Most aquatic macroinvertebrates, especially those that live on or in the bottom sediments of riffle areas, require a specific range of water quality conditions and thus are good indicators of water quality. Aquatic macroinvertebrates can be separated into three general groups on the basis of their tolerance to pollution. Some bottom dwellers like mayfly larvae need a high-quality, unpolluted environment and are placed in Group 1 (Figure 29-4). Dominance of Group 1 organisms in a stream signifies good water quality. Group 2 organisms can exist in a wide range of water quality conditions and include crayfish and dragonfly larvae. Group 3 organisms are tolerant of pollution and include midge and blackfly larvae and leeches.

By looking at the diversity of macroinvertebrates present, you will be able to get a general idea of the health of a stream. Typically, waters of higher quality support a greater diversity (more kinds) of pollution-intolerant aquatic insects. As water becomes more polluted, fewer kinds of organisms thrive. You will collect samples of aquatic insects and separate them in the laboratory into general types to determine the Stream Quality Index Value.

SAMPLING WITH A KICKSEINE. Try to sample from riffle areas only, since these areas usually have a higher quality environment for macroinvertebrates. Sample from pools only if most of the stream is pool area.

Work in groups.

1. Select a riffle area with a depth of 7−30 centimeters (cm), and stones that are 5−25 cm in diameter or larger if possible. Move into the sample area from the downstream side to minimize disturbance.

2. One or two students should hold the kickseine at the downstream edge of the riffle. Be sure that the bottom edge of the screen is held tightly against the stream bottom. (You might want to hold down the edge with a few rocks.) Don't allow any water to flow over the top of the seine or you might lose specimens.

3. The other group members should walk in front of the net and begin the collection procedure. Pick up all rocks fist-sized or larger and rub their surfaces thoroughly in front of the net to dislodge all organisms into the seine. Then disturb the streambed for a distance of 1 m upstream of the kickseine. Stir up the bed with hands and feet until the entire 1-m² area has been worked over. Kick the streambed with a sideways motion to allow bottom-dwelling organisms to be carried into the net.

4. Remove the seine from the water with a forward-scooping motion so that no specimens are washed from the surface. Carry the seine to a flat area of the stream bank for examination.

5. Rinse the organisms and debris collected to the bottom of the screen. Many aquatic macroinvertebrates are very small, so be certain to remove all of them from the screen. Use forceps to remove any that cling to the screen. Place the collection in a collecting jar; drain off as much water as possible and cover the material with alcohol to kill and preserve the organisms. Label each jar to identify the area sampled.

| 29.2 | **Laboratory Analysis—Evaluating Biological Tests and Samples** |

A. Total Coliform Bacteria

Note the reaction after 24 hours of incubation and record it in Table 29-1. A color change from reddish-purple to yellow or yellow-brown indicates the presence of coliform bacteria. If there is no change in 24 hours, incubate for an additional 24 hours and recheck for the color change. If after 48 ± 3 hours of incubation the sample still appears reddish-purple, record the test as negative for total coliform bacteria.

B. PathoScreen for Waterborne Pathogens

Note the reaction after 24 hours of incubation and record it in Table 29-1. A color change from orangish to black, accompanied by a strong smell of sulfur, indicates the presence of potentially pathogenic bacteria.

C. Macroinvertebrates (About 90 min.)

Identification of aquatic organisms can be difficult, to say the least. However, biological sampling results can be translated into a water quality assessment without actually identifying each insect specimen, but by assessing the number of different kinds of collected macroinvertebrates.

MATERIALS

Per student group:

- petri dishes
- white paper *or* white enamel pan

- forceps or tweezers
- dissection microscope *or* magnifying glass

PROCEDURE

1. Pour a portion of a kickseine sample into a petri dish. Place a piece of white paper onto the stage of a dissecting microscope to provide an opaque white background, and then observe the specimens in the petri dish. Alternatively, you might pour a sample into a white enamel pan and observe the specimens with a magnifying glass.
2. Use forceps or tweezers to sort all the organisms into "look-alike" groups, or taxa (Figure 29-4). Look primarily at body shape and number of legs and "tails" to aid in identification. Note the size range of the pictured taxa. Record each taxonomic group present in your sample under the appropriate group number in Table 29-2 (Group 1 = pollution-intolerant taxa; Group 2 = somewhat pollution-tolerant taxa; Group 3 = pollution-tolerant taxa). For purposes of this lab, disregard organisms that are not pictured in Figure 29-4.

TABLE 29-2 Aquatic Macroinvertebrate Survey and Worksheet

Taxa Present in Stream Samples		
Group 1 (Pollution Intolerant)	Group 2 (Somewhat Pollution Tolerant)	Group 3 (Pollution Tolerant)

3. Determine the Stream Quality Index (SQI) Value, a measure of stream ecosystem health, as follows:
   (a) The organisms in each group are assigned a group value as follows:
       Group 1 = group value 3
       Group 2 = group value 2
       Group 3 = group value 1
   (b) Count the number of taxa (*types* of organisms) in each group and multiply that number by the group value. Record the resulting group index value in worksheet space.

	Example:	Group 1 Taxa	Group 2 Taxa	Group 3 Taxa
		Caddisfly	Damselfly	Blackfly
		Mayfly	Crane Fly	Midge
		Stonefly	Clam	
		3 taxa × group value 3 = 9	3 taxa × group value 2 = 6	2 taxa × group value 1 = 2

   (c) Add the respective group index values of the three groups to find the cumulative SQI value. (In the preceding example, 9 + 6 + 2 = 17.)

Number of taxa	×	group value	=	group index value
Group 1 _____	×	3	=	_____
Group 2 _____	×	2	=	_____
Group 3 _____	×	1	=	_____

Group 1 index value	+	Group 2 index value	+	Group 3 index value	=	SQI
_____	+	_____	+	_____	=	_____

The SQI value can be interpreted as follows:

Stream Quality Index Value	Water Quality
23 and above	Excellent
17–22	Good
11–16	Fair
10 or less	Poor

In addition to indicating general water quality, your aquatic macroinvertebrate survey can provide you with information regarding the types of pollutants that may be affecting the stream. If you found few taxa of pollution-tolerant invertebrates, but with great numbers of individuals of these taxa, the stream water may be overly enriched with organic matter or have severe organic pollution. Conversely, if you found relatively few taxa and only a few individuals of each kind (or if you found *no* macroinvertebrates but the stream appears clean), you might suspect the presence of toxic chemicals. A diversity of taxa, with an abundance of individuals for many of the taxa, indicates a healthy stream with good to excellent water quality.

29.3   Analysis of Results

Table 29-1 lists acceptable levels of a few chemicals in water to protect aquatic life, as well as the probable causes of test values that fail to meet those standards. Compare your test results with those values. Also consider your findings from biological observations.

Are your observations, chemical measurements, and biological observations consistent? (Refer to the Stream Environment Characterization Data Sheet, Table 29-1, and Table 29-2.) That is, do they *all* indicate that your stream is healthy, with good water quality? Or conversely, do they *all* point to a stream in trouble, with poor water quality? Or do your results conflict, with some indicators of good quality and some indicators of poor water quality? _____

_____

_____

If your results aren't clear-cut, speculate on why this might be so.

_____

_____

What might you do to increase the consistency and reliability of your results?

_____

_____

(Continues on p. 660.)

Group 1 Taxa: Pollution-sensitive organisms found in good-quality water.

Stonefly Larvae: Order Plecoptera. 1.25–3.5 cm, 6 legs with hooked tips, antennae, 2 hairlike tails. Smooth (no gills) on lower half of body. (See arrow.)

Water Penny Larva: Order Coleoptera. 0.5 cm, flat saucer-shaped body with a raised bump on one side and 6 tiny legs on the other side. Immature beetle.

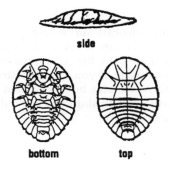

Mayfly Larvae: Order Ephemeroptera. 0.5–2.5 cm, brown, moving, platelike or feathery gills on sides of lower body (see arrow), 6 large hooked legs, antennae, 2 or 3 long, hairlike tails. Tails may be webbed together.

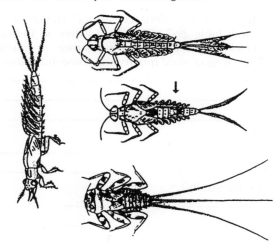

Caddisfly Larvae: Order Plecoptera. Up to 2.5 cm, 6 hooked legs on upper third of body, 2 hooks at back end. May be in a stick, rock or leaf case with its head sticking out. May have fluffy gill tufts on lower half.

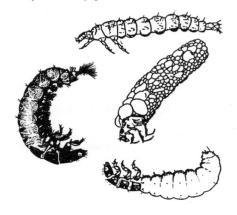

Dobsonfly (Hellgrammite) Larva: Family Corydalidae. 2–10 cm, dark-colored, 6 legs, large pinching jaws, eight pairs feelers on lower half of body with paired cottonlike gill tufts along underside, short antennae, 2 tails and 2 pairs of hooks at back end.

Gilled Snail: Class Gastropoda. Shell opening covered by thin plate called operculum. Shell usually opens on right.

Riffle Beetle: Order Coleoptera. 0.5 cm, oval body covered with tiny hairs, 6 legs, antennae. Walks slowly underwater. Does not swim on surface.

Figure 29-4 Stream insects and other macroinvertebrates. *Continues.*

Group 2 Taxa: Somewhat pollution-tolerant organisms can be in good- or fair-quality water.

Crayfish: Order Decapoda. Up to 15 cm, 2 large claws, 8 legs, resembles small lobster.

Scud: Order Amphipoda. 0.5 cm, white to gray, body higher than it is wide, swims sideways, more than 6 legs, resembles small shrimp.

Fishfly Larva: Family Corydalidae. Up to 3.5 cm long. Looks like small hellgrammite but often a lighter reddish-tan color, or with yellowish streaks. No gill tufs underneath.

Damselfly Larvae: Suborder Zygoptera. 1.25–2.5 cm, large eyes, 6 thin hooked legs, 3 broad oar-shaped tails, positioned like a tripod. Smooth (no gills) on sides of lower half of body. (See arrow.)

Beetle Larva: Order Coleoptera. 0.5–2.5 cm, light colored, 6 legs on upper half of body, feelers, antennae.

Sowbug: Order Isopoda. 0.5–2 cm gray oblong body wider than it is high, more than 6 legs, long antennae.

Alderfly Larva: Family Sialidae. 2.5 cm long. Looks like small hellgrammite but has one long, thin, branched tail at back end (no hooks). No gill tufts underneath.

Clam. Class Bivalvia.

Watersnipe Fly Larva: Family Athericidae (Atherix). 0.5–2.5 cm, pale to green, tapered body, many caterpillarlike legs, conical head, feathery "horns" at back end.

Crane Fly Larva: Suborder Nematocera. 1.25–5 cm, milky, green, or light brown, plump caterpillarlike segmented body, 4 fingerlike lobes at back end.

Dragon Fly Larvae: Suborder Anisoptera. 1.25–5 cm, large eyes, 6 hooked legs. Wide oval to round abdomen.

Figure 29-4 Stream insects and other macroinvertebrates. *Continues.*

Group 3 Taxa: Pollution-tollerant organisms can be in any quality of water.

Aquatic Worm: Class Oligochaeta. 0.5–5 cm, can be very tiny; thin wormlike body.

Midge Fly Larva: Suborder Nematocera. Up to 1 cm, dark head, wormlike segmented body, 2 tiny legs on each side.

Leech: Order Hirudinea. 0.5–5 cm, brown slimy body, ends with suction pads.

Blackfly Larva: Family Simulidae. Up to 0.75 cm, one end of body wider. Black head, suction pad on end.

Pouch Snail and Pond Snails: Class Gastropoda. No operculum. Breath air. Shell usually opens on left.

Other Snails: Class Gastropoda. No operculum. Breathe air. Snail shell coils in one plane.

Figure 29-4 Stream insects and other macroinvertebrates. *Continued.*

Which of your observed or measured factors indicate(s) higher quality water?

_____

Which of your observed or measured factors indicate(s) lower water quality?

_____

Why might you find a low SQI value, even if the chemical and physical parameters you measured are within limits for "good" water quality?

_____

If you found indications of organic or nutrient pollution, what might be some of the sources for this pollution in your stream's watershed?

_____

_____

Do you think most of the pollutants in your stream result from point source or nonpoint source pollutants?

_____

How could the negative impacts on your stream be reduced or eliminated?

_____

_____

_____

PRE-LAB QUESTIONS

_____ 1. A riffle is
(a) the land area surrounding a stream
(b) an area of still, deep water
(c) the living component of a stream
(d) a fast-moving, shallow stream area

_____ 2. Which of these is *not* a type of water pollutant?
(a) dissolved oxygen
(b) toxic chemicals
(c) organic wastes
(d) sediment

_____ 3. Nonpoint source pollutants include
(a) fertilizers from lawns
(b) pesticides from farm fields
(c) soil erosion from construction sites
(d) all of the above

_____ 4. A yellow to orange-red coating on a stream bottom indicates
(a) high dissolved oxygen
(b) possible soil erosion or mine drainage
(c) low nitrate concentration
(d) high chloride content

_____ 5. pH is
(a) a measure of phosphorous concentration
(b) a measure of hydrogen ion concentration
(c) measured by counting the number of different kinds of aquatic insects
(d) measured on a scale from 1 to 100

_____ 6. Dissolved oxygen content in stream water is affected by
(a) organic matter in the water
(b) overgrowth of algae
(c) water nutrient levels
(d) all of the above

_____ 7. Which pollutant would most likely be the source of coliform bacteria in a stream?
(a) fertilizers from a golf course
(b) discharge from a factory
(c) forestry activities
(d) sewage or animal wastes

_____ 8. Most of the aquatic macroinvertebrates in a stream are
(a) clams
(b) insect larvae
(c) worms
(d) arthropods such as crayfish

_____ 9. Group 1 aquatic macroinvertebrates
(a) require high-quality, unpolluted water
(b) require polluted water
(c) are tolerant of a wide range of water quality conditions
(d) include leeches

_____ 10. Nitrates
(a) are suspended sediments
(b) measure hydrogen ion concentrations
(c) are required for animal respiration
(d) contain nitrogen, a necessary plant nutrient

EXERCISE 29

Human Impact on the Environment: Stream and Pond Ecology

POST-LAB QUESTIONS

Introduction

1. What is a watershed? What are some of the major human activities occurring in the watershed of the stream you sampled?

2. Distinguish between point and nonpoint sources of pollution. Provide several examples of each.

3. Why is it important for sewage treatment plants to remove nitrates and phosphates from sewage before discharging it into a river?

4. How can an algal bloom (population explosion of microscopic aquatic plants) affect fish in a pond?

5. Trout are fish that require relatively low-temperature water. Suppose a shaded trout stream has its overhanging streamside trees removed. Explain the possible effects of this action on the trout population over the course of a summer.

29.1 Streamside Evaluation and Sampling

6. Here are the results of physical and chemical sampling of one stream. What do these results tell you about the suitability of this stream as fish habitat? What are likely causes for each of these values?

Parameter	Measurement
pH	5.2
Phosphate	0.15 mg/L
DO	3 mg/L

29.2 Laboratory Analysis—Evaluating Biological Tests and Samples

7. Here are the data from one stream's aquatic macroinvertebrate sample.

Taxa Present		
Group 1 (Pollution Intolerant)	**Group 2 (Somewhat Pollution Tolerant)**	**Group 3 (Pollution Tolerant)**
Caddisfly larvae	Crane fly larvae	Midge fly larvae
Mayfly larvae	Dragonfly larvae	Blackfly larvae
Riffle beetles	Crayfish	
Dobsonfly larvae		

Calculate the SQI value of this stream. What does this sample indicate about the water quality?

8. Referring to the stream in question 7, suppose you also know there are very few individuals of the Group 1 taxa present while midge fly larvae are extremely abundant. Does this information alter your assessment of the water quality of the stream? Why or why not?

Food for Thought

9. List several ways that sediment pollution could be/is being decreased in your community.

10. List several obstacles to improving stream quality in your community.

Estimating the Abundance of a Population of Aquatic Plants (*Lemna minor*, Duckweed)

Abstract

Soil, air, and water pollution can have serious impacts on the biotic component of ecosystems, including effects on human health and well-being. In the investigation reported here, I examine the population abundance of duckweed (*Lemna minor*) within two pond ecosystems on a local college campus. I estimated the population abundance of two separate duckweed populations that are assumed to experience different levels of chemical contamination because of parking lot surface runoff. I hypothesized that the pond closest to the potential pollution source would experience negative impacts on population dynamics. I predicted that the pond closest to the parking lot would support duckweed populations at a lower abundance than duckweed populations within ponds farther from the parking lot. I conducted field sampling using tea strainers to collect data for calculating estimates of population abundance based on frond counts. The results support the hypothesis and indicate that the pond closest to the parking lot supports a less abundant population than the pond farthest from the parking lot. Future studies investigating the effects of various compounds and compound concentrations on aquatic species and communities would be useful for improving our understanding of the ecotoxicological interactions caused by human behavior. Such studies would provide a sound empirical foundation for developing recommendations and strategies for sustainable interactions with the biosphere.

Introduction

Linkages between human actions and environmental inputs arising from those actions have effects on health, survival, and population growth or decline (McMichael 1993). Rapid growth of human populations combined with uncontrolled industrial growth, urban expansion, and agricultural land conversion has led to serious impacts on the environment and human quality of life (Molner and Molner 1999). The release of harmful chemicals into the environment continues, despite environmental activism and involvement from industry and the chemical and agricultural industries, as well as governmental regulations and oversight like that of the Environmental Protection Agency and the U.S. Department of Agriculture (Worldwatch Institute 2007).

An especially significant environmental impact from human actions is freshwater pollution. The Worldwatch Institute, a nonpartisan, independent, interdisciplinary research organization, reports that 81 percent of our nation's community water depends on groundwater sources, and that 53 percent of the population relies on groundwater as its source of drinking water (Worldwatch Institute 2007). Freshwater resources are critical for populations. Ninety-five percent of all freshwater on Earth exists as groundwater. It is imperative that we understand the sources and impact of pollution in order to develop recommendations and strategies for management, reduction, and prevention of pollution, as well as restoration and protection of freshwater resources.

The major sources of fresh water pollution can be classified as municipal, industrial, and agricultural. Freshwater contamination may occur by many routes from these sources, including surface runoff, liquid spills, wastewater discharges, littering, leaching to groundwater, leaking underground storage tanks, and municipal landfills. Among the most significant chemical contaminants are hydrocarbons, heavy metals, herbicides, pesticides, and chlorinated hydrocarbons.

The intensity of pollution and other disturbances can be assessed by understanding the biological responses of individual organisms, populations, and communities to environmental changes caused by freshwater pollution (Almar et al. 1998). These biological indicators can be used to encourage the ecologically sensitive management of freshwaters despite the conflicting demands of today's society.

My objective was to estimate the abundance of duckweed populations within two ponds on the campus of a local college. I hypothesized that duckweed population dynamics would be negatively impacted by surface runoff pollution such as from roads and parking lots. To test this hypothesis, I estimated population abundance of duckweed within two ponds, one adjacent to a large parking lot and the other isolated from the parking lot by both distance and elevation. I predicted that the pond adjacent to the parking lot would experience more surface pollutant runoff. This would lead to contamination of the pond, resulting in lower population abundance of duckweed.

Materials and Methods

Study Site

The study site is located on a local college campus in St. Louis, Missouri. Situated in the northeastern corner of the campus property are two ponds that were the focus of this investigation. These ponds are filled primarily by runoff coming from the areas around the pond that drain rainwater into the ponds. As the water flows into the ponds, it picks up minerals and soil particles. The type of rock and soil through which the water flows determines the type of minerals present in the water. Rocks exposed in this part of St. Louis County are usually limestone, made primarily of calcium carbonate. It is of significance to note that of the two ponds, the northernmost pond, surrounded by woodlands, is situated at a higher elevation and farther away from the large parking lot.

Study Species

The duckweeds (family *Lemnacea*) are a widely distributed group of 22 species found from the subpolar regions to the tropics. They are typically found within ponds, lakes, slow-moving streams and rivers, and ditches. The typical body structure consists of a few flattened, disc-like fronds or thalli that float on the surface. Reproduction is by budding, where new individuals grow from and break off of the "parent" plant, usually after six or so new fronds have developed.

Overall Procedure

For equipment, I obtained plastic tea strainers, white plastic trays, wax pencils, tape measures, and balances. I measured the surface area of the tea strainer and the surface area of ponds 1 and 2. I collected 12 samples from each pond by lowering the tea strainer carefully into the pond, allowing duckweed to redistribute itself once again. I then raised the tea strainer and allowed water to drain, and removed the duckweed attached to the *outside* of the tea strainer and returned them to the pond.

To calculate abundance, I marked the bottom of a shallow, rectangular plastic culture tray with a wax pencil to create a grid of squares 5 centimeters by 5 centimeters. I filled the tray with approximately 1 cm depth of water and emptied the fronds from the tea strainer into the tray. I used the standardized procedure of counting every visible frond. This included any tips of small new fronds that are just beginning to emerge from the pocket of the mother frond. I used a dissecting microscope (10×) for frond counts. I counted the number of fronds over 10 grid squares. To calculate the average population abundance (i.e., number of fronds) of duckweed in the two ponds, I used the following calculations:

1. the total estimated number of plants (N) collected in each tea-strainer sample = (the average number of plants counted in a grid square of the tray) × (total number of squares)

2. the estimated number of plants (P) on the pond = average N × (area of pond ÷ area of the tea strainer).

Statistical Analysis

Summary statistics were calculated for the data from both ponds. A *t*-test was conducted to compare the data.

Results

The results of the *t*-test revealed a significant difference between the two ponds in terms of duckweed abundance ($t = -5.16$, df = 22, $p < 0.0001$). Data are shown in Table 1, and Figure 1 presents the summary statistics for duckweed abundance. Pond 1, which is located closer to the parking lot, was predicted to exhibit lower abundance of duckweed because of assumed greater surface runoff of pollutants from the nearby parking lot. This was supported by the data gathered in May 2007, and therefore the hypothesis was accepted.

Discussion

The results of this investigation indicate that there is a statistically significant difference in the population abundances of duckweed within the two ponds located on the college campus.

The data support my hypothesis of a negatively impacted duckweed population in the lower pond resulting from elevated chemical contamination because of surface runoff from the parking lot.

The assumption that higher levels of chemical pollution are responsible for the decreased abundance of duckweed in the lower pond needs to be assessed. Further investigations into the mechanisms responsible for the observed differences in abundance are warranted. Artificial ponds may be used to conduct research investigations of this nature. Small artificial ponds can be created in the lab or field to investigate the impact of pollutants on pond ecosystems. Heimbach, Pflueger, and Ratte (1991) used 5-m³ artificial ponds to assess the influence of the potential hazards of chemicals to aquatic ecosystems. A study by Hughes et al. (1980) investigated the persistence and biological impact of organophosphorus insecticides within artificial ponds. In the laboratory, petri dishes or bowls may be used to create small artificial ponds under controlled conditions to determine the effect of independent variables. The strength of using such artificial ponds is that the investigator can ensure sufficient replication and control over relevant factors, increasing the strength of statistical evaluations of results (for example, see Rowe and Dunson 1994). The downside is that the artificial ponds may not accurately mimic larger natural ponds. Ideally, results from artificial ponds would be compared to natural ponds to check for similarity of results such as those done by Heimbach, Pflueger, and Ratte (1991).

Sample Abundance Estimate	# of Fronds Pond 1	# of Fronds Pond 2
1	82	115
2	72	111
3	89	99
4	79	78
5	98	102
6	90	122
7	96	112
8	92	104
9	86	118
10	82	128
11	93	120
12	88	109
Mean	87.2	109.8
SD	7.484833	13.16906
SE	2.160685	3.801581

TABLE 1 Summary data of duckweed abundance in the two ponds

Figure 1 Average abundance of duckweed within the two ponds located on the college campus (values are means ± SE)

Of broader significance and potential application would be investigations into the uses of duckweed as a biological indicator for the intensity of pollution on aquatic ecosystems. Duckweeds are excellent model organisms because their growth rates can be measured by counting how many new fronds develop over a five-day period. Among the possible investigations are the effects of different chemical pollutants such as oil, gasoline, copper sulfate, various pesticides, herbicides, insecticides, and various fertilizers. Research such as this will continue to shed light on the linkages between human actions and environmental inputs as well as the consequences those actions and inputs have on health, survival, and population growth or decline. Armed with this knowledge, we may be better able to develop wise, sustainable, ecologically sensitive management and interaction with the world's freshwaters.

Citations

Almar, M., L. Otero, C. Santos, and J. González Gallego. 1998. Liver glutathione content and glutathione-dependent enzymes of two species of freshwater fish as bioindicators of chemical pollution. *Journal of Environmental Science & Health B* (Nov) 33(6): 769–83.

Heimbach, F., W. Pflueger, and H.-T. Ratte. 1991. Use of small artificial ponds for assessment of hazards to aquatic ecosystems. *Environmental Toxicology and Chemistry* 11(1): 27–34.

Hughes, D. N., M. G. Boyer, M. H. Papst, C. D. Fowle, G. A. V. Rees, and P. Baulu. 1980. Persistence of three organophosphorus insecticides in artificial ponds and some biological implications. *Archives of Environmental Contamination and Toxicology* 9(3): 269–79.

McMichael, A. J. 1993. *Planetary overload: Global environmental change and the health of the human species.* New York: Cambridge University Press.

Molner, S., and I. M. Molner. 1999. *Environmental change and human survival: Some Dimensions of human ecology.* Englewood Cliffs, NJ: Prentice Hall.

Rowe, C. L, and W. Dunson. 1994. The value of simulated pond communities in mesocosms for studies of amphibian ecology and ecotoxicology. *Journal of Herpetology* 28(3): 346–56.

Worldwatch Institute. 2007. Pollution. Online at http://www.worldwatch.org/taxonomy/term/109.

APPENDIX 1
Measurement Conversions

Metric to American Standard

Length

1 mm = 0.039 inch
1 cm = 0.394 inch
1 m = 3.28 feet
1 m = 1.09 yards
1 km = 0.622 miles

Volume

1 mL = 0.0338 fluid ounce
1 L = 4.23 cups
1 L = 2.11 pints
1 L = 1.06 quarts
1 L = 0.264 gallon

Mass

1 mg = 0.0000353 ounce
1 g = 0.0353 ounce
1 kg = 2.21 pounds

American Standard to Metric

Length

1 inch = 2.54 cm
1 foot = 0.305 m
1 yard = 0.914 m
1 mile = 1.61 km

Volume

1 fluid ounce = 29.6 mL
1 cup = 237 mL
1 pint = 0.474 L
1 quart = 0.947 L
1 gallon = 3.79 L

Mass

1 ounce = 28.3 g
1 pound = 0.454 kg

The Scientific Method

To appreciate biology or, for that matter, any body of scientific knowledge, you need to understand how the **scientific method** is used to gather that knowledge. We use the scientific method to test the predictions of possible answers to questions about nature in ways that we can duplicate or verify. Answers supported by test results are added to the body of scientific knowledge and contribute to the concepts presented in your textbook and other science books. Although these concepts are as up-to-date as possible, they are always open to further questions and modifications.

One of the roots of the scientific method can be found in ancient Greek philosophy. The natural philosophy of Aristotle and his colleagues was mechanistic rather than vitalistic. A **mechanist** believes that only natural forces govern living things, along with the rest of the universe, while a **vitalist** believes that the universe is at least partially governed by supernatural powers. Mechanists look for interrelationships between the structures and functions of living things, and the processes that shape them. Their explanations of nature deal in **cause and effect**—the idea that one thing is the result of another thing (for example, fertilization of an egg initiates the developmental process that forms an adult.). In contrast, vitalists often use purposeful explanations of natural events (the fertilized egg strives to develop into an adult). Although statements that ascribe purpose to things often feel comfortable to the writer, try to avoid them when writing lab reports and scientific papers.

Aristotle and his colleagues developed three rules to examine the laws of nature: Carefully observe some aspect of nature; examine these observations as to their similarities and differences; and produce a principle or generalization about the aspect of nature being studied (for example, all mammals nourish their young with milk).

The major defect of natural philosophy was that it accepted the idea of *absolute truth.* This belief suppressed the testing of principles once they had been formulated. Thus, Aristotle's belief in spontaneous generation, the principle that some life can arise from nonliving things (say maggots from spoiled meat), survived over 2000 years of controversy before being discredited by Louis Pasteur in 1860. Rejection of the idea of absolute truth coupled with the testing of principles either by experimentation or by further pertinent observation is the essence of the modern scientific method.

Although there is not one universal scientific method, Figure A-1 illustrates the general process.

MATERIALS

Per lab room:

- blindfold
- plastic beakers with an inside diameter of about 8 cm stuffed with cotton wool
- four or five liquid crystal thermometers

Step 1. Observation. As with natural philosophy, the scientific method starts with careful observation. An investigator may make observations from nature or from the written words of other investigators, which are published in books or research articles in scientific journals and are available in the storehouse of human knowledge, the library. One subject we all have some knowledge of is the human body. The first four rows of Table 1 list some observations about the human body. The fifth row is blank so that you can fill in the steps of the scientific method for some observation about the human body, or anything else you and your instructor wish to investigate.

Step 2. Question. In the second step of the scientific method, *we ask a question* about these observations. The quality of this question will depend on how carefully the observations were made and analyzed. Table 1 includes questions raised by the listed observations.

Step 3. Hypothesis. Now we *construct a hypothesis*—that is, we derive by inductive reasoning a possible answer to the question. **Induction** is a logical process by which all known observations are combined and considered before producing a possible answer. Table 1 includes examples of hypotheses.

Step 4. Prediction. In this step we *formulate a prediction*—we assume the hypothesis is correct and predict the result of a test that reveals some aspect of it. This is deductive or "if-then" reasoning. **Deduction** is a logical process by which a prediction is produced from a possible answer to the question asked. Table 1 lists a prediction for each hypothesis.

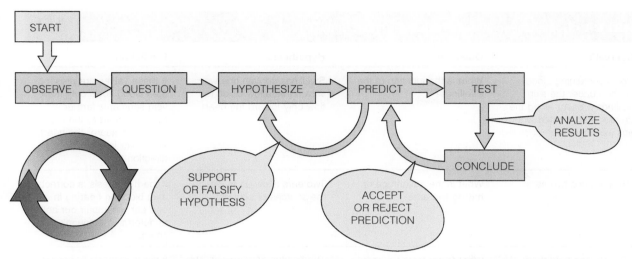

Figure A-1 The scientific method. Support or falsification of the hypothesis usually necessitates further observations, adjustment to the question, and modification of the hypothesis. Once started, the scientific method cycles over and over again, each turn further refining the hypothesis.

Step 5. Experiment or Pertinent Observations. In this step we *perform an experiment or make pertinent observations* to test the prediction. In an experiment of classical design, the individuals or items under study are divided into two groups: an **experimental group** that is treated with (or possesses) the independent variable and a **control group** that is not (or does not). Sometimes there is more than one experimental group. Sometimes subjects participate in both groups, experimental and control, and are tested both with and without the treatment.

In any test there are three kinds of variables. The **independent variable** is the treatment or condition under study. The **dependent variable** is the event or condition that is measured or observed when the results are gathered. The **controlled variables** are all other factors, which the investigator attempts to keep the same for all groups under study.

Note: **The italicized statements show how the scientific method is applied to the predictions in Table 1 or give examples of the scientific method in practice.**

To test the prediction that blocking hearing in one ear impairs our ability to point out a sound's source (row II in Table 1), a group of subjects is tested first with no ears blocked (control group) and then with one ear blocked (experimental group). The independent variable is the blocking of one ear; the dependent variable is the ability to point out a sound's source; and the controlled variables are the standard conditions used for each trial—same test sound, same background noise, same procedure for each subject (same blocked ear, same instructions, same sequence of trials, same time between trials), and recruitment of appropriate subjects.

Sometimes the best tests of the predictions of a hypothesis are not actual experiments but further pertinent observations. One of the most important principles in biology, Darwin's theory of natural selection, was developed by this nonexperimental approach. Although they are a little more difficult to form, the nonexperimental approach also has variables.

To test the prediction that a liquid crystal thermometer will record different temperatures on the forehead, back of neck, and forearm (row IV of Table 1), the independent variable is location; the dependent variable is temperature; and the controlled variables are using the same thermometer to measure skin temperature at the three locations and measuring all of the subjects at rest.

Step 6. Conclusion. *To make a conclusion*—the last step in one cycle of the scientific method—you use the results of the experiment or pertinent observations to evaluate your hypothesis. If your prediction does not occur,

vein segment

valves

(Photo by D. Morton.)

Figure A-2 Veins under the skin.

TABLE 1 Some Observations About the Human Body

Observation	Question	Hypothesis	Prediction
I. Veins containing blood are seen under the skin. Swellings present along the vein are often located where veins join together.[a]	What is the function of the swellings?	Swellings contain one-way valves that allow blood to flow only toward the heart.	If these valves are present, then blood flows only from vein segments farther from the heart to the next segments nearer the heart and never in the opposite direction.
II. People have two ears.	What is the advantage of having two ears?	Two ears allow us to locate the sources of sounds.	If the hypothesis is correct, then blocking hearing in one ear will impair our ability to determine a sound's source.[b]
III. People can hold their breath for only a short period of time.	What factor forces a person to take a breath?	The buildup of carbon dioxide derived from the body's metabolic activity stimulates us to take a breath.	If the hypothesis is correct, then people will hold their breath a shorter time just after exercise compared to when they are at rest.
IV. Normal body temperature is 98.6°F.	Is all of the body at the same 98.6°F temperature?	The skin, or at least some portion of it, is not 98.6°F.	If the hypothesis is correct, then a liquid crystal thermometer will record different temperatures on the forehead, back of neck, and forearm.
V. _____ _____ _____ _____	_____ _____ _____ _____	_____ _____ _____ _____	_____ _____ _____ _____

[a] The portion of the vein between swellings is called a segment and is illustrated in Figure A-2.
[b] This is especially the case for high-pitched sounds because higher frequencies travel less easily directly through tissues and bones.

it is rejected and your hypothesis or some aspect of it is falsified. If your prediction does occur, you may conditionally accept your prediction and your hypothesis is supported. However, you can never completely accept or reject any hypothesis; all you can do is state a probability that one is correct or incorrect. To quantify this probability, scientists use a branch of mathematics called *statistical analysis*.

Even if the prediction is rejected, this does not necessarily mean that the treatment caused the result. A coincidence or the effect of some unforeseen and thus uncontrolled variable could be causing the result. For this reason, the results of experiments and observations must be *repeatable* by the original investigator and others.

Even if the results are repeatable, this does not necessarily mean that the treatment caused the result. *Cause and effect*, especially in biology, is rarely proven in experiments. We can, however, say that the treatment and result are correlated. A **correlation** is a relationship between the independent and the dependent variables.

Severe narrowing of a coronary artery branch reduces blood flow to the heart muscle downstream. This region of heart muscle gets insufficient oxygen and cannot contract and may die, resulting in a heart attack. The initial cause is the narrowing of the artery and the final effect is the heart attack. Perhaps the heart attack victim smoked cigarettes. Smoking cigarettes is one of several factors that make a person more likely to have a heart attack. This is based on a correlation between smoking and heart attacks in the general population but we cannot say for sure that the smoking caused the heart attack.

THEORIES and PRINCIPLES: When exhaustive experiments and observations consistently support an important hypothesis, it is accepted as a **theory**. A theory that stands the test of time may be elevated to the status of a **principle**. Theories and principles are always considered when new hypotheses are formulated. However, like hypotheses, theories and principles can be modified or even discarded in the light of new knowledge. Biology, like life itself, is not static but is constantly changing.

PRINCIPLE

THEORY

HYPOTHESIS

BODY OF SCIENTIFIC KNOWLEDGE

Scientific Writing and Critiquing

The account of one or several related cycles of the scientific method is usually reported in depth in a research article published in a scientific journal. Writing such research articles allows scientists to share knowledge. They provide enough information so that other scientists can repeat the experiments or pertinent observations they describe. The journal *Science,* along with several others, presents its research articles in narrative form, and many of the details of the scientific method are understood and not stated. However, adherence to the modern scientific method is expected, and the scientific community understands that it is as important to expose mistakes as it is to praise new knowledge.

Most scientific journals present research reports in a standard format. This allows scientists to quickly and easily skim through the many new research articles published daily, reading in depth only those of particular interest. By understanding the purpose of each section of a research article, you not only will be able to locate the question, research context, main methods, results, and meaning of someone's research with speed and efficiency, but also learn how to design and communicate your own research investigations along the way! After all, the best way to learn science is to *do* science—reading research articles, exploring and trying out various experimental and observational methodologies that you are reading about, and eventually building on and extending previous research that you have read that particularly interested you. Scientists rarely investigate topics out of the blue; most often they become involved in research that they have either read about or observed that interested them. They then browse the available scientific knowledge base, most often the scientific journal literature, to see what is already known about the topic of interest. If they come across an area where nothing is known—an area of ignorance—then by using the scientific method they may choose to extend our knowledge.

The following sections are most commonly used in the scientific literature. The word counts are suggestions only and offered as guidelines to use when writing your own research reports.

Abstract (~200 words): The abstract contains a brief and concise summary of the main sections of the scientific report. Usually included are the research questions, the broad conceptual framework or relevance of the research topic, the hypothesis and prediction(s), the main methods, the main results and their interpretation, and a concluding statement.

Introduction (~200–300 words): The introduction is a short narrative that describes the research topic in some detail. It explains what is known regarding the research topic, based on previous research. This section concludes with what is not known regarding the research topic, the specific question that the research report focuses on, the hypothesis and prediction(s), and possibly a brief description of how the question will be answered.

Materials and Methods (~200 words): This section explains how the research was conducted. It should provide enough detail that someone could read the research report and repeat the experiment. The statistical analyses that will be used are also described in this section.

Results (~150 words): This section reports the results of the research but does not go into detail explaining or discussing what they mean (that goes in the next section). Here is where any tables, graphs, or figures would be located. The narrative of this section explains what the tables, graphs, or figures show.

Discussion (~200–300 words): In this section, the research question is restated, and the answer that was obtained from the research is given. Data reported in the results section are clearly related to the hypothesis and predictions. The results are interpreted, any unexpected or inconsistent results are explained, and a discussion of what the results mean is provided. The results are also integrated with the work of others, relating the research conducted to the larger body of work already completed and reported in the scientific literature. Finally, the research is related to the big picture or larger conceptual framework within which the research topic lies. New research questions or avenues of research are mentioned as well.

Citations or References: The sources of information that were used in the research report are cited in the text by author, and the details for how to locate the information is given.

It is recommended that you read several research articles to get an idea of how research is reported. This will increase your ability to read and interpret scientific literature as well as increase your ability to communicate through writing. The following is a general guide for critiquing scientific manuscripts.

Evaluating a Manuscript

When evaluating a manuscript, it is important to consider several things. Some of the following questions can only be answered by those who are intimately familiar with the organisms and techniques used. Others concern the structure, style, and soundness of a manuscript and can be answered by anyone with a peripheral knowledge of the subject matter. The ability to consider any of these problems will, of course, increase with experience.

ABSTRACT

Is it informative, concise, and complete?

INTRODUCTION

What is the main point of this study?

Is its relevance to scientific theory (a conceptual framework) apparent?

If it contains a hypothesis, is it stated in a way that is testable?

METHODS

Can the work be repeated on the basis of the methods given?

Are unwieldy technical terms defined?

Are the methods and organisms used appropriate for testing the hypothesis?

To what extent can conclusions drawn from laboratory experiments be extended to interpret events occurring in nature?

RESULTS

Are all important results given?

Were the results properly evaluated statistically?

Are the figures and tables clear?

Do the results contained in the figures and tables support the statements made in the text?

DISCUSSION

Are the data clearly related to the hypothesis?

Are the results properly interpreted?

Are the results integrated with those of other workers?

Are unexpected or inconsistent results explained?

Does the paper provide any new ideas or interpretations?

If the discussion contains any speculation, is it justifiable?

The following is a sample checklist that can be used for peer reviews of scientific reports.

Checklist for Journal Article Peer Review

Clearly critique how well the author sets his or her research topic in context with other scientific studies (the conceptual framework of the article and research).

Use the following outline for critiquing the introduction:

Background overview

Conceptual framework

Specific focus of article (hypothesis and objectives, or premise of a review article)

Significance of specific focus

Synthesis of literature on specific topic as provided by the article's author(s)

Broader impact and relevance of the research question

Evaluate the following:

a. Introduction

_____ Does the author of the article provide a sufficient context or background for the study, relating the specific focus to previous research or conceptual development?

_____ Does the author link his or her research topic to some overarching theory or conceptual framework?

_____ Are the hypothesis and objectives (the specific focus) clear?

_____ Is there a clear rationale and justification for the study (i.e., what is the significance of the study topic, in terms of advancing knowledge and understanding within its own field or across different fields of science)?

b. Methods, results, and discussion

_____ Critique the article (not just summarize), discussing such things as the development of ideas pertaining to the study topic, criteria for evidence, appropriateness and strength of research methodologies, and so on.

c. Conclusions

_____ Discuss the main conclusions (take-home message) of the article.

d. Broader impact

_____ Does the author clearly discuss how the article advances discovery and understanding within or across fields of scientific study (does the article move back to the big picture beyond the specific focus and back to the conceptual framework)?

_____ Does the author provide examples of application and use for the study's ideas, concepts, and findings?

Biological question(s) you came up with from reading the article and its conclusions—that is, questions that may lead to future research:

_____

_____

_____

_____

_____

_____

_____

_____

_____

_____

_____

_____

Statistics and Graphing with Excel

The following are references for commonly used statistical tests.

Nonparametric Tests

Nonparametric statistical tests do not require certain mathematical distributions of the data being analyzed. These tests can be used for measurement or count data as well as data that do not show a normal distribution.

Goodness-of-Fit Test (Chi-Square)

See discussion of chi-square in Exercise 9, section B.2.

Contingency Analysis (Cross-Tabulation of Frequency)

Contingency analysis is used with count data (frequencies) that are arranged in two or more rows, such as recording individuals by their species and their habitat location. This test is used to investigate the association between variables.

The Binomial Test

The binomial test is used when each individual in the sample is classified in one of two categories and the investigator wants to know if the proportion of individuals falling in each category differs from chance or from some previously specified probabilities of falling into those categories.

Parametric Tests

Parametric tests are based on certain assumptions of mathematical distribution of the data being analyzed. The most commonly used distribution is the normal distribution (other tests involve the binomial or Poisson distribution).

Comparison of Variances and Means for Two Samples: The t-Test

The *t*-test is one of the most widely used test procedures for comparing two samples to investigate whether significant differences exist between the two populations sampled.

Using Excel

Excel is an easy-to-use spreadsheet for creating data tables, calculating descriptive statistics, and graphing data. There are many useful online references that provide tutorials and walk you through using Excel. The following are recommended:

The Excel home page: http://office.microsoft.com/en-us/excel/default.aspx

An Excel tutorial: http://www.usd.edu/trio/tut/excel/

How to use Excel: http://serc.carleton.edu/introgeo/mathstatmodels/xlhowto.html

Using Inquiry-Based Module Reports

In the truest sense, science is apprenticeship-style learning by which the student learns from established scientists, often working with them on research projects and learning their "trade" while involved in authentic research investigations. Students locate and read numerous research articles, critiquing them so as to learn the elements of scientific research and communication.

The inquiry-based modules included in this lab manual are designed to teach students about scientific research by having them actually conduct research themselves. The inquiry-based modules not only contain information regarding scientific subject matter related to specific research topics, but also illustrate the scientific process: how science research is conducted and reported. They are designed to engage students in conducting their own research, stimulate higher-order cognitive thinking, and ask students to extend the research being reported.

The following guidelines are suggested for using these inquiry reports:

1. Have students critique the research report in the inquiry module (see sample rubric for peer reviews provided in Appendix 3).

2. Have students come up with their own way of extending the research reported in the module, coming up with their own experimental design (a detailed explanation of the process in the next section and a sample rubric provided later).

3. Have students conduct a background literature search to discover what is known about the research topic they are focusing on.

4. Have students describe their expected results as well as graph these expected results (if possible, also conduct a short pilot study).

5. Have students run their experiment, collect and analyze data, and graph their data.

6. Have students discuss their results and draw conclusions.

7. Finally, have students point to future research on the research topic, discussing ways of extending their research findings.

Creating a Research Proposal

One of the most challenging aspects of scientific research is synthesizing past work, current findings, and new hypotheses into research proposals for future investigation. Research proposals require the careful and thoughtful construction of the conceptual framework, the specific questions and hypotheses of the proposed research, a detailed experimental design and methods that will be used, the projected analysis of the data, and the significance of the proposed research.

The introduction provides background information and places the proposed study within a conceptual framework. Previous research is summarized, leading to the question the current research project proposes to answer. For purposes of clarity, explicit hypothesis/hypotheses are given, with a general statement regarding the main experimental design. (Think of an hourglass, leading from a wide section to a narrow neck. The wide section is the larger conceptual framework or context of the study; the narrow neck is the specific research focus or research question. Later, in the "significance of the proposed research" section, you will again lead to a large section, moving from the specific results of your study to relating these to the larger conceptual framework again.)

The methods section provides more details regarding the experimental design and methodologies you will use. This section is where specific predictions, and the underlying rationales justifying those predictions, are discussed. Background information can be given regarding the particular study site, focal organism, or process being investigated. How you will conduct the study—that is, the specific methods you will employ—are discussed in this section.

The results section for a proposal describes the type of analysis you will use: What type of statistics will be used to analyze the data?

The final section of a research proposal discusses anticipated results and the significance of the research findings. This section is where you expand back into the larger conceptual framework of the study. How will your specific results lead to advances in the field of study? Does your study address a topic that lacks quantitative data, or are their untested assumptions? This section should be pretty clear-cut if you did a thorough enough background investigation. The background review should have provided a clear path to an area within the field of study that requires more research.

Sample rubric for experimental design:

1. What is the research question you will investigate?

2. What is the significance of this question? How will the answer you discover contribute to and advance our understanding?

3. What is your hypothesis and prediction(s) (i.e., what do you *expect* to see *if* your hypothesis is accurate)? (Use the *If . . . , then . . .* format)

4. What is your experimental design? For example, control versus experimental group? Sample size in each group? What you will measure or take data on, your independent and dependent variables, and any statistical tests you will use.

CONTROL GROUP	EXPERIMENTAL GROUP

5. Describe the methods you will use so that someone could read your description and repeat your experiment exactly:

_____

_____

_____

_____

_____

_____

_____

_____

_____

_____

_____

_____

6. Create a data table of the data you *expect* to see if your hypothesis is accurate.

7. Create the *data-recording tables* you will use when you do your experiment; give a copy to your instructor.

8. Create a graph of your expected data and turn it in to instructor.

9. Make sure your equipment is assembled and ready and that your experiment will actually work! Do a *pilot study* run-through with a sample size of 1 in each group.

When you run your experiment, remember that you must be able to organize and graph your data, present your findings to the class, and interpret your results in terms of whether or not your hypothesis is supported or rejected. Be sure to explain your results.

Resources

Day, R. A. 1988. *How to Write and Publish a Scientific Paper* (3rd ed.). ISI Press, NY.

Friedland, A. J., and C. L. Folt. 2000. *Writing Successful Science Proposals.* Yale University Press, New Haven and London.

National Science Foundation. *Grant Proposal Guide.* NSF Web site.

Terms of Orientation in and Around the Animal Body

Body Shapes

Symmetry. The body can be divided into almost identical halves.

Asymmetry. The body cannot be divided into almost identical halves (for example, many sponges).

Radial symmetry. The body is shaped like a cylinder (for example, sea anemone) or wheel (for example, sea star).

Bilateral symmetry. The body is shaped like ours in that it can be divided into halves by only one symmetrical plane (midsagittal).

Directions in the Body

Dorsal. At or toward the back surface of the body.

Ventral. At or toward the belly surface of the body.

Anterior. At or toward the head of the body—ventral surface of humans.

Posterior. At or toward the tail or rear end of the body—dorsal surface of humans.

Medial. At or near the midline of a body. The prefix *mid-* is often used in combination with other terms (for example, midventral).

Lateral. Away from the midline of a body.

Superior. Over or placed above some point of reference—toward the head of humans.

Inferior. Under or placed below some point of reference—away from the head of humans.

Proximal. Close to some point of reference or close to a point of attachment of an appendage to the trunk of the body.

Distal. Away from some point of reference or away from a point of attachment of an appendage to the trunk of the body.

Longitudinal. Parallel to the midline of a body.

Axis. An imaginary line around which a body or structure can rotate. The midline or *longitudinal axis* is the central axis of a symmetrical body or structure.

Axial. Placed at or along an axis.

Radial. Arranged symmetrically around an axis like the spokes of a wheel.

Planes of the Body

Sagittal. Passes vertically to the ground and divides the body into right and left sides. The *midsagittal* or *median plane* passes through the longitudinal axis and divides the body into right and left halves.

Frontal. Passes at right angles to the sagittal plane and divides the body into dorsal and ventral parts.

Transverse. Passes from side to side at right angles to both the sagittal and frontal planes and divides the body into anterior and posterior parts—superior and inferior parts of humans. This plane of section is often referred to as a cross section.

Illustration References

Abramoff, P., and R. G. Thomson. 1982. *Laboratory Outlines in Biology III*. New York: W. H. Freeman.

Boolootian, R. A., and K. A. Stiles Trust. 1981. *College Zoology*. Tenth Edition. New York: Macmillan.

Case, C. L., and T. R. Johnson. 1984. *Experiments in Microbiology*. Menlo Park, California: Benjamin/Cummings.

Fowler, I. 1984. *Human Anatomy*. Belmont, California: Wadsworth.

Gilbert, S. G. 1966. *Pictorial Anatomy of the Fetal Pig*. Second Edition. Seattle, Washington: University of Washington Press.

Glase, J. C., et al. 1975. *Investigative Biology*. Ithaca, New York.

Hickman, C. P. 1961. *Integrated Principles of Zoology*. Second Edition. St. Louis, Missouri: C. V. Mosby.

Hickman, C. P., et al. 1978. *Biology of Animals*. Second Edition. St. Louis, Missouri: C. V. Mosby.

Jensen, W. A., et al. 1979. *Biology*. Belmont, California: Wadsworth.

Kessel, R. G., and R. H. Kardon. 1979. *Tissues and Organs*. New York: W. H. Freeman.

Kessel, R. G., and C. Y. Shih. 1974. *Scanning Electron Microscopy in Biology*. New York: Springer-Verlag.

Lytle, C. F., and J. E. Wodsedalek, 1984. *General Zoology Laboratory Guide*. Complete Version. Ninth Edition. Dubuque, Iowa: Wm. C. Brown.

Patten, B. M. 1951. *American Scientist* 39: 225–243.

Scagel, R. F., et al. 1982. *Nonvascular Plants*. Belmont, California: Wadsworth.

Sheetz, M., et al. 1976. *The Journal of Cell Biology* 70:193.

Shih, C. Y., and R. G. Kessel. 1982. *Living Images*. Boston: Science Books International/Jones and Bartlett Publishers.

Stanier, R., et al. 1986. *The Microbial World*. Fifth Edition. Englewood Cliffs, New Jersey: Prentice-Hall.

Starr, C., and R. Taggart. 1984. *Biology*. Third Edition. Belmont, California: Wadsworth.

Starr, C., and R. Taggart. 1987. *Biology*. Fourth Edition. Belmont, California: Wadsworth.

Starr, C., and R. Taggart. 1989. *Biology*. Fifth Edition. Belmont, California: Wadsworth.

Starr, C., and R. Taggart. 2001. *Biology: The Unity and Diversity of Life*. Ninth Edition. Belmont, California: Wadsworth.

Starr, C. 1991. *Biology: Concepts & Applications*. Belmont, California: Wadsworth.

Starr, C. 2000. *Biology: Concepts and Applications*. Fourth Edition. Belmont, California: Wadsworth.

Steucek, G. L., et al. 1985. *American Biology Teacher* 471: 96–99.

Storer, T., et al. 1979. *General Zoology*. New York: McGraw-Hill.

Villee, C. A., et al. 1973. *General Zoology*. Fourth Edition. Philadelphia: W. B. Saunders.

Weller, H., and R. Wiley. 1985. *Basic Human Physiology*. Boston: PWS Publishers.

Wischnitzer, S. 1979. *Atlas and Dissection Guide for Comparative Anatomy*. Third Edition. New York: W. H. Freeman.

Wolfe, S. L. 1985. *Cell Ultrastructure*. Belmont, California: Wadsworth.